Thomas E. Lightburn served for twenty-two years in the medical branch of the Royal Navy. He reached the rank of Chief Petty Officer and left the service in 1974. After gaining a Bachelor of Education degree with Honours at Liverpool University, he taught for sixteen years before volunteering for early retirement. He then began writing stories for The Wirral Journal and the Sea Breezes, a nation-wide nautical magazine. He interviewed Ian Fraser, VC, ex Lieutenant RN., and wrote an account of how he and his crew, in a midget submarine, crippled the Japanese cruiser, Takao, in Singapore. Tom lives in Wallasey, pursuing his favourite hobbies of soccer, naval and military history, the theatre, art and travel.

THE GATES OF
STONEHOUSE

Thomas E. Lightburn

The Gates Of
Stonehouse

Vanguard Press

A CIP catalogue record for this title is
available from the British Library
ISBN 1 843862 03 4

*Vanguard Press is an imprint of
Pegasus Elliot MacKenzie Publishers Ltd.*
www.pegasuspublishers.com

First Published in 2005

**Vanguard Press
Sheraton House Castle Park
Cambridge England**

Printed & Bound in Great Britain

Dedication

To the late Joseph Woods. Ex Private, 3rd Parachute
Brigade. A firm friend through thick and thin.

And

The late Bill Manley
Without whose help this book could not have been written.

Acknowledgements

I wish to express my deepest gratitude to the following people for their help in writing this book. Commodore Frank Reed, OBE, Royal Navy. Lieutenant Commander John Millward, RN, (Ret'd.) Lieutenant Commander George Story, RN, (Ret'd) Donald Fearnley, ex Fleet Chief, RN, (Ret'd), John Kennedy, Liverpool University, John Haley. MA. Roy Cragg, ex AB, RN. George (Pincher) Martin, ex Leading Seaman, RN. Brian (Doc) Holliday, ex AB, RN. James Kennedy (no relation to John). Mrs Margaret Davidson, for her mortal support and criticism. Sue Sullivan, Editor's PS, Navy News, Mrs J Spargo and staff of Helston Museum, Linda Sanderson, (computer expert) and especially the late William Manley, ex Chief Med Tech (N) RN.

Thank you one and all.

Tom Lightburn,
Wallasey, Merseyside 2005

PROLOGUE

The city lights of Plymouth flickered across the dark waters of The Sound, illuminating Smeaton's Tower and the dull, grassy slopes of The Hoe. Dominating the skyline was the white facade of the Grand Hotel, ablaze with life, and to the right the formidable walls of the Royal Citadel stretched towards the well-lit Barbican.

A yellow moon shone intermittently through darkening clouds, sending shafts of light rippling along the waters of the harbour. Nearby, the imperious statue of Sir Francis Drake, illuminated against the night sky, peered proudly in our direction, as if to welcome us home.

We had dropped anchor outside the breakwater in The Sound, but Customs' officers had refused to let us enter port. There had been some sort of 'administrative error' and we'd been informed they would not be boarding until the morning.

Having completed the first half of an eighteen-month commission, we were eager to get ashore. Instead, we leaned against the ship's guardrail and gazed longingly at the fleshpots of dear old Plymouth.

'Bastards!' moaned Paddy Alexander, 'I could have had an extra night at Gib and bought a few more rabbits,' – rabbits being naval parlance for gifts purchased in foreign ports.

'And a few more beers,' added Taff Leighton, flicking a glowing dog-end into the sea.

'Why can't they come onboard tonight?' I asked. 'Surely they work at night?'

'Maybe the buggers are on strike,' muttered Pincher Martin.

'Just think,' sighed Digger Barnes, a stoker who had come up from below for a quick smoke and a breath of fresh air, 'we could be having a few pints in The Antelope.'

I had been the medic in HMS *Decoy* for nearly a year and had treated everyone on board, from the captain to the most junior seaman. To some, I was a father confessor, to others, a confidant with whom they could share a personal problem. In time, we became a family, sharing laughter, danger, loneliness and death. They were faces of men I could trust with my life.

As the ship slowly swung at anchor, the dense woodland of Drake's Island hove into view.

'Always reminds me of an English Alcatraz, does old Drake's

13

Island,' said Mitch, a small, leathery-faced PO. He came from County Antrim but lived with his family in Plymouth. 'Used to take me missus and the kids there during the summer, I did.'

'Where about in Plymouth do you live?' I asked him, handing him a cigarette.

'We've a cottage in Cattewater, so we have,' he said, 'at the mouth of the Plym, where Drake used to anchor his fleet. I bet my missus is busy making my favourite pasty right this minute.'

'Will she be waiting on the jetty for you?'

'No,' he replied. 'She might go up to the Hoe with the kids and give me a wave, but they're well used to me coming home from sea.'

Ah yes, the crowds on The Hoe. So much had happened since I stood, watching as a warship entered Plymouth Sound, wishing I were one of her crew. Now, four years later, some of my wishes had been fulfilled - others had turned into nightmares.

A biting, westerly wind whipped around my foul-weather jacket, making my eyes water. What a contrast, I thought, to the warmth of the Mediterranean sun we had recently left. HMS *Decoy* had sailed from Malta in late December 1956. After a brief stop at Port Said to off-load stores for the army, we set sail for England.

'Pity we weren't home for Christmas,' muttered Mitch, lighting a cigarette. 'Still an' all, it isn't the first time – but it will be the last.'

'How do you mean?' I asked, giving him a curious glance.

'By this time tomorrow,' he sighed, 'I'll be have done me leaving routine in RNB [Royal Naval Barracks], and be a civilian.'

'Of course,' I replied. 'You're going outside. I'd forgotten.'

Nodding slowly, he replied, 'Twenty-two-and-a-half years. This is my last commission.' He gave me a sideways glance. 'This is your first ship, isn't it, Doc?'

'Yes, it is,' I replied.

Mitch stood back from the guardrail. 'It's been a good trip,' he said, removing his cap and stroking his thin, greying hair. 'Even though we almost got ourselves killed at times.'

Turning up the collar of my jacket, I asked him, 'What made you join the Andrew?'

He gave a short laugh. 'The bloody depression,' he replied, putting his cap on. 'There was no work in Ireland in1934. It were the navy or starve. My first ship was the *Prince of Wales*. And I'll tell you this, I cried like a baby when I heard she was sunk in '41. Your first ship is like your first woman. You never forget her.'

The shrill sound of the bosun's pipe echoed around the ship.

'Pipe down,' came the tired voice of the quartermaster. 'Call the hands will be at 0530.'

Mitch hunched his shoulders, lent heavily against the guardrail and exhaled a stream of blue cigarette smoke into the night. 'What made a young lad like you join up?'

'I wanted to travel,' I replied, trying to sound worldly, 'and the navy seemed the best way to do it.' There was more to it than that but it would have taken too long to tell him.

Later, lying in my bunk, listening to the quiet hum of the engines, Mitch's words rang around my head. I could have easily done two years National Service and re-joined the firm I worked for in Liverpool. Instead, I volunteered for the navy. As for choosing the medical branch, the influence of my Aunt Lottie, a retired nursing sister, had a lot to do with that.

I closed my eyes. My mind went back in time to a warm evening in August 1952. It was a day I would never forget.

1

My hand trembled as I turned the key and opened the front door. I hardly felt the warm August sun on my neck or heard the cries of my sister playing in the street. Even the sound of the traffic seemed dull and distant. I had difficulty in swallowing and thought my heart would explode. My God, I thought, walking into the vestibule. Maybe joing the Royal Navy without telling them wasn't such a good idea after all - in a little while I would find out.

I anticipated Dad would accept the news philosophically. He had served in minesweepers during the war. It was Mum's reaction I was dreading. I visualised her soft, brown eyes darkening and her lips tightening into a thin line, sure sign her Celtic temper was rising.

As I entered the living- room, Mum glanced up from ironing a shirt. 'Och, you're home early, Tom,' she said. 'Anything wrong?'

'No, Mum,' I replied, staring down at the well-worn carpet.

Mum was born in Arbroath and, though she had lived in England for twenty years, her voice had retained a pronounced Scottish inflexion.

The glowing embers of the coal fire fanned my face and the atmosphere was heavy with steam and stale cigarette smoke. From the kitchen came the smell of scouse, our usual Friday night fare. This would normally have made my mouth water – not so today. The very thought of food made me want to throw up.

With a sigh, Mum placed the electric iron on its edge. Her greying, dark hair was tied in a bun and, despite being in nearly fifty, her tired features retained a certain angular attractiveness.

She could read me like a book. 'What's up with you, then?" she said, lighting a cigarette. 'Are you sick or something?'

I gave a nervous cough. 'No, Mum,' I replied, clearing my throat. 'When will Dad be home?'

'He's at work,' she answered. 'Now, for God's sake, what's the matter with you?'

She threw her cigarette in the fire, placed a hand on her hip and glared at me.

This was the moment I was dreading. I took a deep breath and blurted out, 'I've joined up, Mum. I've joined the Royal Navy!'

17

Her expression of disbelief slowly turned to shock.

'You've what?' she gasped.

'I've joined the navy, Mum... this afternoon'

'We'll soon see about that,' she replied, her eyes moistening. 'Just wait till your Dad comes home.'

As tears welled up in her eyes, I suddenly felt guilty. I had forgotten about Tony...

In 1927, at the age of seventeen, Mum married an Italian, Antonio Scala. They lived in Dundee and a year later Tony, my stepbrother, was born. Antonio died suddenly of a heart attack and Mum and Tony came south to Wallasey where she met Dad. They married in 1933 and twelve months later I was born. Ten years later, Alma my sister, came into the world.

As Tony grew up, Dad's resentment of my stepbrother became intense. This often led to terrible arguments between my parents.

'He can do no soddin' wrong, can he?' Dad would yell. 'It's always Tony this and Tony that. Don't forget that I'm the one feeding the bugger.'

If Tony were present, he would shout abuse at Dad. This usually ended up with Tony getting a good hiding.

'Leave the lad alone!' she would cry. 'If you lay a hand on him again, I'm off.'

Sometimes she would hustle Tony out of the house. The front door would slam shut, sending shudders of fear through me. It was a scene I witnessed or overheard many times.

Finally, Tony started playing truant and eventually running away from home. After getting mixed up with local low-life he turned to petty crime.

How well I remember sitting next to Mum in the depressing atmosphere of Wallasey Assizes. Her sobs, as Tony was sent to reform school, kept me awake at night. I was twelve and the agony on Mum's face became indelibly etched on my mind.

In 1946, he went away on two years National Service in the army. Mum later told me he was badly treated when it was found out his father was Italian.

'Why don't you piss off back to Italy, Scala, where you belong?' the sergeant would regularly yell at him. 'You're just a fuckin' wop, aren't yer?'

On one occasion, Tony was hospitalised after someone smashed a bottle over his head during a fight. Mum said he never recovered from this, and started to drink.

I had just turned fourteen when Tony was de-mobbed. He couldn't hold down a job and soon became restless and moody. When asked a question, he would simply reply with a series of meaningless grunts, which annoyed Dad more and more. Things came to a head in November 1948.

Both Mum and Dad were employed. Dad was a river boatman, a job that involved hauling heavy, hemp lines from ship to shore in a small gig – boat. They were nicknamed 'gulls,' and worked in all kinds of weather. It was hard going for a forty-eight years old and required great physical strength and a strong constitution. Liverpool was thriving port and Dad worked steadily throughout the years. The fact Mum was also employed as a part–time laundress only served to make things worse between him and Tony. In Dad's words, my stepbrother was 'an idle, good-for-nothing sod.'

On this particular evening, I was on my own playing in the front room.

Suddenly, the sound of the front door slamming startled me. I heard Tony utter a stream of obscenities as he staggered down the hall. Oh, God, I thought, here we go again.

'Bevied, are yer, eh?' growled Dad. 'You've got money for drink, I see. How about some house-keepin' for your old girl?'

'Give over, Eddy,' I heard Mum cry. 'He gave me some last week.'

'Probably friggin' stole it, more's the like,' retorted Dad.

'Pay no soddin' notice to him, Ma,' Tony's voice was loud and slurred. 'He's nowt but an old windbag.'

The sudden creak of Dad's chair and the anger in his voice made my heart miss a beat. 'Oh, aye,' shouted Dad. 'Come outside and I'll show you what an' old wind-bag can do.'

Mum's sudden scream prompted me to dash into the living room.

A cold draft hit me from the open back kitchen door as Dad and Tony strode into the backyard. I heard the sound of scuffling feet and Tony yelling obscenities.

'I'll kill you!' he cried. 'You fuckin' bastard.'

'Come on,' Dad shouted. 'Just try it on, yer bugger.'

Then came a loud crash as Dad's moped was sent flying onto the ground.

I stood in the middle of the living room, scared out of my wits.

Mum's pleading cries echoed outside. 'For Christ's sake stop it!' she cried. 'You'll kill each other.'

Just then Dad returned. He was out of breath and had an ugly dark bruise on the left side of his head. His face was streaked with sweat and his hair was a mess. The collar of his shirt was torn and he looked pale.

Tony followed behind. His blue jacket was open and his white shirt was ripped to the waist revealing a muscular chest covered in a mass of dark, curly hair.

For a moment they stood in the middle of the room glaring at one another.

'Go on,' hissed Dad. 'Piss off out of me sight, yer useless sod.'

Just as they were about to start again Mum intervened. Her dark, shoulder-length hair normally worn in a neat bun had come undone, and her black skirt was streaked with whitewash from the backyard wall.

'That's enough,' she yelled stepping in between them. 'You're going to wake up the whole neighbourhood. '

Dad slowly sat down in his armchair.

Tony turned away, his eyes black with anger, and abruptly left. 'You wait, you bastard.' I heard him yell as he went upstairs. 'I'll get you.'

Dad lit a Woodbine.

Mum slumped onto the settee. 'I suppose you're satisfied, now?' she retorted angrily.

'What d'you friggin' mean, "satisfied"?' he replied, taking a deep drag of his cigarette. 'If he talks to me like that again, he'll get some more.'

What followed next seemed to flash by in seconds. The living-room door suddenly burst open and Tony rushed in. He carried a knife and threw himself upon Dad.

I heard Mum scream..

'This'll teach you,' cried Tony, as he plunged the knife downwards. To my horror, a trickle of blood suddenly ran down the side of Dad's face. With his free arm, Dad pushed Tony's chin back.

The sight of blood galvanised me into action As he went to strike Dad again I sprang across the room and grabbed Tony's arm. Using my right arm, I locked it around his and held on like grim death. My brother tried with all his might to struggle free, but the sight of the sharp-pointed blade flashing inches away from Dad's neck gave me strength I never knew I had. With my left hand, I grabbed hold of Tony's black wavy hair and wrenched his head back.

'Let go, you little sod,' panted Tony.

I was bathed in sweat and gasped for breath. The sight of Dad's blood-soaked shirt gave me added strength. I just glared at Tony and shook my head.

By this time, Mum was grasping Tony's shoulders with both her hands. I could see the horror in her eyes as she tried with all her might to pull Tony back.

'Are you all right, Eddy?' she cried.

'Don't worry about me, Cora,' he panted. 'Get the police. Dial 999, and for Christ sake, hurry.'

My hands and arms were aching. I clenched my teeth and tightened my grip on Tony's hair. He yelled more obscenities and tried to push his arm down towards Dad, but I grasped his arm firmly.

'Go on, Mum,' I gasped, 'get the police, and be quick.'

Mum suffered from asthma and I prayed she wasn't going to have one of her attacks.

She glared at Tony. 'If you do anything while I'm away, I swear I'll swing for you.'

Mum rushed out the room. I knew she was making for the telephone kiosk at the top of the road.

Meanwhile, Tony, Dad and myself remained locked in a deadly embrace.

Once more, Tony demanded I let go of his hair and release my grip on his arm. 'There'll be a few bob it for you if you do, Tom lad.'

My arm was aching and my hand felt numb. I stared back at him and shook my head.

After what seemed like an eternity, Mum arrived out of breath and bathed in perspiration. 'They're on their way, Eddy,' she said and grabbed hold of Tony again.

Time seemed to stand still.

I heard Alma cry from upstairs and thanked God she hadn't witnessed any of this.

Finally, the sound of screeching brakes told us that the police had arrived. Two burly policemen came into the room and immediately pounced on Tony. One of them twisted his hand and removed the knife, before dragging him off Dad. The other grasped Tony's hands behind his back and quickly placed him in handcuffs.

When I let go of Tony, I thought my arms would fall off.

Mum slumped down on the settee, head in hands, sobbing.

I put my arms around her. 'It'll be all right, now, Mum,' I said. 'I'll look after you.'

'We have him now, love,' one of the policemen said. 'He won't be hurting anyone for a while.'

'Bastards!' cried Tony, as the two officers hauled him away. 'I'll get you. You wait. You fuckin' bastards.' The look of hatred in his eyes told me that he meant it.

Dad was taken by ambulance to Central Hospital, where he had five stitches in his wound.

The police were good as there word. Tony was charged with attempted murder, found guilty and sentenced to five years.

Then followed painful trips across the Mersey to see him in Walton prison.

I dreaded those visits, but always accompanied Mum. Even now I can still smell the dank odour of carbolic and hear the harsh, metallic clink of keys and the sound of steel doors closing.

The sight of Tony in his grey prison uniform always brought tears to Mum's eyes.

'How are you, love?' she would say through the wire mesh separating them.

'O K,' he always replied, adding, 'got any fags?'

Tony seemed quite unconcerned and gave me impression he didn't mind being 'inside.' I think he enjoyed the company of like-minded misfits.

To this day I can see him smiling sarcastically as we left. Mum would smile back, but once the heavy prison doors slammed shut, the tears would flow again.

The visits seemed to age Mum. Her hands would tremble as she lit a cigarette. By the time we arrived home, she was pale and drawn. The effect of these visits on Mum broke my heart and I swore never to put her though such purgatory.

Now, as I stood before Mum telling her that I was about to go away I felt physically sick. Tony was due for release in twelve months, and trouble was inevitable when he and Dad met up.

The scraping of the backyard door opening told me Dad had

arrived. His weather-beaten features appeared at the window as he lent his mo-ped against the wall. With his black oilskin and sou'wester, he reminded me of the fisherman on a pilchard tin. As he entered the living room, his beaming smile produced dimples in each cheek. I smiled back, wondered how long his good mood would last.

'By Christ, it's bitter on that river,' he muttered, rubbing his hands together over the glowing embers of the fire.

Under his oilskin, which he hung up in the hallway, he wore a thick woollen sweater and an old pair of trousers. He sat down and removed his muddy boots. This normally annoyed Mum and she would tell him to go upstairs and change. By now she was composed and sat, arms folded, staring at me.

'Any tea on the go, then?' asked Dad.

I shot Mum a glance and said, 'I'll put the kettle on, then.'

'Oh no you won't,' said Mum, slowly rising from the settee. 'I'll do that.' She glared at Dad, straightened her apron and added, 'Me laddo here has something to tell you,' and went into the kitchen.

Meanwhile, Dad wiggled his toes and sat back in his chair. 'What's up, son?' he said, giving me a sly wink. 'Don't tell me you've got the sack.'

Before I had time to reply, Mum shouted from the back kitchen.

'You're son's joined the bloody navy. That's what's up.'

I sat rigid on the settee and stared at Dad. His dimples became even more pronounced than usual and he burst out laughing.

'You've what?' he exploded. 'You've joined up? Well bugger me, two years in the old Andrew'll do you the world of good.'

The term, 'Andrew' was the navy's nickname for itself, after an 18th century press-gang officer of the same name.

My insides churned over. Christ, I said to myself, he thinks I'm only going in to do my National Service. I felt the blood drain from my face. With a quick flick of my tongue over my lips, I took a deep breath and blurted. 'It's not me National Service - I've joined for twelve years!'

Mum returned from the kitchen, threw her dishtowel on the table. 'Twelve years,' she cried. 'Over my dead body!'

Meanwhile Dad's startled expression had changed to a grin. He lit a Woodbine and offered one to Mum.

She ignored him.

'Sit down, Cora,' he said. 'Keep a level head. The navy did me no bloody harm.'

I settled back into the settee with relief. Suddenly, the strain of the day caught up with me. My legs felt like jelly and my head ached.

Mum remained standing and lit a cigarette. She took several quick puffs and once again tears welled up in her eyes. 'There was a bloody war on then,' she replied.

'There's still a friggin' war goin' on,' replied Dad, flicking his ash onto the dying embers of the fire, 'Out there in Korea, or hadn't you heard?'

Mum glared at Dad. 'Course I have,' she replied, blowing her nose. 'Aye, and if your son ends up there, it'll be your bloody fault if anything happens to him. You and your soddin' war stories.'

I lit a Bar One, inhaled deeply and began to relax. But Dad's reminder about Korea made things worse. Mum put her cigarette out, sat down on the settee and covered her face with her apron. The sight of her crying cut right through me. I put a consoling arm around her shoulder.

'I won't be going to Korea, Mum, so don't worry,' I said. 'Anyway, it'll be all over by the time I join.'

Peace talks had broken down and the war in Korea was still raging – Bill Speakman had even been awarded the Victoria Cross. At night I imagined myself on the bridge of a destroyer ploughing through the China Sea, firing off depth charges while under attack from MIG fighters. 'So you've nothing to worry about,' I said, giving her a hug.

Mum stood up, wiped her eyes with the back of her hand, and went into the kitchen.

'This is all your bloody fault, Eddy,' said Mum, raising her voice over the clatter of dishes. 'You put him up to this.'

Dad smiled and winked at me. 'Don't be soft, Cora,' he said. 'The lad's old enough to know 'is own mind, aren't you son?'

'Yes, Dad, I think I am,' I replied confidently.

Mum returned, carrying a tray containing two plates of stew and potatoes.

'He's only bloody seventeen,' she said, carefully placing the food on the dining table. 'That makes him under age, doesn't it Tom?'

'I suppose so,' I replied sheepishly. 'But I've got the papers here.' I took two folded forms from the inside pocket of my jacket.

Dad and I sat at the table. Mum, in a defiant mood, banged some knives and forks on the table. 'You can sign the damn things, Eddy,' she cried angrily. 'Because I bloody-well won't.'

I began to toy with my food.

'Ah, come on, Mum,' I said rather mournfully, 'I want to see a bit of the world. You know I've always wanted to join the navy.'

But I had to admit Mum had a point. Over the years, Dad had held us spellbound with his countless war stories. Told with typical Scouse humour, his yarns about Sicily and Italy seemed to come alive. When he spoke his infectious laugh and facial expressions made us shriek with laughter.

The story I liked best happened in Augusta, shortly after the invasion of Sicily in 1943. On their way back onboard their minesweeper, Dad and his pal, Harvey Rawlinson, stopped to relieve themselves against a door of a chemist shop that had been bombed.

I can see Dad now wearing a blue collarless shirt and red braces holding a bottle of strong ale. As he spoke, his brown eyes sparkled with humour.

'We needed a leak, y'see,' Dad would say, with an expression of mock innocence. 'Well, we lent on this large door. Anyways, the door opened. Just like Ali Whatisname? and the forty thieves.'

Dad went on, 'Well, guess what? We found two large bottles of Eau de Cologne. Harvey began to panic. 'Don't touch them,' he cried. 'They're probably booby trapped.'

'Now, you must remember,' said Dad, 'perfume was hard to come by, there was a war on. Keep a level head, I told Harvey, and we decided to 'liberate' them.'

They smuggled the bottles onboard then proceeded to mix the perfume with some whiskey. It was against naval regulations to smuggle alcohol onboard a RN warship. However, the 'Sparrows', as the men in minesweepers were nicknamed, simply ignored this. All were volunteers and didn't pay much attention to such petty rules.

Shortly afterwards the 'brew' began to take effect. Everyone started to sing and break wind.

'The smell was lovely,' Dad would say, roaring with laughter, while Mum pretended to be disgusted. 'It brought tears to our eyes,

I can tell you.'

The aroma soon drifted up onto the upper deck. The Officer of the Watch, a young sub-lieutenant who, in Civvy street was a chemist, suddenly sniffed the air.

'I know that smell,' he was heard to say. 'They've got women on board. Call out the duty watch.'

Suddenly, four tired-looking sailors invaded Dad's mess.

The captain, a tall, distinguished-looking man named Lieutenant Peter Reid, RNVR, was startled by the noise and came up from his cabin to investigate.

By this time, Dad and his mess- mates were singing their heads off.

Harvey, who was the captain's personal steward, was standing on the mess-deck table frantically conducting the drunken choir.

When the duty watch came into the mess, Harvey collapsed on top of the captain and let out the most resounding fart.

Needless to say, no women were found, but the smell was so overpowering that the duty-watch soon beat a hasty retreat

Dad and Harvey received a week's stoppage of leave, by which time they were being bombed by German Stukas while clearing the channels of mines ready for the invasion of Italy

My imagination had also been stirred by reading C.S.Forrester's wonderful *Hornblower* books and Nicholas Monseratt's *The Cruel Sea*. Films such as *In Which We Serve,* and *The Gift Horse* also gripped me. As for the travelogues, they made me even more determined to see the world.

I was seventeen, and would soon be eligible for National Service. My two best friends, Joe Woods and Jock Forbes, who were apprentice shipwrights at Camel Lairds, were deferred until 1954.

'I pity you when you go in,' said Joe. 'All that bloody square-bashin'

'Aye, an' I bet that fuckin' uniform itches like hell,' said Jock, knocking back his whisky.

We were sitting in the King's Arms, our favourite meeting place on Liscard Road. Momentarily I thought about telling them of my decision to join the Royal Navy, but changed my mind. .

'Oh, it might not be so bad,' I casually replied. 'After all, it's only for two years.'

Still, I thought as we left the pub, anything was better than my job sitting at a desk licking stamps and posting letters.

I worked for Leonard Baines and Company, paint pigment exporters in Old Hall Street, Liverpool. My desk overlooked the River Mersey. Every day I gazed enviously as ships came and went, wondering where they had been, or were going to. As for warships with their sleek, grey lines, whenever one cruised down-river, I was beside myself with excitement.

I had already secretly visited St John's Recruiting Office in Liverpool, to obtain a brochure telling about the various aspects of the service.

Although Dad had been a seaman, I had long ago made up my mind to join the medical branch of the navy. My Aunt Lottie was a nursing sister during the war. Dad's stories always made me laugh, but Aunt Lottie's accounts of hospital life intrigued me. It made good sense to combine medicine with the navy. That way I could see the world, and follow a noble calling - who knows, I told myself, one day I might even become a doctor. Wishful thinking perhaps, but I was young and fired with ambition.

I finally made up my mind. During my lunch break on a warm, sunny day in August 1952 I left the office, and with my pulse racing, made my way to St John's Lane.

Smoking my last Bar One, I nervously stood outside the recruiting office, staring at coloured posters encouraging men and women to join up.

My heart pounded and my nerves felt on edge. After all, I was about to take a momentous decision that would change my life forever. I took a deep breath, threw my dog-end away and went inside.

Behind a large, well - polished desk, reading the *Liverpool Echo* sat a thick-set man in a blue uniform. He was almost bald, with tufts of grey hair at each temple. Two empty wire-mesh trays labelled 'IN' and 'OUT' lay at each corner of his desk.

As I entered, his heavily jowled face looked up.

Placing his newspaper down he, fixed me with a steady stare.

'What can I do for you, me beauty?' He sounded like Robert Newton in Treasure Island.

On his left breast were two rows of medal ribbons. Behind him, on a blue painted wall, was a large white ensign. Nearby were several black and white photographs of warships. A model of an aircraft carrier stood in a glass case on top of a bookcase. A brass plaque read, HMS *Ark Royal,* built in Cammell Lairds, Birkenhead, in 1938.

I nervously cleared my throat. 'I want to join up, sir.'

His face broke into a toothy grin. 'Then you've come to the right place, my bird,' he replied. 'And don't call me 'sir.' These three buttons on me arm 'ere says I'm a chief petty officer, right?'

I nodded quickly. 'Right.'

When I told him which branch I wanted to join, he nodded his approval. 'A poultice-walloper, eh?' he said with a grin. 'Good men they are. Patched me up good and proper after Dunkirk.'

He took out a form from a drawer and told me to fill it in. After doing so, the chief stood up.

'Follow me, my 'andsome,' he said.

Walking with a slight limp, the chief led me through a door into a small room.

After that it was, as it were, plain sailing.

After passing a thorough medical examination, I took a test in basic arithmetic and English. I was then told to wait in the main office.

The waiting played havoc with my nerves. The chief sensed this and tried to make me feel at ease. He told me he had been in the navy nearly twenty- two years.

'And loved every minute, I can tell 'ee,' he said. 'Only 'ave a few months to do afore me pension. Met some grand lads. Saw a few killed, too, God rest their souls.'

He asked me what my parents thought about me joining for twelve years.

I gave a quick shrug of my shoulders and muttered, 'All right, I suppose.'

He pursed his lips. 'Mm, I see,' he said, giving me a look of disbelief.

He then stood up, gave me a wink and said. 'Back in a jiffy,' and disappeared through a side door.

I began to bite my nails. The waiting was almost too much to bear.

After what seemed like an eternity, the chief came back. His beaming smile told me everything and I felt like hugging him.

'You'll do, matey,' he said. Then with a sly grin, handed me two large white forms. 'But you'll have to get your folks to sign these. If you gets 'em back 'ere on Monday, we'll have you in

Pompey on the twenty-third o' next month.'

I emerged into the warm sunshine feeling exhilarated. This state of euphoria didn't last long – my watch told me I was almost two hours late for work.

By the time I arrived at work, I was sweating and out of breath. I hardly noticed my tie was undone and my jet-black hair a dishevelled mess.

The first person I met was the corpulent figure of Mr Baines, dressed, as usual, in a blue double-breasted suit. He was smoking one of his favourite Churchill cigarettes. I knew this because it was my job to buy forty of these for him every day. Over a pair of horn-rimmed spectacles he glared at me.

'And where, may I ask, have you been till now?' he scowled. 'One of the girls had to buy my cigarettes.'

'Sorry, sir,' I stuttered. 'You see, I've just joined the Royal Navy, for twelve years.'

His expression immediately changed. He raised his bushy black eyebrows and gave me a look of surprise. 'Have you, by Jove?' he said, smiling. 'Good for you. I was in the RAF, you know.'

He put his arm around my shoulders and led me to the centre of the office.

The typists stopped work and the two managers, Mr Croasdale and Mr Roberts looked up from their desks. Glancing around, he announced. 'Young Tom, here, has just joined the Royal Navy.'

I felt my face redden especially when Dorothy Hinds, the boss's buxom secretary, gave me a wet kiss on the cheek. The typists turned to each other with a look of surprise and giggled. Mr Croasdale, who had been a pilot in the Fleet Air Arm, was especially pleased.

'Congratulations, Tom,' he said, pumping my hand. 'You'll look really smart in navy-blue.'

After everything settled down, I finally plucked up enough courage to hand in a week's notice. Much to my relief Mr Baines accepted this with a smile; he even gave me a ten bob note and told me to go home early. Now all I had to do was tell my parents.

Dad eventually persuaded Mum to sign my forms. But the shock of learning that I would be on my way to Portsmouth in just over three weeks showed in both their faces. Even Dad couldn't raise a smile. The only person who became hysterical was Alma.

She burst into tears and she threw her arms around my waist.

'No...no,' she cried. 'You can't go away, I won't let you.'

I knelt down and with a handkerchief, wiped away her tears and looked up at Mum. Her face was pale and she was crying also. For once, Dad was silent and sat eating his dinner.

Then, I remembered Cynthia, my girlfriend. My God, I thought. What on earth was I going to tell her?

2

After the Second World War, New Brighton boomed. Despite continued rationing, everyone was determined to enjoy themselves. The all-night, ferry boat service across the River Mersey gave easy access to anyone seeking to escape the austerity of post-war Britain. This often meant a Saturday night out at the biggest dancing arena in the north of England, the fabulous Tower Ballroom in New Brighton.

People came from as far afield as Southport, Chester and North Wales. Visitors could hardly miss the Tower Building. It loomed high in the sky, like a huge, red-bricked sentinel casting a lengthy shadow across the nearby football ground of New Brighton FC.

Crowds would pile out of the coaches, laughing with excitement, hell-bent on dancing to the big band sounds of Bill Gregson, Bert Yates or Harry Gold and his Pieces of Eight.

It was here, on a warm July evening in 1951 that I met Cynthia.

The night began quietly enough. The smoke-filled bar of 'The King's Arms' was packed with the usual Saturday crowd. Joe and I were sitting at a table enjoying our second pint. He sometimes called me 'Bud,' a term copied from the American movies. I didn't mind as I occasionally referred to him by his surname, 'Woods.' He didn't seem to mind either.

'According to the *Echo*,' said Joe, 'there's going to be some sort of river pageant and a fire-work display for the Festival of Britain on the 19th. Sounds great, don't it?'

'Yeah,' I replied, emptying my glass. 'My Dad says the Royal Navy's sending several ships. Now, that really will be worth seeing. By the way, it's your round.'

Joe's face with its crinkly grin always reminded me of Tommy Steele. 'D'you fancy goin' to the Tower tonight, Bud?' he said, running his fingers through his mop of fair hair. 'I've a feeling in me water this could be our lucky night.'

We had a saying: 'If you can't dance, you've got no chance.' That didn't apply to Joe. Unlike me, he was a terrific ballroom dancer.

'Sound all right to me,' I replied, pushing my empty glass

towards him. 'But it's still your round.'

It was still daylight as Joe and I made our way down New Brighton's busy Victoria Street. Making our way through the crowd, we passed the Tivoli Theatre, an early venue for up and coming comedians such as Ken Dodd and Jimmy Tarbuck.

We joined the happy hordes making their way into the fairground. People clustered around brightly-painted stalls, trying their luck with rifle, dart or cloth ball. Couples strolled, arm in arm, lazily licking *Walls* ice-creams or clouds of pink candy-floss.

The warm air helped to increase the mouth-watering odour of fish and chips, hot dogs and doughnuts. The strong smell of tobacco hung in the air and from every corner came the sound of syncopated ragtime, barrel-organ music and the jingle-jangle of the carousel.

Children's cries from the Big Wheel merged with the rattle of the figure-of-eight roller coaster carriages. To this was added the ear-splitting roar of motor bikes warming up for the Wall of Death ride. The atmosphere was charged with excitement, and like Joe, I too sensed something special was going to happen.

The red-bricked Tower Building stood, like a medieval fortress, overlooking the fairground. At each end, two pagoda-like structures surrounded by four smaller pointed towers jutted upwards. To this was added an enormous steel tower. Standing 621 feet above sea level, it was the tallest structure in Europe. Completed in 1900 at a cost of £120,000, this imposing edifice was the pride of Wallasey.

Dad once told Joe and me that from the top you could see the Isle of Man.

'Just the job, eh, Bud?' said Joe, grinning. 'D'you fancy that?'

'No, not me,' I replied. 'It's all right for you, Woods. You've a head for heights. I get a nosebleed on the top deck of a bus.'

The Tower building not only housed a ballroom, but also a spacious theatre where Rob Wilton, George Robey and Vesta Tily once topped the bill. Because it dominated the skyline, ships coming into Liverpool used the steel structure as a navigational aid. This came to an end after the First World War.

A few years ago, Dad told me about the time when he and his older brothers, Sam and Jack, watched it being dismantled.

'Rusted to hell, it were,' he said, sitting in his favourite armchair, smoking. 'It were just after the first war. I'd be about fourteen or so. Council said it were a danger to the public. Our Jack and me watched as the men lowered those bloody big steel parts down on a crane. Like ants they were. No safety nets in them days. My oath, there weren't. Four men were killed buildin' it, y' know. It was sad to see it come down. Some of them judies who were watchin' cried, like babes, so they did.'

But, thank goodness, the Tower Ballroom, our target for tonight, remained.

As we climbed up the steps, Joe rubbed his hands together.

'Come on, Bud,' he cried. 'I still have that feeling in me water.'

We paid our three shillings entrance fee and made for the bar. After downing a couple of pints we retreated to the toilet.

Standing in front of a mirror, combing our hair, I couldn't help but notice the difference between Joe and myself. He had a fair complexion whereas mine was dark and swarthy. Joe was slightly smaller, but broader than me. We even enjoyed different sports. Joe was keen on snooker and could handle a cue with expertise. I played soccer and supported Liverpool.

Furthermore he came from a large Catholic family. Mine were Protestants with Spanish antecedents. Joe preferred sports jackets like the fawn one he had on that night, while I wore my one and only grey suit complete with white shirt and dark red tie. Oh, yes, I almost forgot. Joe liked blondes, but I fancied brunettes, which, as things turned out, was just as well.

However, there was one thing we did have in common. We trusted one another completely, and as the years passed this developed into a bond of unbreakable friendship.

We lit a Woodbine, straightened up and like two gladiators entering the Coliseum, strode into the ballroom.

We were met by a blast of warm air, heavily tinged with perfume, tobacco and sweat. The ballroom was a mass of colour and movement. Couples in close proximity, moved to the strains of Bill Gregson's band playing *"Blue Moon"*. It was here, over the years, that many a tango had led to a waltz up the aisle.

Among the dancers was a smattering of service uniforms, including a few GIs from Burtonwood, an American base just outside Liverpool.

Joe once told me the dance floor was the biggest in England and was specially sprung. I remember him saying, 'You know, Bud, this bloody floor is so good, Fred and Ginger could dance on it.'

Immaculately dressed in black tuxedoes, the musicians contrasted sharply with Bill Gregson's pristine white dinnerjacket, complete with red carnation. The band struck up Cole Porter's "*Anything Goes*". With every movement, their instruments caught the light, dazzling couples as they swayed past the bandstand.

The beat of the music reverberated around the green and cream decorated walls. Joe and I watched as the men whirled their partners around the floor. The girls, in flowing dresses, gave more than a glimpse of stocking as they rustled past the eyes of the ever-watching males.

Suspended from the high ceiling by an almost invisible cable rotated a huge silver sphere. With each movement, flecks of luminescence filtered down onto those below. When the lights dimmed, an umbrella of intimacy descended upon the dancers. Warm cheeks were pressed together, bodies moved closer and passions became aroused.

Set back from the floor, people sat at tables under a balcony supported by archways. Those, like Joe and myself, who couldn't find anywhere to sit, lounged against the wall, smoking and eyeballing the talent.

Joe decided it was time for us to make a move.

The next dance was a waltz, the only one I could do. It was, however, one of Joe's specialities.

'D' you fancy them?' said Joe, with a sideways nod of his head.

I turned and saw two girls sitting at a table. One had dark hair and wore a yellow dress. The other was a blonde in something pink.

'All right,' I replied, 'but I'll take the one in yellow. O.K?'

As we pushed our way towards them, Yellow Dress gave a quick glance at us and pretended not to notice. Then, like women do, she sent a telepathic message to her pal, who also turned her head away.

I nervously approached her, half expecting to be refused. To my surprise she looked directly at me, smiled demurely, and said. 'Yes, thank you, I'd love to.'

She stood up, straightened her dress and picked up a small black handbag. Her head came up to my chin, and as I stood aside to let her past, the fragrance of her perfume sent my pulse racing. She wore black, high-heeled shoes and carried herself like a model. The colour of her dress contrasted sharply with her dark brown hair that fell gracefully around her shoulders.

When we reached the floor, I put my hand around her narrow waist. She looked up and in a soft voice, said, 'I'm afraid I'm not a good dancer.'

'That's all right,' I replied, 'just follow me.' But just as I was thinking how delicate her hand was, we collided into a couple. Now it was my turn to apologise.

The collision pushed us closer and I could feel the softness of her breasts against my chest. She quickly pulled away and we carried on in silence.

I tensed up and my feet just about managed to keep in time to the strains of *"The Tennessee Waltz"*. Joe and his blonde moved past, showing off a few fancy steps before disappearing into the crowd.

'Is the girl you're with your mate?' I asked, avoiding yet another couple.

'Yes,' she replied in a clear, refined voice similar to those high school girls I sometimes heard on the bus. 'Her name's Janet. We live near each other.'

'Where's that?'

'Gorse Crescent. Do you know it?'

'Oh, yes, off Gorsey Lane. Not far from the docks.'

We were continually being jostled closer and I became aroused. Beads of sweat formed on my brow and I broke off dancing. We then walked for several steps, arms around each other keeping in time to the music.

I caught another glimpse of Joe and Janet. He gave me a quick 'I think I'm on here' wink and disappeared again.

When we resumed dancing, she pressed herself against me and I decided to show off by attempting a double turn. In order to do this, I placed my knee between her legs to affect an easier movement. She grasped my hand and I could feel that familiar feeling rising again. When the music stopped I was bathed in sweat.

As we stood quietly waiting for the band to strike up the next waltz, I sneaked my arm around her waist. When we began to dance, I plucked up enough courage to ask her name.

'Cynthia Peters,' she replied, 'and yours?'

'Tom,' I said, carefully avoiding another couple. 'Lightburn.'

'You're very dark, aren't you?' she said, looking up at me.

'Are you foreign?'

I gave a laugh. It was a question I was always being asked. 'No,' I said grinning. 'My grandparents were Spanish. And before you ask, no, I can't play the castanets.'

She tilted her head back and laughed, displaying a row of even, white teeth. Suddenly the ice was broken. Her hand tightened around mine and we both relaxed.

'Haven't I seen you in Jones's Milk Bar?' she asked. 'Do you go there?'

'Yes,' I replied. 'That's where we all meet – the lads of the football team, that is. I've never seen you there, though. I would have remembered.'

'D' you have any brothers or sisters?' she asked. 'I have a little brother, Henry. He's seven.'

Her question made me feel uncomfortable. How would she react, I wondered, if I told her that Tony was doing a stretch in Walton for attempted murder? She would probably say 'thank you,' and rapidly disappear. 'I have a sister, she's eight, and a brother, who's, er, away.'

'Is he working?'

'Yes, he's working,' I replied avoiding her gaze. Much to my relief, that satisfied her curiosity.

She looked at me and smiled. 'Are you a keen footballer?'

'Yes, I play quite a lot.'

Suddenly I felt even more confident and drew her closer to me. I had my hand on her back and could feel the straps of her bra under her dress. Christ, I thought, she's almost naked. I became bolder and gently rested my cheek against her head. I was afraid to hold her too tight, and for a while we drifted around the floor, oblivious to everyone and everything.

When the dance finished, we walked to her table.

She was the roughly same age as me, and worked for a solicitor. I told her I was a clerk in a Liverpool office, adding rather cockily, I was due for promotion. This wasn't true, but it seemed to impress her.

After another dance, Joe and I invited them for a drink.

'We'd love one,' said Cynthia. 'Wouldn't we, Jan?'

'Yes,' replied Janet, glancing at her friend. 'But we're not eighteen. Will they serve us?'

'You'll be all right with us,' said Joe, trying to sound manly.

I grinned and took Cynthia's arm. 'Come on. Nobody will notice.'

And nobody did. The girls had a port and lemon and Joe and I drank a pint of bitter each. Cynthia passed her Senior Service cigarettes around and we talked about school days.

I told Cynthia I went to Wallasey Technical and it came as no surprise to learn she had attended the local high school.

'Cynthia and Jan live near each other in Gorse Crescent.' I said, kicking Joe under the table.

Joe gave Janet one of his famous grins. 'That's handy,' he said. 'I live in The Grove, not far from you.'

Janet raised her eyebrows in mock surprise. 'Mmm, you don't say,' she said teasingly, picking up her handbag. 'Come on, Cynny. Let's go to the Ladies.'

While they were away, Joe and I had a crafty shot of whiskey.

'Don't forget, Bud,' said Joe, gleefully rubbing his hands together. 'If we get separated, we'll meet in "The Kings" tomorrow at one. OK?'

Cynthia and I stayed together for the rest of the evening. Joe and Janet got swallowed up in the crowd and we didn't see them again.

Shortly before eleven, Cynthia and I left the dancehall. Hand in hand we dashed to catch the last bus.

We got off at St Martin's Lane and walked though Central Park. After the smoky atmosphere of the ballroom, the warm air felt cool and refreshing. A full moon cast a silver sheen across the waters of the lake. The stillness of the night was palpable, disturbed only by the occasional snorting of water hens. We stopped walking and instinctively put our arms around each other and kissed. Her lips felt warm and soft and, as her tongue found mine, I could feel the blood pounding in my head.

'Come on, Tom,' she gasped, breaking away from me. 'My mother will kill me. It must be almost twelve.'

'OK,' I said, smiling. 'I can't have you changing into a pumpkin.'

After crossing Poulton Road, we finally arrived outside her terraced house. She stood up and gave me a quick kiss on the lips.

'Thank you, Tom,' she whispered. 'I've had a lovely time.'

'Can I see you again?' I asked anxiously.

'I'm on holiday next week,' she replied. 'Mum and I are going to see my aunt in North Wales. We'll be back on Wednesday afternoon. I could see you after that.'

'Great,' I replied. 'I finish work at five. Meet you outside the Queens at seven OK?'

She smiled and nodded.

Just then the lobby light suddenly went on and a tired female voice called out. 'Come on, Cynthia. It's time you were in.'

We still held hands. When I looked down and couldn't tell which were her fingers or mine, I knew that 'something special' I had sensed earlier had happened.

The next day Joe and I met as arranged. Straight away the mischievous glint in his eyes told me he had scored with Janet.

'All right, you dirty bastard,' I said, sitting down at the table. 'What happened to you last night, as if I couldn't guess?'

'Bingo!' he replied, pushing my pint to me. 'What about you, did you get a bit?'

Normally, I would have lied, but this time I couldn't bring myself to brag about something I hadn't done. 'Well, not exactly,' I replied, 'I'm seeing her on Wednesday.'

'Don't worry, Bud,' said Joe, finishing his black and tan. 'You'll be all right there, but remember to use a johnny.'

I ignored his lecherous leer and finished my drink.

Buying condoms could be a bit embarrassing, especially if there was a girl serving in the chemist. I usually ended up buying a toothbrush. One day Mum asked me what I was doing with so many toothbrushes, she must have thought I was obsessed with cleaning my teeth.

Condoms were also sold in barbers' shops. Joe's eldest brother, Jim, bought them for us. He had recently been de-mobbed from the RAF. They were three for two and sixpence, and came in small, purple packets marked 'Durex.'

Wednesday arrived and each passing hour seemed like a day. Shortly after five o'clock I hurried along Old Hall Street and made my way to the Pier Head. I could see the mast and red funnel of the ferryboat over the curved canopy of the slipway. I joined the jostling crowd and boarded the ferry that would take me across the Mersey to Wallasey.

The ferryboats worked a shuttle service between Liverpool, Wallasey and New Brighton. My vessel was the MS *Leasowe,* and in the distance I could see her sister ship, the MS *Egremont*, pulling away from Wallasey's Landing Stage.

I glanced up at the two pairs of Liver Birds perched high on the twin towers of the Liver building. According to Dad they were half eagle and half cormorant, and made of copper. He also told me that the face on the Liver clock was twenty-five feet in diameter and was bigger than that on Big Ben. He may not have had much formal education, but he certainly knew a lot about Merseyside.

During the Second World War, Hitler bragged his Luftwaffe would knock the Liver Birds off their perch. Of course, they never did. The German bombardiers must have been blind because the birds, a symbol of the city, were certainly big enough.

The compartment where I found a seat was stuffy and cramped. Suddenly, the engines revved up sending a shudder throughout the vessel, as it slowly pulled away from the landing stage.

The wooden benches were uncomfortable, and the smell of stale tobacco and fresh make-up made me feel a bit queasy. Tired eyes scanned magazines and early issues of the *Liverpool Echo*. Seeing the headlines, 'Royal Navy Arrives This Week', reminded me of their forthcoming visit. I lit a cigarette and went outside.

The fresh air cleared my head and I found space against a guardrail. I took a deep breath and flicked my dog-end into the river. Christ, I thought, would this journey never end?

The reflection of the cloudless sky turned the calm waters dark blue. Riding high on the ship's thermals, clusters of seagulls circled like hungry vultures. According to Greek mythology, these birds were the souls of dead sailors. Judging by the mess they made on the deck, they didn't think much of the ferry service.

Finally, the engines slowed down. The vibrations ceased as the boat turned to port, leaving a frothy mass in its wake.

In the distance, the New Brighton fairground and Tower buildings dominated the Cheshire skyline. Not far away from the ferry terminus stood Wallasey's majestic Town Hall. From its stone roof rose a neo-classical temple topped up with a gigantic copper urn. At each corner, lying in reverent pose four statues representing Courage, Industry, Peace and Prudence gazed down at the populace. Dad, in his inimitable Scouse humour, thought they looked as if they were sitting on the toilet.

Further along I could see the Mariner's Home. This imposing, red-bricked building faced the river, thus enabling its inhabitants to feel close to the sea. And further along, the thick black line of New Brighton pier jutted into the Mersey, like an extension of the peninsula

The ferryboat squashed against two huge, rubber fenders forcing passengers to steady themselves before disembarking. Strong hands slid open the solid, wooden doors. At the same time the clanking of chains being unlatched allowed the gangway to be lowered. This hit the deck with an ear-splitting clatter letting people ashore.

With a turn of speed that would have done justice to Billy Liddell, I flashed my pass and jumped on the number fourteen bus.

As I opened the front door, the smell of fish and chips made my mouth water. After a brief hello, I dashed upstairs, had a quick wash, and changed my clothes. .

'After the geese again, eh?' commented Dad, as I entered the living room.

'Pay no attention, to him, Tom,' said Mum, placing a plate of egg and chips in front of me. 'You look very smart. I think that brown checked jacket goes well with your white shirt and tie. Going somewhere nice?'

'Ha!' snorted Dad. 'He must have a date.'

I grinned and hurriedly made two large chip sandwiches.

'Can you lend me two and six, please, Mum?' I gabbled through a mouth full of food. 'I'll pay you back on Friday.'

'Must be a heavy one,' laughed Mum. From her purse she took out half-a-crown. 'Here you are, Errol Flynn, I hope she's worth it.'

I already had two shillings. Now I could afford a packet of Bar One, pay for the flicks and have some left over for an ice cream. I gulped down the remainder of my supper, checked my hair in the mirror, gave Mum a quick kiss on the cheek and left.

The Queen's picture house was a few minutes walk from my house in Rappart Road. I arrived ten minutes early.

There was nobody outside the cinema as the first house started at five-thirty. I passed the time by nervously looking at the technicoloured photographs in large glass cases either side of the entrance. The film showing was Walt Disney's *Cinderella,* which didn't appeal to me.

I gave my brown shoes a quick rub on the back of my trousers, lit a cigarette and checked my watch. It was almost seven. She was nearly five minutes late.

I began to feel self-conscious and hoped none of my mates would see me. Just as I was about to slink around the side of the cinema, I saw her.

With her head slightly tilted upwards, there was a sexy aloofness in the way she walked. Her high-heeled shoes accentuated her well-shaped legs and in her left hand she casually swung a small handbag. A breeze blew against her green dress, outlining the contours of her thighs, making me think thoughts I could be locked up for.

'Hi,' I said, stubbing out my cigarette. 'You look really nice.'

With a quick bow of her head, she replied, 'Thank you, kind sir. Sorry to be late. Had to do the washing up. Where shall we go?'

She took a step back and looked up at the billboard. For the first time, I noticed how attractive her turned-up nose was.

'I'm afraid I've seen this one,' she said. 'Dad took me to see it last week. What about a drink at Jones's?'

'Great,' I replied. 'Maybe we could get some chips later on?'

'Yes,' she said. 'It's too hot for the pictures, anyway.' She took hold of my hand. Suddenly, I did feel like Errol Flynn.

The milk bar was only a few hundred yards down the road. Through the large glass window I could see the diminutive figure of Henry Jones and Agnes, his buxom wife. Clad in her usual white apron, Agnes was busy wiping down the white marble counter. From inside, the jukebox blared out Ted Heath's orchestra playing *'Intermission Rif.'*

Henry, in his customary brown overall coat, was making milk shakes. As we entered he looked up and gave us a toothy grin. 'Hello, what have we here, then?' he sneered, placing two drinks on the counter. 'Young Tom with a girl, eh?'

I felt my cheeks redden.

'Shut up, Henry,' snapped Agnes, 'and mind your own business. Now, what would you and your lady-friend like, Tom?'

I ordered two milk shakes and we sat down at one of the Formica-topped tables.

On the cream-coloured walls, now stained brown by tobacco smoke, hung tattered posters advertising Woodbines, Walls Ice Cream and Tizer. A few pals from Ashville, the soccer team I played for, sat with their girlfriends. They were drinking milk shakes and smoking. Cynthia knew one or two and gave a wave.

She talked to them, while I discussed football with the lads. One or two gave me a sly wink and laughed.

Three girls dressed in black, pencil skirts, waspie-belts and coloured sweaters, lounged against the jukebox. All were smoking and chewing gum. Frankie Lane singing *Jezebel* had taken over from Ted Heath. With an air of indifference, they tapped their feet to the beat of the music, while blowing smoke rings in the air.

We finished our milk shakes.

'Come on, Tom,' said Cynthia. 'It's very stuffy in here, isn't it? Shall we go?'

The girls gave each other a furtive glance and the lads sniggered.

Peter Morris, our burly, redheaded centre-half winked at me. 'Don't forget training next week, Tom' he said 'Johnny Dennett will do his nut if you don't show up.' Johnny Dennett was the team manager. He had served in the Royal Navy during the Second World War, and was a stickler for discipline.

Our quicksilver left winger, Norman Spearing, added, 'Aye, if he's got any strength left.'

Just as I turned to him, Cynthia grabbed my arm.

'Pay no attention, Tom,' she said, pulling me away. 'He's only joking.'

The girls giggled, and as we left I mouthed a silent obscenity at Norman.

Outside it was almost dark. 'Do you fancy some fish an' chips, Cynthia?' I asked.

'No, thanks Tom,' she replied. 'I'm not hungry. And call me Cynny. Everyone else does.'

'O.K,' I said, smiling, 'Cynny it is.'

'Have you always lived in Wallasey?' she asked me.

'More or less,' I replied. 'We moved into our house in 1941, just before Dad went into the navy. What about you?'

'I was born in Birkenhead. My Dad was in the army during the war. He's always going on about it.'

I gave a laugh. 'Just like mine.'

'Were you evacuated during the war?'

'No,' I replied, 'me Mum and I stayed here. Under the stairs, mostly.'

'My God,' she said, as we reached the end of the road that led onto the promenade. 'Were you frightened?'

'Not really. I collected a lot of shrapnel, though.'

High above, a full moon peeked from behind a cluster of clouds. The warm breeze fanned our faces as we strolled, hand in hand towards the waterfront. Neither of us noticed the occasional bus or car, and by the time we reached the promenade, darkness had fallen.

'What a lovely night, Tom,' whispered Cynthia, looking across the river. 'There's hardly any wind.'

The glare from the Liverpool docks sent daggers of light shimmering into the inky-black waters of the river.

We watched the anonymous figure of the lamplighter cycling along the promenade. At every gas-lamp he reached up with his hooked pole and pulled a lever producing an eerie yellow light.

'I don't know how he stays on that bike,' murmured Cynthia, cuddling up to me. 'I'd probably fall off.'

We arrived at the foot of the Town Hall. Three flights of wide steps led upwards with grassy slopes on either side.

'Do you fancy sitting down and a ciggy?' I asked. 'We could go and sit up there on the grass.'

'Yes, all right,' she replied, with a coy smile.

But we never did have that cigarette.

As soon as we sat down our arms went around each other and we kissed as if the world was coming to an end. What happened next became a kind of blur in my mind.

As our lips pressed together, I thought my heart would burst. Her body pressed hard against my chest. Our breathing came hard and fast, forcing us to break away. As our lips met again, my hand instinctively sought one of her breasts. It felt soft and pliable under the thin material of her brassière. My sexual experiences were limited to a quick fumble last Christmas with some girl I picked up at a party. Cynthia seemed more experienced. She gave a low murmur, and pulled me closer. The next thing I knew she was lying on top of me.

It was over all too quickly. Afterwards, we lay side by side, clothes in disarray, oblivious to everything, except the hammering of our hearts and the warmth of the wind.

After a while Cynthia stood up, and with a quick movement, pulled her dress down. She rummaged into her handbag, found a comb and carefully ran it through her hair. Feeling self-concious, I adjusted my trousers.

'Are you all right, Tom?' she said, putting her comb into her handbag. 'You're very quiet.'

'Yes,' I replied sheepishly'. I'm, sorry about –'

'Forget it, Tom,' she replied, placing a finger over my lips. 'There'll be other times.'

And she was right. We did it everywhere, on the beach, in Central Park, and in the seclusion of the sand-hills.

We almost succeeded in doing it in her front room. Her parents were in the kitchen listening to the *The Charlie Chester Show*.

Suddenly, a voice came from the direction of the kitchen. It was Cynthia's mother. 'Would you two like a cuppa and some crumpets?'

With the speed of lightning Cynthia pulled down her dress and quickly hid her white knickers under a cushion. Still wearing the condom, I adjusted my pants and quickly stood up. Cynthia's Mum entered the room carrying a tray containing two cups of tea and a plate of hot, well-buttered crumpets.

Cynthia's Mum placed the tray on the table near the settee. 'Don't let this get cold, now.' she said, with a smile. 'Must get back, Arthur Askey's on shortly.'

When she had gone, Cynthia and I looked at each other and burst out laughing. 'Here,' she said, putting her arms around my neck. 'Do you fancy a bit of crumpet, Tom?'

We arranged to meet the next day to watch the warships sail down the river.

'According to the *Echo'*, I said, 'they are due to arrive at twelve o'clock tomorrow afternoon.'

Cynthia squeezed my hand. 'I could catch the eleven-thirty boat from Wallasey and meet you at the top of the slipway in Liverpool. by the newspaper stand.'

That night I lay in bed, going over in my mind every little detail of the past few hours. Every time I closed my eyes I could feel her body next to mine. It was a long, frustrating night that seemed to go on forever.

Cynthia gave me a little wave as I dodged the trams and ran towards her. Dressed in a pale blue blouse and dark skirt, she looked gorgeous.

'Hope you haven't been waiting long,' I said, catching my

breath. 'I see the ships are here.'

I took hold of her hand and we found a good view of the river by the side of the slipway.

My heart raced as I watched the sleek warships, bedecked in bright-coloured bunting, move gracefully down the river. Led by the Norwegian warship *Arendal*, the destroyers *Battleaxe, Sluys, Cadiz, Scorpion* and *St Austel Bay*, cut a spectacular sight sending frothy bow waves curling in the air.

In the middle of this flotilla, dwarfing her escorts, the aircraftcarrier, *HMS Indomitable,* moved in stately splendour.

'Look,' Cynthia cried, pointing excitedly at the aircraft carrier. 'They've got aeroplanes on them.'

From where we were standing we could see the grey wings of several rows of aircraft lined on the flight deck. 'Yes, they're called Sea Furies and Firebrands,' I said, trying to impress her with my knowledge. 'I read it in the *Echo* last night.'

We watched, fascinated as *Indomitable* slowly came to a halt and heard the rumble as the anchor splashed into the river. Suddenly, everyone, including Cynthia and I, cheered as a tall, blue-uniformed figure, complete with a rows of glittering medals, appeared.

'Who's that?' yelled Cynthia, jumping up and down like an excited child. 'He's got a silver sword, as well.'

'That's Admiral Sir Phillip Vian,' I said. 'He got the DSO during the war for capturing the *Altmark* and rescuing survivors from ships sunk by the *Graff Spee.*'

'How do you know all this?' asked Cynthia quizzically.

'Me Dad told me last night,' I said, laughing. 'I think he read it in the *Echo* as well.'

'Don't the sailors look smart in those blue uniforms?' Cynthia said, looking up at me. 'I think you'd look great dressed like that.'

Now, twelve months later, as we sat in Central Park, I remembered how prophetic her words were.

'Twelve years!' she exclaimed. 'How…how could you?'

'Ah, come on, Cyn,' I said. 'There's nothin' for me around here, and you know I've always wanted to join the navy. I've spoken about it often enough.'

'But twelve years is a long time, Tom. What am I to do?'

'What d' you mean?'

Cynthia looked away and stared at the ground. 'I've missed my period,' she whispered, 'that's what I mean.'

At first I wasn't quite sure what she meant. Then, with a sudden sense of shock, the importance of her words hit home. 'You mean you're...you're going to have a baby?'

'I'm not sure yet,' replied Cynthia, with a sigh. She sat back, took out a packet of Senior Service from her handbag and gave me one.

'When are you going?' she asked, taking a deep drag and exhaling a steady stream of smoke.

'The twenty-second,' I replied.

'I might not know by then.'

A feeling of dread gradually crept over me. I puffed heavily on my cigarette. Poor Cynthia, I thought. Her parents will go mad when they find out, as would mine. Suddenly, I felt very helpless. 'What are we going to do, Cyn?'

'What do you mean "we"?' she retorted. '*You're* the one who's going away. *You'll* be all right. It's me that'll have to face the music.'

Later, in bed I reflected on the events of the evening. I knew things would be difficult, but I didn't think it would turn out to be a nightmare.

The next day I told Joe. He stared at me in amazement.

'You silly-born bastard,' he yelled.

We were in the pub and a few of the lads turned quickly and looked at us.

'Not so loud, Woods,' I replied, cringing in my seat. 'Everyone'll hear you.

'Talk about fuck 'em and forget 'em,' he raged. 'You take the bloody cake. Why didn't you use a jonnie? I gave you enough of them.'

I finished my pint in one gulp. 'I did,' I replied weakly. 'Well, most of the time. Anyway, she says it may be all right. Something about a false alarm.'

'You'd better hope so, Bud.' replied Joe, shaking his head. 'Or else you could end up the youngest married sailor in the navy.'

The next three weeks seemed like an eternity. I met Cynthia every day. But to our utter misery her periods didn't arrive.

I hardly slept at night.

Joe's comment about being married rankled in my mind. Until

I was eighteen, according to naval regulations, I was classified as a 'boy.' I wondered what Cynthia would say to that.

We tried to carry on as if everything was all right. On the Saturday before I was due to leave, the four of us went to the Tower Ballroom. Things were going reasonably well until two young American GIs sauntered up to our table. One was a corporal with two inverted chevrons on his arm. The other was a private. They asked the girls to dance.

'On yer way, pal,' I snapped, glaring up at the corporal. 'They're with us.'

'Yeah, piss off,' snarled Joe, staring at the private.

The girls looked nervously at one another. Suddenly, Cynthia stood up, smiled at the corporal, and turned to me. 'We'll please ourselves who we dance with,' she said defiantly. 'Won't we, Jan?'

Janet nodded in agreement. She then stood up, and with an all-knowing smile, moved next to Cynthia. Both of them then took hold of the Americans' arms, and made their way onto the floor.

I was livid. My hands shook with anger. How, I wondered, could she humiliate so? I could feel the blood pounding through my head, and was about to go after them.

'Wait, Bud,' said Joe, placing a hand on my arm.' I think Cynthia's playing a game with you. She's trying to get her own back.'

Joe had a point, but it didn't make me feel any better.

'I don't fuckin' care what she's doing,' I replied. 'We'll get those two Yanks when they come back.'

But we didn't. The girls wisely left the GIs on the floor as soon as the dance finished.

The girls sat down, a smug expression written all over their faces.

'There, now. No need to be jealous,' said Cynthia, trying to sound innocent. 'They're a long way from home and feeling lonely.'

I gave Cynthia a piercing look. 'Lonely my arse,' I grunted. 'What was it they said about the Yanks during the war? Over here, over-paid and over-sexed.'

Cynthia looked across me with raised eyebrows and let out a false laugh.

'Over-sexed!' she screamed. 'My God. You should know all about that.'

Janet burst into a fit of hysterical laughter. She clearly knew about Cynthia and me. She grabbed Joe's arm, and still laughing, pulled him onto the dance floor.

I felt my face redden as anger once again boiled up inside me. 'That was a bloody rotten thing to do, Cyn,' I rasped. 'I'd have smashed his head in if he'd come back.'

'Oh forget it, Tom,' she said, 'it's over with. Come on. Let's dance.'

I didn't see much of Cynthia during the week. She told me she was ill and didn't even come to my farewell party that Johnny Dennet, our team manager, threw at his house. When I called round to say goodbye, she looked pale and tired.

Her parents were out and she was looking after her little brother. We were in the parlour, sitting on the settee.

She seemed remarkably composed, considering the plight we were in. 'Nothing' happened yet,' she said dryly. 'We'll just have to hope something does, that's all.'

'Don't worry, Cynny, love,' I said, putting my arms around her. 'I'll do anything. No matter what happens, I'll stand by you.'

As we said goodbye, tears welled up in her eyes and she tried to smile. When she closed the front door, a lump came in my throat. Poor bugger, I thought. What the hell will become of us?

3

Monday, 22nd September, dawned bleak, with a biting south-easterly wind. For most of the night I lay in bed chain-smoking. I finally fell into a fitful sleep before Mum's voice filtered into my sub-consciousness.

'Here you are, son,' she said, placing a mug of tea on my bedside table, 'it's half past five. Drink this, and don't fall asleep. How d' you feel?'

'Ta, Mum,' I replied, rubbing my eyes and sitting up. 'Thanks. I'm O.K.'

I don't think anyone except Alma slept much that night. In between bouts of half-sleep I could hear Mum pottering about downstairs. Sometime during the night I heard the dull bump of the back door closing, telling me Dad was home from work. Normally he would have gone straight to bed. This time, however, he remained downstairs.

The smell of bacon frying failed to stimulate my taste buds. When I entered the living room, the warmth of the coal fire that hit me full in the face made everything seem unreal. The headlines in Dad's *Daily Express* reporting the war in Korea made me feel uncomfortable. Bloody-hell, I thought, this might be my last meal at home.

Dad glanced up from his newspaper and put his hand in his back pocket. 'Here, son,' he said, passing me two crumpled pound notes. 'Yer might need this.'

A lump came into my throat and I found it hard to swallow. I suddenly wondered if the other five lads I was due to meet outside the recruiting office were feeling the same.

'Ta, Dad,' I replied, toying with the food on my plate. 'I'm not sure when we'll be paid,' was all I could say.

Shortly afterwards I collected my case and started to leave.

'Say tara to Alma,' I muttered. 'Tell her I'll bring her some sweets.'

Sweets were still rationed so I knew this would please her.

'Sure you've got everything, Tom, love?' said Mum, tears in her eyes. 'Be careful, and write as soon as you can, love.'

I shook Dad's hand. 'Keep a level head, son,' he said, trying to smile.

I nodded, and for a few seconds reflected on the irony of what was happening.

My thoughts went back to another morning in 1942. Dad was about to go away in the navy. After kissing Mum, Dad picked me up.

'Take care of yer old girl, son, do you 'ear, now?' he said, giving me a hug, 'an' I'll bring yer back a German 'elmet.'

I never did receive a Jerry tin hat, instead, he sent me a sailor's knife, complete with marlin-spike-it would come in handy later when I joined the sea scouts.

Mum clasped me to her side as we watched him walk up the road, kitbag slung over his shoulder and his matelot's cap firmly placed on his head. At the top of the road, he turned, gave us a quick wave, and disappeared. We didn't see him again for two years.

Now, ten years later, it was my turn and a similar scene was being re-enacted, only this time I was the one who was leaving. However, the one thing that hadn't changed was the sound of Mum quietly sobbing.

Mum and Dad watched as I walked up the road. Then, just as Dad did a decade ago, I gave them a wave before starting on a journey that would change my life forever.

The others were waiting in the recruiting office. The tallest, whose name was Harry Small, told us he had served in the army. He was well over six feet, dark and unshaven and was immediately nicknamed 'Lofty'.

The chief looked us up and down, and said, 'Lofty here is in charge. He has the travel warrants and passes for the London underground. From Euston, you go on the Northern Line to Waterloo, then catch the train to Portsmouth, Southsea. Any questions?'

There were none.

We boarded the train, found a compartment and, as we left the station I sat wondering when, or indeed if, I would see Liverpool again.

'Christ,' sighed one of the lads.' I hope I'm doin' the right fuckin' thing.'

'Well,' said Lofty, with a half-hearted laugh. 'It's too bloody late now, mate.'

Gradually the compartment fogged up with cigarette smoke.

Outside the black clouds sent lines of rain slanting across the window. The dull rumble of the train, and the warm, claustrophobic atmosphere made one or two feel drowsy.

I yawned, glanced at my watch and thought of Cynthia. By now she would be at work. How the hell can I help her? I thought. Perhaps, I could allot her some money as I was doing for Mum. Even if we got married, I wouldn't be around.

With a sigh, I closed my eyes, imagining myself onboard a destroyer, bandaging wounded men while shells burst all around. I saw myself being awarded a medal and making headlines in *The Liverpool Echo*. Then, there were all those nurses with black stockings and starched uniforms....

According to the naval brochure, I could become an X-ray technician, laboratory assistant or physiotherapist – and promotion to leading hand or petty officer was also possible. With hard work, I could gain a commission, but somehow I couldn't see myself making admiral.

Lofty and I were the only ones in the group hoping to be medics. After being de-mobbed from the RAMC he had had difficulty settling down in civvy street. 'I missed the lads,' he said, 'and the fact that you could always rely on your mates. You'll find out what I mean.'

After a while the conversations dried up. Once more we became lost in our thoughts. With a million things running through my head, I fell asleep. After what seemed to be only a few minutes, I was awakened by Lofty vigorously shaking my shoulder.

'Come on, wake up, yer lazy bugger,' he yelled. 'We're here, we've arrived in Smoke.'

'Keep together, now,' cried Lofty, as we left the compartment.

Lofty had obviously been here before, and we clustered behind him.

The journey from London to Portsmouth was uneventful.

From our compartment the grey waters of the Thames and the Houses of Parliament flashed by. The next thing I remember was waking up and hearing a loud-speaker telling me we had arrived in Portsmouth.

Portsmouth-Southsea was a small, bustling station situated in the city centre. The roads and pavement were still wet from the rain, and the dark clouds threatened more inclement weather.

A matelot wearing white gaiters approached us. On his right

arm he wore two silver crossed guns. I later learned this signified he was a gunnery rating.

'Party for Victoria Barracks?' he asked

'Yes,' replied Lofty, and handed him an envelope containing our documents.

'Right. Follow me.'

We clambered into a blue lorry with a large RN painted in white on its side. Lofty and I sat up front with the driver.

Upon leaving the station we passed an imposing grey-stoned building with stout Corinthian columns and an elegant clock tower.

'What's that?' I asked the driver.

'The Guildhall,' he replied. 'But I expects you and your oppos will be more interested in "The Sussex or The Ship Leopard."'

I gathered these were the names of some of Pompey's notorious pubs.

We drove through the city and arrived at the high, red-bricked walls of Victoria Barracks. Waiting at the main gate was a pugnacious-looking chief petty officer. He was six feet tall with creases in his trousers sharp enough to cut butter. Tucked under his left arm was a swaggerstick. I quickly discovered he was a chief gunnery instructor, the scourge of trainees and regulars alike. From under a shiny peaked cap, a pair of steely eyes stared at us.

'Get out, shut up and follow me,' he growled in a sharp, Yorkshire accent. We climbed out of the lorry, collected our suitcases and ambled through the main gate.

Once inside, the walls looked even bigger. I found out later the barracks had been built by convicts in 1880. One of them enjoyed the experience so much, he volunteered to continue the work when his sentence was completed. Maybe the food was better then than it was in 1952.

On our right was a large building, guarded by another matelot in white webbing, holding a rifle. This, we were told was the 'Guard-Room' where we had to report on entering or leaving the barracks. A big white ensign fluttered gently at the top of a flagpole, from which sets of rigging angled down into a large, well-kept lawn.

I noticed a sailor saluting in the direction of the flagpole. This, I was told later on, was the sacred 'Quarterdeck,' and had to be saluted by everyone who walked past.

Rows of tall Victorian buildings faced each other on either side of a huge, rectangular parade ground. The sharp voices of Chief Gunnery Instructor drilling groups clad in blue fatigues, gaiters and caps echoed around the parade ground.

We followed the chief through a door, passed toilets, and washbasins which, in naval parlance, were called the 'heads'. An acute smell of disinfectant and polish wafted under my nose. We then entered a large room with rows of double bunk beds on either side. Sitting around long, wooden table were several lads dressed in blue fatigues called 'number eights.' A few were reading newspapers, while others wrote letters or lay on their bunks, smoking. All of them looked in our direction as we entered.

'Stand when an officer enters the room, and get off those fuckin' bunks,' snapped the chief. Everyone immediately leapt onto the highly polished floor. Unaware of what was happening, a tall lad with a spotty complexion strolled into the room. He was naked except for a pair of red rubber flip-flops and a white towel draped loosely around his waist. In one hand he carried a bucket full of freshly washed clothes. With a startled expression, he dropped the bucket and stood rigidly to attention. Everyone, except Lofty Small, looked petrified.

The chief stopped, clasped both hands behind him. 'Find a spare bunk. There's a key in each locker. Stow your gear. You'll be issued with uniforms in due course.'

'When do we get our rum?' I asked with a grin.

A ripple of laughter went around the room. The chief glared at me. His face turned a deep shade of purple and for a second I thought he might spontaneously combust. 'You'll get a kick up the arse. There's no rum issue for trainees. Call the hands is at 0630, and don't be adrift.'

He then turned, and with a ramrod back, marched out of the room. As he did so, he kicked over the bucket full of washing belonging to Pale Face. 'Stow that lot away, d' yer hear?' he snapped, without moving his head.

'Yes, sir,' said the lad, standing rigidly to attention. Then, much to his embarrassment, the towel fell from his waist into a crumpled heap on the floor. Pale Face's reactions were slow. He momentarily remained at attention before covering his crotch with both hands.

'You can stow that ugly thing away too,' growled the chief, then slammed the mess door and disappeared.

'Whew,' I gasped, putting my case on the floor. 'Who was that?'

'That,' said Pale Face, retrieving his towel, 'is Obadiah, our friendly instructor, and he's as mad as a hatter.'

'Fuck me,' I gasped. 'I wonder what the rest of them are like.'

During the next six weeks, a whole new way of life opened up for me. Each morning the shrill sound of the bosun's pipe woke us up at precisely 0630. The 'D' in my official number, D/MX 919173, stood for Devonport, in Plymouth. After training, this would be my home depot.

'Learn, memorise and inwardly digest, your official numbers,' bellowed Obadiah. 'If you forget them, not only will you get no pay, which in the navy is every fortnight, you will cease to exist.'

Many of the men had accents I had never heard before. There were 'Paddies,' 'Taffs,' 'Jocks'and others, such as big Geordie Wellings, who nobody, could understand. Pale Face, whose name was 'Chalky' White hailed from Lambeth, London. He baffled everyone with his Cockney rhyming slang, but we soon got the hang of it.

One lad, Mickey O'Hanlon, a small, stocky lad from Dublin, livened the mess up by playing a few Irish jigs on his mouthorgan. Jock McBride, who slept in the bunk below me, gave us all a laugh when he showed us his tartan kilt.

'Wait till old Obadiah sees you in that, boyo,' cried 'Taffy' Williams. 'He'll send you over to join the Wrens.'

Another budding medic was Cedric Morgan from Cardiff. He was a tall, thick set man, with wiry black hair and a perpetual five o'clock shadow. One Saturday morning during Divisions, (parade inspection), Obadiah stopped in front of Cedric, raised his eyebrows and peered closely at him. 'Did you put a blade in your razor this morning, lad?' he rasped.

'Yes, sir,' replied Cedric, staring straight in front of him.

'Well it don't look like it to me,' snarled our illustrious leader. 'You look more like Desperate Dan.'

From then on, the name stuck.

Desperate's great weakness was toffees and despite rationing, he always had a bag handy. 'A toffee a day, boyo,' he said one day, handing them around, 'keeps you frisky, so the lads in the rugby club at 'ome say.'

'In that case I'll have two, Taffy Bach,' said Lofty, stuffing one in his mouth. 'They'll make up for the bromide they're putting in the tea.'

They seemed a good bunch and we got on well. - that is, all except one man. His name was Marlowe. He was a 'Brummy' with straight, dark brown hair, close set eyes and a thin, pointed nose. He spoke in a high pitched voice and had served in the R A F. Most of the others seemed to ignore him. This puzzled me, because I found him quite pleasant.

One evening I was lying on my bunk. Jock was in the bathroom doing his washing. I reached across the top of my locker for my cigarettes when Marlowe appeared. 'Here,' he said, smiling, 'use my lighter, Thomas. You can hang on to it, I've got another one.'

'No thanks, Brum,' I replied. 'I've got a lighter, thanks all the same.' He smiled again, gave me a friendly pat on the thigh then went away. I couldn't understand why some of the others were sniggering. I soon found out.

Two nights later, after lights out, the sound of someone shouting woke me up. At first I thought it was a fire drill. Then, the mess lights suddenly came on. I sat up and was surprised to see Geordie and Marlowe writhing in a heap on the deck.

'The bastard tried to grope me, he did,' shouted Geordie, who was on top of Marlowe. He raised his clenched fist. 'Try this on, you bugger,' he yelled, and hit Marlowe on his nose. Marlowe screamed and blood suddenly spurted down his face onto his blue-striped pyjamas.

The duty petty officer arrived demanding to know what was going on. By this time everyone was wide-awake. Marlowe staggered to his feet and grabbed hold of a white towel from the end of a bed and held it to his nose.

'What the hell's gong on here?' barked the PO.

'This sod tried t' grab 'old of me cock, sir,' cried Geordie. He put his hand doon in me bed-clothes, the little bastard.'

The PO looked at Marlowe. 'What have you to say, lad?' Marlowe, who was busy with the towel, didn't speak. He just blinked nervously and shrugged his shoulders.

With eyes blazing, Geordie went to grab Marlowe again, but the PO intervened.

Marlowe was ordered to get dressed and told to report to Sick

Bay. Lofty Small was detailed to escort him.

The PO glared at Geordie. 'Go and get a mop and clean this blood up,' he said. 'The rest of you, turn in. We'll deal with this in the morning.'

'What was all that about, Jock?' I asked, climbing back into my bunk.

'Och, that bloody Marlowe,' replied Jock, lighting up a cigarette, and flicking one up to me. 'He's a fuckin' gristle – grabber.'

'A what?' I replied, more than a bit perplexed. 'What hell's that?'

'A shirt-lifter, a queer,' said Jock. 'You must have led a sheltered life, Scouse, or don't they have 'em in Liverpool?'

Jock was right. Maybe I had led a sheltered life. This was the first time I had met anyone who was a homosexual. It wouldn't be the last.

We didn't see Marlowe for a few days. Geordie was sent for and questioned by the Provost Marshal. Marlowe returned from sick bay and kept away from everyone. I felt sorry for him. After all, like me, he was away from home. And although I didn't fully understand what all the fuss had been about, we were, to coin a phrase, all in the same boat.

One evening I went into the heads and was alarmed to find Marlowe leaning against a washbasin, crying. 'What's up, Brum?' I asked, putting my hand on his shoulder.

He slowly turned his tear-stained face towards me. There was a look of desperation in his eyes. 'They might chuck me out, Thomas,' he muttered. 'I don't know what I'm to do.'

'No they won't, Brum,' I replied, trying to cheer him up. I had overheard that homosexual behaviour was a serious offence in the navy. However, I didn't mention this to Marlowe. 'Come on, mate, have a fag. You'll be all right.' Before leaving, I studied him closely. He had stopped crying, but was standing quite still, staring out the window.

The next day he hung himself.

His body was discovered by the duty Petty Officer while we were being drilled. Apparently, Marlowe complained of headaches. Instead of reporting sick, he went into the mess.

When the chief told us what had happened everyone looked at one another in horror. I was probably the last person to speak to

Marlowe, and felt physically ill. We sat in grim silence. I glanced at the drawn expression on Geordie's face. It said what many were thinking. Maybe if they had been more understanding, Marlowe might still be alive.

During the next six weeks we had our hair cropped short, watched a film on Venereal Disease, which, although making us laugh, gave us food for thought. From slops, the naval term for the clothes store, we were issued with everything from underwear to what was colloquially called a 'Housewife.' This was a blue pouch-like bag containing, needles, buttons and reels of cotton – which, thanks to Mum's tuition I knew how to use.

The chief drilled us relentlessly, but I still couldn't get used handling a rifle. Once, after dropping it, Obadiah glared at me. 'Pick it up, there's a good boy,' he sneered sarcastically. My arms ached for days after running around the parade ground holding the damn thing in the air.

A week later we were placed in a group called the Supply and Secretariat Division. This consisted of potential cooks, stewards and writers. It also included Jock, Lofty, Desperate and myself.

Jock was a thrifty Scot, tall and slim, with a shock of red hair, and a witty sense of Celtic humour.

A week after our arrival, everyone collected three hundred cigarettes from the slop room. I had never owned so many cheap fags in my life. The cigarettes came in packs of a hundred and cost a meagre five bob. The regular sailors called them 'Blue Liners,' due to the markings down the side of each cigarette. Like everyone else, I began handing them around. Pretty soon the atmosphere was like a peasouper on the Mersey.

'Och, make sure y' keep your dog-ends, Tom,' said Jock, stowing used butt ends in an old tin can. Rubbing his hands together, he added, 'You never know when you might need a wee drag.'

Our main headache was kit musters. These took place every Saturday morning after Divisions and involved meticulously laying out all our gear. They were also used as punishment for a myriad of misdemeanours. I fell foul of a petty officer who caught me walking across the parade ground. 'Run, you lazy bugger!' he cried. 'And lay your gear out at 1600.'

The Duchess of Kent barracks, an establishment for trainee Wrens, was across from our parade ground. Each morning, as the

Wrens marched to their own 'part of ship', the men strained to catch a glimpse of black-stockings or swaying hips.

One of our instructors, a Scot, treated our sex-starved ogling with contempt. 'Keep yer eyes in yer sockets,' he roared, 'and yer balls in yer pockets, yer dirty wee wasters.'

However, Obadiah was a law unto himself and ignored the Wrens. Each morning, straight as a dye, he would yell. 'My name is Obadiah, and I always pull my fuckin' wire. What do I do?'

We, in all innocence, had to yell back, 'Pull your fuckin' wire, chief.'

If anyone smiled or, perish the thought, laughed, they would be made to double around the parade ground or do twenty press-ups. One sunny morning we were fallen in on the parade ground. I was in the middle of the front line. As usual, the Wrens appeared in their smart, dark blue uniforms. Obadiah, at the top of his voice, promptly issued his obscene directive.

Our illustrious leader was facing us. He therefore couldn't see the girls, or the portly chief petty officer Wren approaching his rear. She came towards us like a battleship closing for the kill. Her face wore the expression of a female Rottweiler. With a stamp of her foot, she came to a halt directly behind him.

'Chief G I Ramsbottom,' she screamed.

Obadiah's eyes nearly popped out of his head and he did a swift about turn. He raised his hand as if about to speak but was quickly interrupted.

'Must you use such coarse language in front of my Wrens? They are new to the service and you are embarrassing them. Do I make myself clear?'

For once Obadiah was almost lost for words. He turned pale, and in a quiet, unrecognisable voice, meekly replied, 'Agnes, please. Not in front of the men.'

'Rubbish,' she snapped, before turning around and striding across to re-join her girls.

I couldn't help myself and broke down laughing, closely followed by the others. Had we known Agnes was Mrs Ramsbottom, Obadiah's wife, we would have collapsed in hysterics.

At long last, after four, weeks we were allowed shore leave. Dressed in our new, single breasted, blue serge uniforms, white shirt and black tie, we fell in outside the Guardroom.

Obadiah ran his beady eyes over us. 'And remember, you

future poultice-wallopers, leave expires at 2300. Don't be adrift.'

As we marched out the main gate, I ran my hands down the sides of my uniform, thrust out my chest and thought how proud Cynthia and my parents would be if they could see me.

I wrote home as soon as I could. Mum's reply told me all was well, but Cynthia's two pages didn't say much. She still hadn't started her periods, she also said not to send any money.

Putting my domestic problems behind me, we piled into the NAAFI Club. Oblivious to the fact that our new uniforms identified us as trainees, we sauntered up to the bar. Jock ordered four beers, which after nearly five weeks abstinence tasted like nectar.

After a couple of pints, we decided to try our luck in the dancehall. Several couples were waltzing to a Mantovani record. I looked around and noticed a pretty blonde Wren sitting alone. The beer had given me Dutch courage, and I asked her to dance.

'No thank you,' she replied haughtily, looking me up and down. 'I don't dance with sprogs. Come back when you've got some time in.'

I felt my face redden and quickly joined the others. We had a good laugh and decided to have a meal in the canteen. Afterwards, we retired to the lounge. As we sat eyeing up the talent, Cedric pulled out a bag of toffees.

'Not eating again, are yer, Desperate?' I moaned. 'You must have cast-iron guts.'

'Hey, laddie, what's fallen out of your pocket?' said Jock, pointing to two small, green packets lying on the floor close to Desperate.

He quickly bent down and picked them up. 'Bloody Hell, mon, it's me frenchies,' he said, with a grin. 'The lads in the rugby club gave 'em to me before I left, just in case me luck changed, they said.'

We grinned at him. 'Wishful bloody thinking, Desperate,' commented Lofty. 'Best stick to toffees.'

It was Jock who suggested going to the pictures. 'Och, there's that filthy French film, *La Ronde*, on down the road,' he said. 'I saw it advertised on the board as we came in. We could have a few more drams then go to the first house.'

Half an hour later, feeling more than a little bleary-eyed, we went into the cinema.

The Gaumont British News was on, showing the war in Korea

59

and British troops fighting Mau Mau terrorists in Kenya.

A heavily-rouged usherette gave us a smile, tore our tickets, and showed us to our seats. I overheard her whisper to Lofty, 'My boyfriend's a sailor, and a right randy git he is too, I can tell you.'

'You don't say,' replied Lofty. 'Where is he now, then?'

'Onboard HMS *Ocean*, an aircraft carrier,' she said, patting her hair. 'Somewhere in the Far East.'

Before Lofty had a chance to reply, Jock took his arm. 'Come on, you,' he said. 'We want to see the film, even if you don't.'

We found our seats and settled down. Much to my annoyance, Desperate kept on making growling noises whenever a flash of female nakedness appeared on the screen. 'Pack it in, will you, mate,' I muttered, 'you sound like a bull on heat.'

A few minutes later, all hell broke loose.

A girl next to Desperate let out an ear-splitting scream. 'Take it away! Take it away!' she cried, and began hitting Desperate with her handbag. 'Pervert. Pervert.' bellowed the woman.

Everyone turned to see what the commotion was about. I lent forward and tried to grab the girl's arm as she lashed down at Desperate. 'Hey, give over,' I cried, dodging the handbag. 'Are you mad, or something?'

Suddenly, the manager, a stern-faced fellow with a military moustache, arrived at the end of the row.

'I say, what the blazes is going on 'ere?' he snorted, blinding everyone with the beam of his torch. 'You're disturbing everyone.'

'This man, 'ere,' cried the girl. 'Put this in me hand, he did.'

By this time the place was in an uproar. People were yelling, telling her to shut up and sit down. Others suggested that Desperate should be thrown out.

'Put what in your hand, madam?' was the impatient reply from the irate manager.

'This,' cried the girl who quickly stood up, and barged her way along the row. She then handed the manager a small object.

He took one look at it, and glared at us. 'Right, you lot,' he bawled. 'Out. All of you, before I call the police.'

With his fist raised, Desperate made a lunge at the manager. Lofty and Jock grabbed him and held him back. 'Why the hell should we leave?' growled Desperate. 'We've done nuthin wrong.'

'Right, Mavis,' said the manager quickly taking a step backwards. 'Call the police, and the naval patrol.'

The words, 'police,' and 'naval patrol,' immediately stirred us into action. With bewildered expressions, we glanced at one another. The film was still on and the audience was becoming hostile. Throw them out, was the cry, and other suggestions not so polite.

'Come on, lads,' growled Jock. 'I don't what the hell's going on, but we better leave.'

As we left the picture house, the manager, closely followed by the usherette, glowered at us. 'And don't come back,' he shouted.

Then Mavis joined in. 'All the same, you sailors,' she screeched at us. 'Sex mad, the lot of you.'

Jock gave them two fingers. Lofty mouthed an obscenity at the manager, and we hurriedly left.

'What the fuckin' 'ell were you up to, Desperate?' gasped Lofty, as we walked down the road. 'Were you trying to tap her up or what?'

'Bugger off, Lofty,' replied Desperate. 'I put me hand in me pocket to offer that mad bitch a toffee.' We stopped to catch our breath and looked him. 'I was so busy, watchin' the girl in the film taking off her clothes that I put a Frenchie in her hand by mistake.'

'Bugger me,' cried Jock, grinning his head off. 'So much for your luck changing.'

By the time we reached the barracks our sides were aching.

Finally, the day of our passing-out parade dawned. Along with several other groups, we fell in outside our messes. As Obadiah ordered, 'Quick march,' the Royal Marine Band struck up *Hearts of Oak*. Pride welled inside me - I thrust out my chest and started to march. With arms swinging, we strode past the Commanding Officer, who, along with several other officers, stood on a wooden dais. Each section received a salute as they went by.

When Obadiah gave us the order, 'eyes right,' I suddenly felt a lump in my throat. The first hurdle was over and I had passed with flying colours.

Now, the real test was about to start.

4

On a bitterly cold November morning our section was fallen in outside the mess. Each of us carried a brown canvas kitbag and a suitcase case, called a 'Pusser's Green.' Anything and everything in the navy was referred to as belonging to 'Pusser.'

'You lot are to be sent to Portsmouth,' snapped Obadiah, glancing at papers on a clipboard. 'You Probationary Sick Berth Attendants will be billeted in HMS *Collingwood*. From here you will travel every day to the Royal Naval Hospital, Haslar, for instruction. Any questions?'

'Will we get an issue of rum, chief?' chirped Desperate with a wide, toothy grin.

Obadiah gave him his customary glare. 'No. Rum is not issued in hospitals,' he snorted. 'And from what I hear, toffees are more in your line.'

Everyone stowed his gear inside a lorry. As we climbed into a coach, Lofty asked the driver, 'Where's this place called *Collingwood,* mate?'

'It's an electricians' training base outside Fareham,' replied the driver. 'Just around the other side of Pompey harbour. Named after one of Nelson's Admirals.'

'So much for sexy nurses,' mumbled Lofty, 'nothin' but hairy-arsed matelots, I bet. Ugh.'

Obadiah stood with on his hands on his hips facing us. When we were all in the coach, he gave us a wry smile. 'Good luck, lads,' he said. 'You're going to need it.'

After leaving Portsmouth, the driver told us that the high ground to our right was Portsdown Hill. Behind this was a shore base called HMS *Dryad*. 'That's Fort Southick,' he said. 'Where Monty and Ike planned the D-Day landings.'

After a short journey we arrived at the place which would be our home for the next three months. We drove past a well-guarded main gate and up a roadway flanked by huts. Behind a large parade ground rose several large brick buildings which we later learned housed senior rates. To our right was a covered area which, I assumed, was used for divisions during wet weather.

The coach and lorry stopped and we took our gear inside one

of the huts. A tall, stern-faced three-badge petty officer showed us where to stow our kit. 'My name is Miller, and I'm your divisional PO,' he said, slowly walking up and down. 'Fall in outside at 1100. Who is PSBA Small?' he asked. Lofty put up his hand. 'Right,' said the PO. 'You're in charge. Call the hands is at 0630. Muster outside at 0800. Rig'o the day is number eights. Make sure nobody's adrift. Got it?'

Lofty nodded.

'Me again,' groaned Lofty after the PO left. 'Why am I always in charge?'

'If you can't stand a joke,' laughed Pete Cronin, a tall, thin-faced lad from Huddersfield, 'you shouldn't 'ave joined, mate.'

The huts were warm and well ventilated with brown linoleum on the floor. Four circular white lampshades with bulbs hung from a stout, wooden ceiling by thick, well-insulated flexes. Alongside every bed was a metal kit-locker and behind each an overhead light was attached to the wall. Each hut was connected to a long corridor with bathrooms and heads. The green curtained windows left us gaping with admiration.

'Look you, now, this is what I calls comfort,' cried Desperate, throwing his kitbag onto the bed next to mine. 'I wonder what the grub's like?'

Twelve PSBA's had arrived a few days earlier.

One of these was a tall, athletically-built lad from Kingston, Jamaica, called 'Simbo' Johnson. He was a first class cricketer and had a wonderful sense of humour.

One Saturday afternoon, Simbo was lying on his bed reading a magazine. Desperate sauntered up and sat down beside him. 'Tell me, Simbo,' he asked with a curious inflexion in his voice, 'how come your teeth are so white?'

Simbo gave Desperate a quizzical look. 'Well, my friend,' he said with a gleam in his eye, 'it's hereditary, you see.'

Desperate stared intently at Simbo. 'What d'you mean, boyo, hereditary?' he replied, frowning.

Simbo put his magazine down. 'You see, Desperate, it's like this,' he said. 'My folks used to eat *white* people. That's why my teeth are so white. See?' At which point, Simbo thrust his face close to Desperate and bared his teeth.

Desperate was taken aback and quickly moved away. 'I don't believe a word of it, boyo,' he muttered, taking a paper bag from his pocket. 'Here, have a toffee, they'll do your teeth far more good!'

'You lot'll have to do yer joining routine,' remarked a big lad with a Liverpool accent. The name above the left pocket of his number eights read D. Wilson. 'Make it last till secure at 1600. There is rounds every evening at 2100, and mess inspection each Saturday at 1100.' He gave us an all-knowing wink, as if to say, 'stick with me and we'll show you the ropes.'

From then on Dave was always referred to as 'Scouse.' Jock and the others called me Tom to avoid confusion. And although Lofty was from Huyton in Liverpool, he kept his nickname.

We soon found the NAAFI. Desperate immediately had his pay-book stamped and bought his weekly nutty, (naval slang for sweets and chocolate) ration. 'I wonder what the beer's like,' he said, sucking a toffee. We soon found out.

The NAAFI canteen was a large, smoke-filled bar that sold beer and local apple cider called scrumpy. After several pints we felt decidedly unwell and made a dash outside.

The next morning the mail arrived, but there was no word form Cynthia. After many a sleepless night, I finally decided to ask Cynthia to marry me. At the time it seemed like the best solution to our problems. However, during the coming weeks I would have other things to think about.

The Royal Naval Hospital at Haslar is situated at the tip of Gosport peninsula. The journey from *Collingwood* took took twenty minutes. It was raining, so we mustered in the main arcade.

We fell in and were confronted by a petty officer and a tall, dark-haired officer. 'I am Wardmaster Sub-Lieutenant Millward,' he said, 'and I will be your Divisional Officer while you are here.' He paused, placed his hands behind his back and added, 'This hospital was built in 1753. The cobblestones you are standing on were put there during Nelson's time.'

Several of us reacted to this by glancing down.

'Face the front,' barked the PO.

The officer pursed his lip and went on, 'The training you are about to receive will enable you to serve on His Majesty's shore establishments, and in ships not carrying a doctor. This is a grave responsibility and one I hope all of you will consider carefully. A good sick-berth attendant is worth his weight in gold, not only to himself, his crew and captain, but to the service as a whole.'

We listened intently, hanging on to his every word. 'And

remember,' continued the officer, 'a medic who earns the trust of his ship's company will be play an important part in the efficiency of his ship.'

It was a short but effective address and made me think.

During the weeks that followed, I began to realise exactly what the officer meant. We were issued with exercise book, pencils and, most important of all, a BR 888, *The Handbook of the Royal Naval Sick Berth Personnel.* This was a thick, red, hard-backed book dealing with every subject from basic anatomy to tropical diseases.

'This is the sick-berth attendant's bible,' retorted a stocky, fair-haired chief petty officer. With an all-knowing air, he introduced himself as Chief Petty Officer Bryant. 'I am the chief in charge of you lot, so you'll be seeing plenty of me.'

We were sitting at desks in a well-lit classroom. He picked up a copy of the handbook from his desk, and held it in the air. 'You will learn, and inwardly digest every word in this. Do I make myself clear?'

'Every word, chief?' asked Simbo Johnson, with a toothy grin.

The chief looked at Simbo and threw his BR 888 at him. With the expertise of a slip-fielder, Simbo caught the book with one hand.

'Now, open it at any page and tell me the number. The rest of you keep your books closed.'

Simbo did so, looked up and said, 'Page 207, Chief.'

'Regional Surgery,' came the chief's emphatic reply.' Right?'

'Yeah,' replied Simbo, glancing around the class. 'How did you...'

The chief cut him off and without blinking, added, 'Top of the page reads: 'Treatment. The thumbs should be well-padded' etc.'

'Right,' replied Simbo, suitably impressed. 'Bloody-hell, you must have a photographic memory, chief.' After everyone had checked their books, a buzz of admiration went around the room.

The chief placed the manual on a table. 'Now,' he said, surveying our attentive faces, 'that's how well you will have to learn it. Right?'

'Right!' we replied in unison.

At first, the journey from *Collingwood* to Haslar fascinated everyone. But, as time went by, Fareham, Gosport and the Victorian houses of Alverstoke became familiar landmarks, and we lost interest.

A high, grey-stone wall surrounded the hospital. Behind, in a small, deserted area lay a disused cemetery full of cholera victims from days gone by. Close by was HMS *Hornet*. This was a motor torpedo base, used in the Second World War. Near the entrance was amounted MTB Boat.

Spanning Haslar Creek was a fragile-looking structure called Pneumonia Bridge – so named because of its height. It was also a sobering shortcut from Gosport following a boozy run ashore.

Over the next twelve weeks our lectures covered every aspect of nursing from tropical medicine to the treatment of the mentally ill. At first, it was all a bit bewildering. Only Lofty, who had been in the Royal Army Medical Corps, appeared to understand what was being said. Nevertheless, we scribbled away, hoping the words would eventually make sense - and in time they did.

One Monday morning we sat yawning as a PO droned on about first aid. After a short while he stopped and glowered at Scouse Wilson, who was sound asleep. Scouse's freckled face lolled to one side and a thin line of spittle appeared at the side of his mouth. His chest moved with each gentle snore.

'You, there, PSBA Wilson,' bellowed the PO, his face red with anger.

Someone dug Scouse in the ribs. 'What's up? What's up?' spluttered Scouse, gazing around.

The PO peered at Scouse while drumming his fingers on his desk, then growled, 'What's the first thing you do when you find an unconscious body, Wilson?'

'Erm... frisk him for his wallet, PO,' replied Scouse, innocently.

Everyone, except Scouse, burst out laughing. That night, poor Scouse was kept busy writing out a large slice of the First Aid Manual. 'Miserable bugger, 'he grunted, scribbling away. 'I've seen more unconscious bodies in Scotty Road on a Saturday night, than he's had bunk ups.'

Then there were the nurses – or should I say, the lack of them. Everyone, especially Lofty, was in danger of developing, 'the swivel-headed syndrome.' From our coach we preened our heads in all directions, piping any we saw. 'Cor! Look at the arse on that one, Tom,' breathed Lofty, as we flattened our faces against the coach window.

Clad in flowing blue capes with vivid scarlet linings, white caps and sexy black stockings, they laughed and gave us a wave.

This only served to make Lofty and the rest of us howl with pleasure. 'Pack it in, you sex mad buggers,' ordered PO Miller. 'You're nowt but a bunch of animals!'

Lofty and I looked at each other and gave a low growl.

It was just as well the nurses were lectured separately from the men – those we received about venereal disease would have been more than embarrassing in mixed company.

This subject was the pet subject of Chief Petty Officer Farmer, a small, grey-haired man, with sleepy eyes and horn-rimmed glasses. A smile played around his mouth as we sat watching him fiddle with a film projector. 'You must all pay close attention to this film,' he said in a rather high pitched voice. 'It will teach you to behave yourselves when you go ashore in dirty places like Port Said and Alexandria.' This immediately produced a round of giggles.

He ordered all the curtains to be drawn and the room darkened. We had seen films about VD in Portsmouth, but they hadn't prepared us for this one.

'In my day,' began the chief, with an all-knowing sneer, 'there was no such thing as penicillin. We had to flush out the demons with potassium permanganate and other such medicates.'

On the screen we saw a series of coloured slides showing the extreme effects of VD. One showed a male nurse inserting a long needle directly down a grossly inflamed male organ. 'That's what I mean by flushing out,' continued the chief. At that moment Jock McBride, who was sitting in front of me, gave out a low moan and fell sideways onto the floor in a dead faint. 'My goodness!' exclaimed the chief, clasping his hands together. 'Isn't it amazing what the sight of a small prick can do to a grown man?'

Every day, I eagerly awaited a letter from Cynthia, but none arrived. However, when Joe's letter told me she had been seen dancing at the Tower, I was more than a little concerned.

I sought the advice of Lofty, who was divorced and had two daughters living with his ex-wife. 'Let's see, now,' mused Lofty. We were in the mess, sitting on his bed. 'Even though she's two months gone, dancing would be OK, I guess. As long as she took it easy.'

'But she shouldn't be out with other men, Lofts,' I sighed. 'What the hell's goin' on?'

'Probably nothin', mate, so quit worrying,' said Lofty, putting a reassuring hand on my shoulder. 'Anyway, we'll be on leave in a few weeks. You can sort it out then.'

His well-meaning words helped. But I still lay awake, thinking about Cynthia and seeing those lovely brown eyes staring at me.

Every Saturday morning we had Captain's Rounds. This involved meticulous bulling up of toilets, corridors and messes.

Each rating, dressed in well-pressed number eights, stood to attention at the end of their bed. The mess door leading out onto a small parade ground would be opened wide. The rating in charge then stood and waited at the doorway at the other end of the mess. This allowed a free passage of fresh air to blow down the mess.

The inspection party would be heralded by the shrill sound of a bos'un's pipe. On this particular Saturday, we awaited the arrival of the Captain, PO Miller and the Master-at-Arms.

I was anxious to get away early to travel to Portsmouth to watch Liverpool play. My team were in danger of relegation to the Second Division and Fratton Park, where Pompey played, was a fair distance from the camp.

The piercing notes of the bos'un's pipe drew near. 'Attention for rounds,' barked Lofty. Heels snapped together. 'Mess ready for inspection, sir.' retorted Lofty, chopping off a text book salute.

Like everyone else, I was standing rigidly to attention. I could feel the stiff breeze blowing through the mess on the side of my face. The dull echo of shoes on the linoleum came nearer. The Captain appeared in front of me. I stared directly ahead, but could feel his eyes looking through me. He quickly looked me up and down, before moving on until he reached the end door. Suddenly he stopped. 'What the hell's that, Master?' he cried. I turned my head slightly. The officer was pointing to a crumpled piece of greaseproof paper lying on the deck. 'Pick that thing up,' he cried. All eyes focussed on Lofty as he bent down and picked up the offending article.

A look of astonishment came over Lofty's face. 'It's a toffee wrapper, Master,' replied Lofty in a hoarse voice.

The Captain frowned. 'Master,' he cried, 'dig me out. I'm up to my neck in shit. This mess is to be re-inspected at 1400.' And stormed out.

The Master glared at Lofty. 'I'll be back,' he snorted. 'See that this mess is properly cleaned up by then.'

As soon as they were gone, everyone made a beeline for

Desperate. We pinned him to his bed while someone went through his pockets.

'It wasn't my fault, fellers,' he choked, munchuing a toffee. 'It were the wind'

However, I never did get to Fratton Park – just as well as Liverpool lost 1-0.

At long last we were allowed to buy a dress uniform. Everyone had to make out a monthly allotment of a few pounds to a naval tailor. The tailors contracted to the service were Bernards, Greenburghs and Coopers of Harwich. I chose the latter, remembering Dad was stationed there during the war.

The tailors carried their wares in vans and congregated outside the NAAFI each Saturday afternoon. They sold everything from toothpaste to well-tailored civilian suits. After signing the necessary forms, we were duly measured up. A week later we collected our smart, double-breasted, doeskin uniforms.

'It suits you fine, son,' said the tailor, a small man, immaculately dressed in one of his own suits. 'You'll have to fight the girls off when you go into town.'

The following Saturday I celebrated my eighteenth birthday in the NAAFI. The top of my locker was bedecked with cards, but, sadly, none from Cynthia. My expression must have told its own story.

'Cheer up, mate,' said Lofty, slapping me on the back. 'My missus always forgot mine as well.'

'Aye,' chimed in Ernie Fielding, a thickset Geordie. 'And look what happened to you, eh?'

'Pay no attention to that Geordie bugger, Tom lad,' interrupted Scouse Wilson. 'Just think of all them free pints you're gonna get tonight.'

The next morning, arms draped over the sides of the urinals, I brought up my greasy breakfast of bacon and eggs. Suddenly I realised I was, officially, a man and entitled to a rum issue – and immediately threw up again.

The next three weeks seemed to fly past. Much to surprise, I passed my intermediate examinations with flying colours. Nobody in our class failed, and as first leave approached, excitement mounted.

The day before leave, we were addressed by Sub-Lieutenant Millward.

'I will be brief,' he said, as usual, placing his hands behind his back. 'You have all done well in your exams, and are to be congratulated.'

Everyone shuffled his feet. One or two grinned at each other, while some glanced at the ground anxious for 'stand easy,' and a quick fag.

Millward took his hands from behind his back and placed them, thumbs showing, in his jacket pocket. 'However,' he continued. 'When you return, the real work begins. You will be sent on the wards, and,'- at this point he stopped. His lips curled up and a crocodile smile slowly spread across his face. 'You will administer your first injection – using sterile water – to yourselves – into your thigh.'

With a look of horror on several faces, a low murmur of disquiet echoed around the room.

'Carry on,' said Millward, and with a sneer, added, 'And, er... have a good leave.'

Desperate was standing next to me. 'Have a good leave, he says,' spluttered Desperate, bending down and feeling his thigh. 'The man's mad, look you. Soddin' mad. You won't catch me sticking no needle in my leg, boyo, I can't stand pain.'

'You'll have to stick it your big, fat head, then,' scoffed Simbo. 'There's no feeling there, mon, so you'll be all right.'

Before going on leave, we removed the wire grommet that kept the stiff, round shape to our caps. We then stretched the cap cover backwards, giving it a rakish appearance of a seasoned veteran.

'Bloody hell, mate,' said Lofty, as we admired ourselves in the mess mirror, 'we look like Dutch Admirals, so we do.'

I had managed to save my cigarette issue, being careful not to exceed the two hundred allowed on leave. This did not included a tin of tobacco, called 'tickler,' for Dad, as I knew he liked to roll his own. My allotment to Cooper's came in handy. I bought a doll for Alma, a pair of fur-lined booties for Mum, warm, leather gloves for Dad and a set of sexy underwear for Cynthia.

'What size is your girl?' the Cooper's rep had asked, sorting out various boxes from the back of his van.

'About five foot two,' I replied, somewhat bemused.

'Not how tall she is,' sighed the tailor, 'her bust, her tits. How big are they?'

For a moment I stared, open-mouthed, unable to answer. I had no idea of Cynthia's vital statistics. Glancing around I saw Jock McBride. He was about to peel an orange. I hurriedly snatched it from his hand, and with a nervous gesture, shoved it under the tailor's nose, and said, 'About this size...I think!'

Christmas leave 1952 was my first in the navy and was to prove memorable.

Cluching suitcases and grips, we boarded the coaches that would take us to Corsham. This was a small railway station near Fareham, where we would catch trains to Waterloo.

'I suppose you'll be going to see that crummy football team o' yours,' laughed Ernie.' We play you at Anfield on New Year's Day. Big Jackie Milburn'll get a few, you wait an' see.'

'Ten bob says the reds will win,' I replied, with a smirk on my face. 'And I'll give you the draw. OK'?'

We shook on it, and he left.

The platform was crowded with hundreds of men in uniform.

'See you next year, Taff,' yelled Jock. Several faces turned towards and looked in the direction of the speaker. I am sure that if someone had shouted, Scouse, Jock, or Paddy, it would have received a similar response. Taff Taylor, a quiet lad from The Mumbles, instantly recognised Jock, and gave him a grin and a friendly wave. It was strange how these geographical nicknames stuck; and even though you might become close friends, you never used their proper first names; Taff Taylor did tell me his Christian name, but, to this day, I'm darned if I can remember what it was.

'Have a good leave, Scouse,' said Lofty, shaking my hand. He was taking his leave in London. 'And remember, women are nothin' but a pain in the arse.'

When we parted at Waterloo the familiar faces I had lived with during the last two months vanished. Suddenly, I felt quite alone. Then, the unmistakable voice of Scouse Wilson brought me back to my senses.

'Come on, Tom,' he said, putting his arm around my shoulders. 'There's a bar over there. Let's get a few bevvies down us, eh lar.'

Armed with several bottles of Nut Brown ale, we piled into an empty coach at Euston Station. Scouse was an Evertonian, and arguing about football took my mind off Cynthia.

Finally, the streets and houses of Liverpool came into view. As the train rumbled agonisingly slowly into Lime Street, my heart pounded with excitement.

Scouse was greeted by his girl friend. Even though I had written, there was no sign of Cynthia.

'This is Wanda, 'said Scouse, hugging her. 'Isn't she a smasher?'

I gave a half-hearted laugh. 'Yea, nice to meet you,' I replied, shaking her hand.

Shivering in the cold, north-westerly wind I made my way down Nelson Street to the Empire Theatre. Here I waited for a bus to the Pier Head.

Across the busy road, St George's Hall stood with its wide, decorated pediment supported by a row of massive Corinthian columns. In the foreground, on a cobbled courtyard, proud equestrian statues, commemorating past glories, guarded the entrance. Away to the right rose the majestic complex of the Picton Library, Walker Art Gallery and law courts. All lay under the protective gaze of the Duke of Wellington's statue, imperiously looking down from the top of his column. Like so many servicemen throughout the years, I welcomed it as a sight for sore eyes.

The journey across the Mersey was rough, and I loved every second of it. The ferryboat tossed and turned like a cork in a bath. Huge waves cascaded over the bows as white horses rolled angily in from the Irish Sea. I pulled my peaked cap down and gripped the guard-rail. For a few moments I imagined myself on the bridge of a destroyer with needles of icy spray biting my face. However, the jarring squelch of the ferryboat arriving alongside the jetty brought me back to reality.

It was nearly six o'clock when I arrived home. This time there were no trembling hands as I opened the front door.

Mum was sitting down playing patience.

Dad, legs stretched out in his usual armchair, was reading the *Echo*.

Mum's eyes lit up. 'Tom, love,' she cried, scattering her playing cards on the floor.

A huge grin spread across Dad's face. 'Aye, aye,' he quipped. 'The wanderer returns.'

The curtains were drawn and I could smell fish and chips. They were obviously expecting me.

Alma came rushing downstairs. She dropped her dolls and flew at me, crying, 'It's Tom, Mum, Tom. Where's my sweets?' And wrapped herself around my waist.

Mum reached up and took my face in both hands and kissed me. I instantly recognised that familiar body odour of sweat and hard work. 'Welcome home, son,' she said, tears filling her eyes. 'I'm sorry we couldn't meet you, your Dad and I were at work. It's lovely to see you.'

A lump the size of the Rock of Gibraltar prevented me from answering. I just kept my arms around her and grinned.

Dad's eyes glistened as I took an arm away from around Mum's waist and shook his hand. 'You look in good nick, lad,' he said. As he spoke, those dimples I knew so well appeared in both cheeks. 'Been feedin' yer all right, have they?' I nodded, and kept hold of his hand. I looked around the room. Nothing had changed except a new set of yellow and green curtains. The ornaments on the mantle-piece were the same and the coal fire still glowed like a welcoming beacon. The only changes would be the squares of newspaper hanging in the outside lavatory.

Everyone was pleased with the presents. Mum's face beamed as she tried on her booties.' Och, they feel lovely,' she said, smiling at me. 'Just like silk, I'll be the envy of the street.'

Dad was especially pleased. 'Ta, son,' he said, his eyes sparkling. 'Haven't had any of this for years.' He then took out his old roller and produced a perfect 'home made.'

Alma's eyes nearly popped out her head when I produced a half dozen milk chocolate bars from my suitcase.

Mum lit up a cigarette from a packet of duty free blue-liners. 'Oh,' she said, letting a stream of smoke trickle from her nose. 'There's a letter here for you.' She picked up a white envelope from the sideboard and handed it to me. 'It came yesterday.'

I immediately recognised Cynthia's handwriting and hastily tore it open.

Suddenly, I felt the blood drain from my face.

Her words bounced off my eyes. 'I've met someone else... I love him.... He's foreign. We are going to be married...' My hand started to shake and I felt sick.

'What's up, son?' said Mum. 'You look pale. Are you all right?'

Dad took a drag of his cigarette, put down his newspaper and looked up.

'Yes… I'm…I'm OK, Mum,' I tried to swallow, but my mouth felt like sandpaper. 'It's from Cynthia, she's…' my voice trailed. I stood in silence, staring at the letter. How could she do this to me, I thought. Why a letter? Why not tell me to my face? A dozen questions ran through my mind. She had not even mentioned being pregnant. I slowly handed Mum the letter. 'She's met someone else,' I heard myself say. 'And she's getting married.'

'What!' exclaimed Mum. 'Met someone else?' As she read the letter, she cried. 'The rotten bitch, how could she do such a thing…?' Handing the letter to Dad, she said. 'Here, Eddy, read this.'

He read the letter and glanced up at me. 'The bloody shit-house,' he said venomously. 'Took a ball o' chalk, has she? Anyway, lad. There's plenty more, you'll see. She couldn't have been much good, son, to do a thing like that.' He gave me back the letter and tried to smile, but his eyes had lost their sparkle.

I couldn't face Mum's fish and chips. 'Keep them warm, Mum,' I said. 'I'll eat them later. I'm going out.'

Mum and Dad looked at one another, concern written all over their face. 'Keep a level head, son,' said Dad,' d' you hear, now?'

I nodded and went upstairs and changed into civvies. My sports coat and shirt felt pleasantly different after weeks of blue serge. Lofty Small was right, women were a pain in the arse.

I had intended going straight to Joe's house, but I changed my mind. As if drawn by a magnet, I walked in the direction of Cynthia's house.

There was hardly a soul about as I made my way up Brentwood Road and down Lyncroft. A foggy haze drifted in the cold night air and the glow from the street lamps cast pools of pale light on the pavement. Only the throbbing sound of a the occasional motor car or bus disturbed the night

With my hands thrust deep in my overcoat pockets, I walked slowly past dimly lit houses. Behind heavy curtains, snug and warm, people sat listening to the wireless or playing cards, contemplating the oncoming of Christmas.

I turned into the curve of the crescent where Cynthia lived and abruptly stopped. Outside her house was a black car. Suddenly, the noise of a door slamming pierced the stillness of the evening. The unmistakable figure of Cynthia hurried from her house and dashed into the car. I called out her name and started to run.

My breath came in short gasps. 'Cynthia!' I yelled. But it was no use. The car quickly disappeared. Suddenly, everything was quiet. Not a soul stirred. The only sounds I heard were my cries of anguish as I slumped against a garden wall.

'Whey-hey, where the heck have you been, Bud?' cried Joe, as I walked into the living room of his house. Joe's mother was a stout, Irish lady, with short, dark hair held in place by a sagging hairnet.

'He's been waiting for you, so he has,' she said, holding a ball of yellow wool in one hand. Using her free hand she opened the door. 'It's nice to see you again, Tom, come in out of the cold, now.'

Joe stood up as I walked into the room. He was wearing his customary brown bomber jacket and black polo-necked sweater. His father, a small, stocky man from Kilarney, sat in front of a glowing coal fire, smoking a cigarette. His greeting was warm and friendly. 'Well, well' he said, with a smile. 'If it isn't the Jolly Jack Tar, himself. How are you Tom, m' lad?'

'Fine, thank you, Mr Woods,' I replied. 'How are you?'

He stood up, yawned and stretched his arms.' Ah, just dandy,' he said, reaching for an old, black overcoat that hung limply on the back of the kitchen door. 'I'm off now, mother,' he went on, smiling at his wife. 'Big darts match on to-night.' He gave his wife a quick kiss, turned to us, and with a gleam in his eyes, said. . 'Stay sober, you two,' laughed. 'Some hope, eh?' he added. He then placed a battered old trilby on his head and walked jauntily from the room.

Joe turned to me. A wide grin instantly spread across his craggy features. 'Great to see you, Bud,' he said, shaking my hand. His eyes narrowed slightly. 'Hey, what's wrong? You look knackered.'

'Watch your language, now, Joseph Woods,' said his mother sternly. 'Away now with both of you and let me get on with me knitting.'

'Bloody'ell, Bud!' exclaimed Joe. We had stopped under the street lamp at the corner of Canterbury Road. He glanced up from reading Cynthia's letter. 'No fuckin' wonder you looked pissed off, I don't blame you.'

'No mention of her being up the duff,' I remarked, lighting a cigarette and giving one to Joe. 'What do you think, mate?'

Joe took a long drag before answering. 'I think she was havin'
you on, Bud,' he said. 'Trying the old diamond ring caper. Just as
well you didn't fall for it. Now, what you need is a few bevies.'

The next day Joe called around. 'Get up, you drunkard,' smiled
Mum, as she came into my room holding a steaming hot cup of tea.
'It's eleven o'clock and Joe's downstairs.'

I vaguely remembered we had arranged to meet for a
lunchtime session in "The King's Arms".

The tea nearly scalded my mouth and I had a head like
Birkenhead. I gingerly made my way downstairs, feeling like death
warmed up.

'Fancy a nice greasy piece of bacon on a drippin' butty, Bud?'
It was Joe's idea of a joke. I merely smirked at him and sat down.
Dad was at work and Alma was out playing.

'Very funny,' I Mumbled, holding my head in both hands.

'What you want is a hair of the dog,' said Joe. 'Come on, a
drop of whisky will put you back on your feet.'

The thought made me feel worse. However, I reluctantly
agreed. The football team were in the King's Arms having a liquid
lunch before a match.

'Shagged any o' those Wrens yet, Tom?' quipped Billy Cotton,
Ashville's wiry goalkeeper.

'Wrens be buggered,' laughed Dave Simms. 'What about those
nurses, eh? I hear they love it.'

'Christ,' I said. 'You're just as bad as Lofty Small, a mate of
mine. He's sex mad, too.'

'You bet,' cried Pluto Williams, the team's gangly left half. He
turned and leered across at Hazel, the barmaid and drooled. 'What
are you doing tonight, love?'

'Not you, that's for sure,' she replied. 'I'm fed up, not hard
up.'

After a few pints I felt better. 'Do you fancy the Tower
tonight, Joe?'

He gave me a quizzical look. 'The Tower?' he said. 'Not a
good idea, really, especially after . . . well, you know?'

'Why not?' I replied confidently. 'Like me Dad said. She's not
worth bothering about.'

Joe rubbed his hands together gleefully. 'Whey-hey,' he cried.

'You're on, providing you wear your rig. Women love men in uniform. Meet you here at seven. OK?'

A few hours later I was in the living room brushing my uniform. 'Looks real tiddly, doesn't he Cora?' said Dad, sipping a cup of tea.

'Och, so he does,' replied Mum, with a touch of pride. 'Especially with that lovely redcross I sowed on his arm. He'll have the girls swooning, he will.'

Although we hadn't passed our finals, the lads decided to sow our Red Cross on during leave. Needlss to say, it would have to come off before we returned to camp. 'Cheers, folks,' I replied, trying to put all thoughts of Cynthia out of my mind. 'Here's hoping you're right.'

Joe was waiting at the bar. A dark Macintosh hung over his arm and he wore his usual brown sports coat, white shirt and tie.

After downing a few pints, we caught the bus to New Brighton.

As we approached the Tower, memories of Cynthia returned. I felt the tension rising inside me and wondered if Joe had been right after all.

'What's up, Bud?' asked Joe, as we queued up to put our gear in the cloakroom. 'You've gone quiet all of a sudden. Are you OK?'

I gave him a curt nod. 'Yeah,' I replied flatly.' Let's go to the bar.'

Not surprisingly, the bar was crowded. There were several servicemen, so I didn't feel out of place.

'Come on, Bud.' said Joe, as we finished our second pint. 'Let's see if that uniform of yours works, eh?'

Much to my surprise, it did. A girl with red hair and a nice smile asked me if I was in the Red Cross. I explained what the insignia on my right arm meant.

'The Royal Navy,' she gushed, turning to her friend. 'He's an officer in the navy, Joan.' I was about to contradict her, but thought better of it when she asked me to dance.

I gave Joe a quick nod towards her mate. 'Meet you here if we get separated, Joe. All right?'

The dance was a quickstep, not one of my specialities. We had gone half way around the floor when suddenly, my stomach lurched. There, in the crowd was Cynthia. Her long, dark brown hair hung down her back and she was wearing the same floral dress she had often worn for me. I also recognised her partner. It was that same cocky American corporal who asked her to dance when we were here the last time.

My heart beat like a drum as I closed in on them. Suddenly, they turned and I saw her face. She didn't see me as she reached up and gave the American a passionate kiss. Anger and jealousy engulfed me. Beads of perspiration ran down my face. My hands felt clammy and I missed my step, kicking Red Hair in the ankle. 'Ouch' she yelped, hopping on one foot. 'You're not doing the horn-pipe now, you know.'

I Mumbled an apology. When the dance ended, Red Hair sniffed the air and left. My eyes followed Cynthia and the American. They walked slowly, arms wrapped around one another, and sat down at a table on the edge of the dance floor.

With a fury generated by months of frustration, I strode over to them. Blissfully unaware of my approach, they held hands and gazed into each other's eyes.

'Remember me?' I shouted. Both immediately looked up. My face was burning with rage. 'I'm the idiot who thought you were having a baby. Remember? You lousy sod.'

With startled expressions they stared up at me. 'T...Tom,' stuttered Cynthia. 'What! What are you doing...?' She was quickly interrupted by the American.

'Say, Mac. Who d'ya think you are?' he drawled, slowly standing up. 'I don't know what you want, but get lost before I loose my temper.' I glared at him, my fists clenched. He was tall and athletically built. With one hand he pushed me away.

Joe appeared next to me. After that, pandemonium broke lose.

I remember hitting him and feeling a sharp pain in my hand. He fell backwards onto a table behind, blood spurting from his mouth.

'Orville! Orville!' screamed Cynthia, as he crashed against her, knocking over glasses and spilling drinks onto her dress. 'Oh my God. Don't hurt him, Tom. Don't hurt him.'

A crowd had gathered around, and some other girls began screaming.

Using the back of his hand, the American wiped blood from his mouth, and staggered to his feet. 'You Limey bastard,' he grunted. 'I'm gonna give ya a real whippin'.

'Oh yeah,' I gasped, pushing his chin upwards with my hand.

'You and whose fucking army?'

The corporal's pal stood up and Joe immeditely floored him with a left hook.

The four of us crashed into another table. More screams ensued as the corporal's pal quickly got up and traded blows with Joe.

Cynthia's continued screeching, 'Orville, Orville,' as I got in another punch. He gasped and let out a stream of obscenities.

At that moment I felt a pair of strong hands on my shoulders. 'Right, mate,' came a gruff voice, pulling us apart. 'That's enough.' Two stockily built, men in tuxedoes grabbed Joe. Two other bouncers held the Americans.

'It were his fault,' sobbed Cynthia. Others nodded in agreement. 'He—' she sobbed, pointing at me, '- hit Orville, right in his mouth.'

'OK. Out with the pair of you,' snorted the biggest of the bouncers. 'Go on, Charlie, throw these two buggers out,' indicating Joe and myself

With great satisfaction, I saw Cynthia's American sitting on a chair, pale-faced and holding a blood-soaked handkerchief to his nose. Cynthia, her face streaked with mascara, placed a consoling arm around his shoulders. 'I never want to see you again,' she cried, glaring at me, 'Never! Never!'

'I'll get you for this,' came the muffled voice of the American from behind the handkerchief. .

'Anytime, Yank, anytime,' I called out to him, as Joe and I were manhandled out of the ballroom.

The band hadn't stopped playing, and I remember hearing *"The Tennessee Waltz",* the same tune they played when I met Cynthia.

Sometime later we were sitting on a wooden bench along New Brighton promenade. 'Are you all right, Joe? There's a bit of blood on the side of your mouth.'

He gingerly touched it with his finger. 'Just a scratch,' he replied, taking out a handkerchief and dabbing the blood away. 'I'm OK. No problem. How about you?'

'A few bruises. Nothin' much. I wonder what happened to the Yanks?'

He gave a quick shrug of his shoulders. 'First aid, I expect' he grinned, handing me a cigarette.

I struck a match and gave him a light.

He took a deep drag , then with a pained expression on his face, Mumbled, '*Orville*? I ask you?'

'I'll have to go and visit him,' said Mum with a deep sigh. 'Nobody else will and it is Christmas.'

Mum was sitting on a chair, peeling potatoes. Two days had elapsed since the 'Battle of Tower Hill,' as Joe called it, and I was helping to prepare the dinner.

'I know, Mum,' I replied. 'I'll come with you, all right?' I was sitting in Dad's chair, scraping carrots, and using last night's newspaper to catch the skins.

Mum was referring to Tony, who was still in Walton Prison. He was due out some time next year. I glanced across at Mum. The grimy potato skins curled gently away from her knife and fell onto the newspaper. She looked pale and drawn with dark circles around her eyes. The greyness in her short, brown hair appeared to have increased during the past few months.

Outside, the harsh, wintry wind sent sleet rattling against the kitchen window. I warmed my hands on the fire and pitied Dad being tossed about on the river in his small boat. I could hear bursts of laughter coming from the front room where Alma and her friends were playing.

'Don't tell your Dad,' said Mum, cutting the potatoes into small chunks, and dropping them in a large saucepan. 'Just say we're going to see your Aunt Lottie. You know what he's like about Tony?'

Aunt Lottie was Mum's sister. She and Uncle George lived in New Brighton. A visit there usually took all afternoon, so it was a watertight alibi.

Without looking at her, I nodded while slicing the carrots into a large saucepan. I gave a worried sigh. We were both only too aware of what might happen when Tony was released. Mum had to live with this every day and, even though I was away from home, the thought of Tony and Dad under the same roof sent shivers down my spine.

Mum wiped her knife on her pinafore. 'You've done well with those carrots, son,' she smiled. 'Do you fancy doing the turnips while I nip out for a piece of mutton? Your old man loves a nice hot pan of Scouse.'

We sat in silence as the Number 20 tram rattled along Scotland Road. The high, grey walls of Walton prison looked even greyer under the cold, December sky. The familiar tinkle of keys announced the opening of the heavy, iron door. Once inside, we waited in a well-lit room with wooden partitions and wire mesh windows. A few decorations hung from the walls and a small Christmas tree, suitably tinselled, stood on a table.

Mum sat with the collar of her coat turned up even though it was warm. The inmates slouched in, eyes lighting up when they recognised a visitor.

A smile lit up Mum's face as Tony appeared. He hadn't changed. His pale, angular features and thick, black, wavy hair looked the same. As he sat down he gave us his familiar boyish grin. 'Hello,' he said, in a whisper, 'got any ciggies?'

Mum reached across and touched the wire mesh. Tony kept his hands on the small wooden bench in front of him. 'You look well, son,' she muttered. 'How are they treating you?'

Tony shrugged. 'OK,' he replied flatly.

'I've given the guard a cake and some cigarettes. You'll get them later.'

He never said, 'please,' or 'thank you.' With his shy, arrogant manner he took everything for granted. Little did he know that Mum had to scrimp and save money to buy him things.

He nodded at me. 'How's the navy, eh?'

'Great,' I replied, trying to sound enthusiastic.' I'm gong to Plymouth soon. I've given Mum some Navy fags for you. They're in the parcel.'

He took out a dog-end from the top pocket of his grey siren suit and lit it.

I gave Mum one of mine, and for a while nobody spoke.

'I'll be out of 'ere next year, y' know?' he said, in between drags on his cigarette. Then, with a dry smile, said. 'Better get me room ready, eh?'

His words gave me a sudden jolt. I could feel the tension rise as Mum, tight-lipped, straightened up. 'Do you thinks that's wise, son?' she said without looking at him.

'What do you mean! Wise?' he replied angrily.

I could see and feel the unease in Mum's eyes. Before she could reply, I interrupted them. Feeling awkward and more than a bit scared, I said 'Wouldn't it be best if you kept away?'

'Look,' replied Tony, his eyes darkening. 'Don't tell me what to do. Do you hear now?'

'He wasn't telling you what to do, Tony,' cried Mum, glancing at me. 'He's only trying to help. You know Dad won't let you in the house.'

Tony stood up. He angrily stubbed his dog-end out with his foot and glared at Mum.. 'We'll see about that.' He turned to leave. Mum craned her head forward. . 'Tony,' she pleaded, 'sit down, please. I don't know when I'll be able to come again. Sit down, son.'

He sighed as if it were an effort and muttered. 'I've got to go. Ta for the things.'

'Look after yourself, son, and write,' cried Mum, her voice fading into a whisper. He nodded, flashed his trademark grin, and walked away. Suddenly, the tension was gone, but Mum's tears remained.

Dad and I put up a Christmas tree in the front room while Joe, Alma and Mum festooned the place with decorations. On Christmas Eve we had an impromptu party in the house after a hectic session in "The Brighton". Joe arrived with his current girl-friend, a plumpish blonde called Rita,. Jock Forbes and June, his 'wee lassie,' came. Two old mates, Phill Leatham and Reg McKnight, both on leave from the Royal Navy also showed up. Along with several neighbours, we piled into the front room. Mum made corned beef sandwiches and everyone danced and sang to the strains of Slim Whitman, Frank Sinatra and Teresa Brewer.

On New Year' Day, Joe and I squeezed into the Kop at Anfield to see Liverpool play Newcastle United. We needn't have bothered. The Magpies won 1-0 and Jackie Milburn scored the winning goal.

One evening at the Grosvenor, where the lively trio of Ernie Hignet played every Tuesday and Saturday, Joe and I got lucky. We met Monica and Jessie, two sisters who lived with their deaf mother in Leasowe, a few miles away. We didn't get home till five o'clock the next morning.

It had been a great leave. Two days into 1953, on a cold January morning, I said a tearful farewell to Alma and Mum.

As the ferryboat pulled away from the jetty, I could see Dad, standing on the promenade by the side of the slipway. He wore his dirty, old, brown Macintosh, and from under his flat cap sprouted tufts of grey hair. He smiled and waved. It was a scene that was to be repeated many times during the coming years.

'Now, everyone, pay close attention.'

It was the day after we returned from leave, and everyone stood around a wooden plinth. On it lay Desperate, stripped down to his white shirt and gym shorts. With eyes anxiously wide open, he gazed up at us.

Sister Jasper was an attractive woman. Dressed immaculately in her blue uniform, complete with a white starched cap almost concealing her ash blonde hair, she looked down at her 'victim'. Normally all eyes would have been focused on her. Not so today – sex was the last thing on our minds.

Our nervous eyes were riveted on the sixteen, silver kidney dishes laid out in front of us. In each gleaming container lay the 'instruments of torture,' a metal syringe to which a thin, sharp needle was attached.

The sister gently folded up the hem of Desperate's shorts and placed her hand on his thigh. This immediately brought a smile to Desperate's face. 'Mmm,' he murmured, 'do that again, sister.'

'Be quiet, Morgan,' she retorted. 'And keep still.' She looked at us and continued, 'You will give yourself an injection – here.' She stabbed the outer aspect of Desperate's thigh with her finger. This made him jump.

'Ouch,' he cried, 'that hurt.'

All eyes followed as she picked up a syringe. 'Note how I disperse any air bubbles by flicking it,' she said. She then picked up a blob of cotton wool soaked in surgical spirit.

Before wiping the area to be injected, she smiled sweetly down at Desperate who, by this time, was a dithering wreck.

'This won't hurt, and remember, you will get a pint of beer from the Chief for volunteering.'

We watched, fascinated, as she expertly plunged the needle into his thigh. Desperate, wide-eyed with terror, let out a cry.

'Keep still,' snapped Sister Jasper and went on. 'Always withdraw the plunger slightly to see if you're in a blood vessel, before injecting, so.' The "patient" gave a slight moan, flattened his body and fainted!

'Och, that lad will do anything for beer,' growled Jock, nudging me in the ribs.

Then it was our turn to inject ourselves. For the next hour, we sat down, syringe in trembling hands, trying to pluck up enough courage to do the dastardly deed. Only Lofty completed the job. This encouraged us and in due course even Desperate, with eyes tightly shut, managed the job. Yet another hurdle had been overcome and we all felt justifiably proud of ourselves.

The week before our final examinations, we experienced our first taste of ward duty.

'I wonder what D3 is?' I said, seeing my name on the main notice board.

'Medical,' came the husky voice of Chief Donnelly, standing behind our group. 'Diabetes, hepatitis and all that lot.'

'Oh, yes,' I replied. 'Sounds interesting. What have you got, Des?'

Before Desperate had time to reply, Simbo Johnson chimed, 'They're sending old Des to the mental ward for rehabilitation.' Simbo's face dropped a mile when he found out that he, and not Desperate was being sent there.

D3 was a large ward, with sixteen beds on each side and high windows. An ugly-looking coal fire, enclosed in a marble-topped grate, glowed in the centre. Next to this stood a black coal-scuttle with a metal shovel resting inside.

The place was a hive of activity. The sister was standing by an open cupboard, busy preparing medicines and tablets. Nearby, a stockily-built rating with fair hair checked a stack of bed-tickets. I later learned this was in readiness for medical officer's rounds.

Everyone was busy, their long white gowns almost tripping them up as they went about their work. The sharp smell of antiseptic stung my nostrils as I watched a Sick Berth Attendant energetically drag beds into the centre of the ward. The deck was polished and beds returned. This process was repeated on each side of the ward.

A nurse pushing a trolley gave each patient a fresh water carafe. From the bottom shelf, she selected and squeezed out a piece of lint from a basin of antiseptic and wiped each locker. Every time she bent down the patients and staff would give her uniformed backside and shapely legs a quick admiring glance.

'Pack it in, Harry,' said one of the patients to his mate in the opposite bed. 'You'll end up having another heart attack.'

'Ah,' he replied, with a sigh, 'it might be bloody-well worth it, mate.'

The rating examining bed tickets stopped what he was doing, looked up and gave me a toothy grin. 'Aye, aye,' he said. 'You must be the PSBA we're expecting?'

'Yes, I am,' I replied nervously. 'I'm here for the week.'

'Right,' he replied, in a somewhat officious manner.' I'm the leading hand of the ward. LSBA Joslyn. Josh to you. After you've stowed your gear, I've got a special job for you. What's your name?'

'Lightburn,' I replied. 'Tom Lightburn.'

'OK, Lightburn,' he said, 'report to me when you've got your gown on.'

LSBA Joslyn introduced me to the ward sister. 'This is PSBA Lightburn, sister,' he said. 'We have him for a week.'

The sister, a tall woman with dark hair, smiled. 'I'm Sister O'Malley,' she said. 'Do your best, my boy, and don't be afraid to ask questions. You hear now?' Before I could answer, she turned away and busied herself at a nearby cupboard.

Josh turned to me, placed a fatherly arm around my shoulders, and said, 'you, my son, are going to be given the most important job on the ward. You are going to be "King of the Heads."'

Much to my disgust I found myself scrubbing sinks, scouring urine bottles, cleaning toilets and mopping floors. Every so often, Josh would pop his head around the door, flash a toothy grin, and say, 'You're doing a great job there, Tom. Keep it up, my son.'

On Wednesday, we had Medical Specialist's rounds. Promptly at 11.00am, Josh called the ward to attention. The sister greeted a portly figure in a white coat, unbuttoned to reveal a bulging blue waistcoat. He had a beard similar to James Robertson Justice and wore a pair of rimless spectacles perched on the end of his nose. Around his neck, dangling like a badge of office, hung a stethoscope.

'That's Surgeon Commander Terraine Williams-Ithell,' whispered SBA Ray Milton. 'TWIT for short.'

I suppressed a laugh and stood rigidly to attention as he passed by, followed closely by the block chief and an officer.

'Just follow on behind, PSBA,' whispered Dusty Miller, another member of staff.

The Medical Specialist and his retinue arrived at the bed of a rating who had just been admitted. His face was bright yellow and he looked rather ill. As far as I knew, the only people with yellow faces were Chinese.

'Ah,' said the doctor, raising his eyebrows and looking expectantly at everyone. 'Has any of the junior staff any questions they would like to ask about this patient?'

I pushed my way between Josh, Ray and Dusty. 'Why is he so yellow, sir?' I nervously enquired.

All eyes fell upon me. Suddenly, I felt my face redden. The doctor gave me a benign smile. 'Good question, young man. Who are you?

'PSBA Lightburn, sir,' I answered.

'Ah, a trainee,' he replied, stroking his beard. 'Well now, this man has jaundice. His colour is due to an excess of bile passing into his blood stream. Caused, no doubt, by some obstruction to his bile duct. But...' He paused and stopped stroking his beard. Then, peering over his spectacles at me, he added, 'We shall see. Does that answer your question, young man?'

I did not fully understand what he meant, nevertheless, I replied. 'Y...yes, thank you, sir.'

Every evening we had our books out, swotting up for our forthcoming finals. Everyone, that is, except Desperate. 'You're gonna fail, Des,' threatened Lofty. 'And it'll be back to the valleys for you, me-laddo.'

Desperate was stretched out on his bed, reading a comic. 'Oh, I'll be all right, boyo,' he replied, stuffing a toffee into his mouth. 'Besides, I knows me stuff. You wait.'

I was also lying on my bed, reading our medical bible, the BR888. 'Right, boyo,' I cried, sitting bolt upright. 'What's the signs of German Measles?'

With an air of resentfulness, Desperate put his comic down on his chest. 'That's easy,' he replied, in between chews. 'You break out all over in little, black swastikas, see.' Several groans echoed around the mess and someone threw their BR 888 at him.

The examinations lasted three days. Under the eagle eye of Sub-Lieutenant Millward, we sat in a cold, damp room and answered written questions. The subjects ranged from medical and surgical nursing to first aid and service administration. There was even a paper on dispensing, requiring us to translate a doctor's prescription from Latin to readable English.

Everyone wrote frantically. Everyone, that is, except

Desperate. Ever time I glanced up, he was staring at the ceiling, chewing the end of his biro.

'Everything all right, Morgan?' enquired Sub-Lieutenant Millward. 'Having any difficulties, are we?'

Everyone stopped work, and looked at the silly grin on Desperate's face. 'Oh no, sir,' he nonchalantly replied. 'Just thinking.' I wondered what exactly he was thinking, because one of the questions was about German Measles.

Wednesday was the final day and we were all keyed up for the last and probably the most important part of the examinations. The oral tests.

'Who's the doctors taking the exams, chief?' asked Jock. 'It's no the Surgeon Rear Admiral, is it?' We were in a room, bare except for the chairs we sat on and two windows. This was the tough one, as nobody knew what to expect. 'No it's not,' replied the chief, cheerily. 'And, even if I knew, I wouldn't want to spoil your fun.'

Everyone waited, stomachs churning and pulses racing. All eyes became focussed on a sign pinned to a closed door which read, 'Silence. Oral Examinations in Progress.'

My God, I thought. This is worse than waiting for the dentist. Suddenly, the door opened and out came Geordie, white-faced but relieved. As he left the room, the chief placed his finger over his mouth indicating silence, thus preventing Geordie from passing on any relevant information.

Desperate was next. After twenty minutes or so, he also emerged looking as if he had seen a ghost. Lofty was next, followed by Jock, Scouse Wilson and Simbo. By the time my name was called, I was a nervous wreck.

As I stood up, my legs felt weak. My shirt stuck to my back with sweat and my mouth felt dry. I took a deep breath, opened the door and went inside.

'Ah, sit down, young man,' said a familiar voice. I couldn't believe my eyes. Sitting behind a large desk, clad in a white coat, was the TWIT. His pale grey eyes peered benignly over his spectacles. I sat down and anxiously awaited my fate. He lent back in his chair and made a steeple of his fingers on his chest. 'Now, my boy, what can you tell me about jaundice…?'

With mounting anticipation, we scanned the notice board on Friday morning. As each individual saw a 'pass,' by their name, they gave a whoop of relief. Much to our delight, everyone, including Desperate, managed to pass.

We were fallen in outside the training divison in Haslar on Friday morning. 'Well done, all of you,' announced the chief, with a grin. 'Now, pay attention. Those of you with official numbers prefixed with D will be drafted to the Royal Naval Hospital, at Stonehouse, Plymouth, on Monday. Have your gear packed, and outside your messes by 0800.'

Lofty, Jock, Desperate, Scouse Wilson, and Simbo turned to one another and grinned. We were all Devonport ratings and would be going to Plymouth together.

That evening, with glowing pride, we sowed on our Red Crosses.

At long last, we were no longer sprogs.

5

The yardarms of HMS *Victory,* towering over the dockyard, offered their own farewell as the train pulled out of Portsmouth Harbour Station. Gradually, my eyes felt heavy and I fell asleep.

The jolting of the train woke me up. A glance outside told me had reached Eastleigh.

'I see the bloody Yanks are taking a pounding,' remarked Lofty from behind his *Daily Mirror.* 'Says here, " Casualties mount as American forces fight around Inchon. "'

'Where's Inchon, for Chrissake?' said Desperate. Jock and I were sitting next to him,with Lofty and Scouse Wilson seated across from us, jackets undone and legs stretched out.

Lofty raised his eyebrows in mock surprise. 'Korea, you berk,' he replied. 'Didn't they teach you anything at school?'

'I wonder if there's any chance of us going out there?' I said, passing a packet of blue–liners around. 'What do you think, Lofts?'

'Why not,' he replied, glancing over his newspaper. 'Churchill's calling up more reservists, so we might end up on a ship. We've got quite a few out there at the moment, including two aircraft carriers, HMS *Ocean* and *Albion.*

'I'd prefer a destroyer myself,' I said, flicking my ash onto the floor. 'My Dad used to say, " Small ships are the best ships. " And he ought to know. He was in mine– sweepers during the war.'

'Bugger that,' muttered Scouse Wilson. 'I didn't join up to get frigging shot at. No thank you.'

'I don't know what you're blathering about,' said Jock, wiping the grimy window with his hand and peering out. 'None of us have enough experience, so you can all forget it.'

The train arrived at Salisbury and an elderly couple came into the compartment. Both were out of breath and the man carried a heavy–looking suitcase. They wore spectacles, were medium height and quite stout. She had a pale, round face, alert blue eyes and several doublechins. Except for tufts of grey hair at each temple, he was quite bald. Desperate immediately stood up and helped the lady off with her coat, while Jock took the case from the man and placed it on the rack.

'Thank you both,' said the elderly lady, peering over her

spectacles. 'That was very thoughtful of you.' She opened her handbag and took out a small paper bag. 'Would any of you like a toffee?'

Desperate's face lit up like a Belisha beacon. 'Oh, ta very much,' he beamed, dipping into the bag. 'I don't mind if I do.'

'And mind where you put the wrapper, Des,' quipped Jock, winking at me.

The couple settled down. She opened a copy of *Housewife* and flicked through the pages. He removed his spectacles, wiped them with a handkerchief, and said, 'On your way to Guzz, are you lads?' He spoke with the same dialect as the chief in the Liverpool recruiting office.

'Guzz?' replied Lofty, shooting a curious glance at him. 'Where's this Guzz? We're on our way to Plymouth.'

'Aye,' added Jock. 'The naval hospital.'

'Sick bay tiffies, I see,' said the man, glancing at our red crosses. 'Spent some time in Stonehouse during the war, I did. Shrapnel in me leg, see.' He pulled up his right trouser and proudly showed us a long, white scar.

The elderly lady hit him playfully with her hand. 'Pull your trouser down, Henry. The boys don't want to see your hairy leg.'

'They'll see worse than that in the hospital, Ida, I can tell you.' He hurriedly obeyed his wife. 'As for what Guzz means,' he went on, 'that was the old W/T call sign for ships coming into Devonport. Now it's the sailors' nickname for Plymouth.'

'Why do they call the hospital Stonehouse?' I asked, offering them a cigarette. Ida politely refused, but Henry accepted one. Lofty struck a match and gave him a light.

'Named after the area in Plymouth where the hospital was built,' he said, 'called Stonehouse Creek, a small river running past the hospital. Used to land sailors from the dockyard in the old days. Nearly dry now.'

We hung on to his every word. Desperate even stopped chewing his toffee.

'Is it an old hospital, then?' asked Scouse.

'Oh aye,' retorted Henry, his blue eyes twinkling. 'Laid down in 1758 it was. The same year Nelson was born. Completed in 1762. Finest in the land. Even the Frogs came over to see it. Copied, it so they did.'

'During the war with France?' I asked.

'Much before that, my handsome,' replied Henry 'Still looks much the same too. Was in there a few months ago. You remember, Ida?'

Ida nodded and carried on reading.

'We visited old Charlie Adams in H2 ward. Had a heart attack, so he did.'

'Och, so it's pretty big, then?' asked Jock. 'As big as Haslar?'

'Don't know about Haslar, my bird,' went on Henry. 'All I knows is that it has these huge blocks of wards. Made out of grey granite, so they are. They've got large lawns and pathways running up and down between them. Nice big football field, too. Watched a match there once.'

'Sounds great,' I said, glancing at the others. 'Might get a game, eh?'

'Plenty of nurses, then?' asked Lofty, with a grin.

'All the same, you sailors are,' muttered Ida from behind her magazine.

'Oh, they've a big staff, all right,' replied Henry. 'Big walls too. Used to be a handsome set of gates at the main entrance. They were moved into the hospital for safety reasons. Many a young sick bay tiffy passed through them, I can tell you. So you'll have a lot to live up to.'

The train arrived in Exeter. 'This is where we get off,' said Ida. 'Moved here last year from Plymouth. Have a nice little pensioner flat, now, we have.''

'Aye,' said Henry, with more than a trace of nostalgia in his voice. 'But there's nothing like a quiet stroll on Plymouth Hoe on a sunny afternoon. Good luck to you lads.'

When they had gone, the compartment felt strangely empty. We had learned a lot about our next home, couldn't wait to get there.

Our journey continued along the Devon coast passing Exmouth and the picturesque towns of Dawlish, Teignmouth.

Dusk was falling, and the lights of Exmouth reflected in the calm waters of the bay. Vivid scarlet rays from the setting sun streaked from under the black clouds, making sea and sky resemble a Turner painting. It was as if the heavens were giving us a personal welcome. By the time we reached Plymouth darkness had fallen.

A naval lorry outside North Road Station took us to the hospital.

'Och, old Henry was right lads,' said Jock, looking out from under the lorry's canopy. 'Those bloody walls are high all right.'

'Not half,' added Scouse. 'They must be over twenty feet high. Bigger than those at Walton, I'll bet.'

How right you are, I thought, as a policeman waved us through the main gate.

The hospital was just as old Henry described. I later learned that each ward block was made of rough marble with flat, Purbeck stone decorating each corner. A glass-panelled solarium ran along a colonnade supported by stone pillars.

The lights were on and I tried to imagine what was happening inside. I would soon find out.

The lorry stopped outside a large, yellow-stoned building with a light above an arched entrance. A tall, fair-haired SBA in shirts-sleeves waited by an open door.

'This is the staff quarters,' said the PO. 'Take your gear and go up the stairs onto the first floor.'

We walked up a spiral staircase onto a landing. A strong smell of food made my stomach rumble. As if he read my thoughts, the PO said, 'The dining-room is there.' He pointed to two closed doors at the side of the landing. 'The chef has kept you some stew and figgy-duff. SBA Budding here will show you where your mess is. Report to the regulating office at 0800 tomorrow. OK?'

'Where's that, PO?' enquired Simbo.

The PO sighed and shot the SBA a tired glance. 'You tell them, Dave. I'm going for a pint.'

'Pay no attention to Nick Carter,' said Dave as we walked down a well-lit corridor. 'He's been on duty all day and it gets to you. By the way, the RO is in Trafalgar Block, just at the top where you came in. Stow your gear and take the kitbags to the baggage store tomorrow. That's just past H Block.'

'Hello, hello,' shouted someone as we entered the mess. 'More pigs for the trough. Welcome to the bone-yard, lads. All the more the merrier.'

A couple of SBA's in civilian trousers and shirts approached us. 'Where are you lot from, then?' asked a stocky lad, with a mop of untidy, brown hair. I immediately recognised his accent.

'Pompey. Just passed out,' I replied. 'And what part of Liverpool are you from?'

'Kirkby,' he answered. 'Stan Major's me name. What's

yours?'

'Tom Lightburn.' We shook hands. I introduced him to Scouse Wilson.

'You'll find a lot of Devonport ratings come from the north-west,' said Stan. 'The same way Pompey ratings come from the south. I suppose it's draftee's idea of a joke.'

'Och, away with you,' ranted another SBA, who told us his name was Jock White. 'The bloody place is being taken over by you Scousers. It wouldna be so bad, but your football team is down the drain.'

'Of course,' interrupted Stan, 'he means Liverpool. Me, I support the 'Toffees.' He glanced across at Jock White. 'That's Everton – a proper team.'

'Toffees,' repeated Desperate, looking around at everyone. 'Now that's a great name for any team.'

Lofty and the rest of us just grimaced and shook our heads.

The chief in the regulating office was at his desk, talking down the telephone. I was the last to go in. The others waited outside in the colonnade. He was a fresh-faced with straight, dark brown hair, slightly greying at the temples. Behind him at a smaller desk, an SBA pounded away at a typewriter. I noticed a large map of Plymouth on the wall and shelves containing several files. On a chart there was a series of red-and-blue cards, slotted in columns. Above this was a sign which read 'Watch Bill.'

'All right, all right, Sam,' growled the chief down the phone. 'I'll tell him when he gets here. You and your bloody football team!'

He sighed and replaced the telephone on the receiver. 'Right,' he said, sorting through a stack of documents. 'I'm Chief McKenzie. You must be Lightburn.' He drew a file from the bottom of the pack and opened it. 'This is yours. Mmm, good exam results. Ah, ah.' His eyes lit up. 'You are the one that plays football. Good. When you've finished your joining routine, report to Petty Officer Small. You'll find him somewhere on C Block, most probably chatting up a nurse. He's our illustrious e team manager. You'll be on H2 ward, and in 1st of Starboard Watch. Carry on.'

On our way to the baggage store I told Lofty the watch I was in.

'Not that it means anything to me,' I added, with a shrug of my shoulders.

'Ha!' exploded Lofty. 'I'm in 2nd Starboard and we are duty weekend. That is what it bloody-well means.'

We watched two members of staff push a trolley across the wide, tarmac pathway. The head of a young man peered at us over a few layers of blankets. He gave us a wide grin, and said, 'Broken foot, going to get me photo taken.' The SBA's with him laughed and steered the trolley up a wooden ramp into the x-ray department.

'It's very compact,' commented Jock, staring around. 'If it were raining, you could walk right around the place without getting wet.'

After depositing our kitbags, we walked across the inner walls of the hospital to the Pay Office. Inside, several civilian clerks were busy writing in large, open ledgers.

A white-haired man with horn-rimmed spectacles looked up as we entered. 'Morning,' he said. 'Doing your joining routine, I see. My name is Mr Ferris. I'm the pay officer.' He spoke with a rich Devon accent. 'Now. I expect you'll be wanting a sub till pay day, which isn't till next week?'

'Wouldn't mind a few quid,' replied Desperate, who seemed to have appointed himself spokesman for all of us. We were paid fortnightly and this was 'blank week.'

Later, at dinner, Lofty was sitting next to a small, redheaded SBA. 'Where's the nurses, then, Ginge?' enquired Lofty. 'Don't they eat here, then?'

'Naw,' replied Ginger. 'They all go to Wingfield Mansions, up the road from here. I don't think old 'Bogey' Knight trusts us.' He was referring to Wardmaster Lieutenant Knight, the officer in charge of the staff. 'By the way,' he added. 'My name's Ginger Valentine.'

Lofty introduced himself and carried on eating.

The following morning I reported for duty.

Unlike the wards in Haslar, H2 was square-shaped, with a large partition in the centre. The walls were pale green, with several windows on either side, shining light onto a highly polished floor. On a table stood a vase of early spring daffodils whose smell was overpowered by that of anti-septic.

All the beds were full. Some patients were sleeping. Others sat upright, reading newspapers and magazines. Tall, oxygen cylinders, painted black and white, with rubber tubes and masks attached, stood like sombre guardsmen alongside several beds.

A thickset medic with a mop of black hair and large, humourous eyes looked across at me. 'What can I do for you, then, boyo?' He sounded just like Desperate.

'Er...The reg office told me to report here.'

His face broke into a broad grin. 'Ah,' he cried, rubbing his hands together. 'A new member of staff, eh? Welcome.' He held out his hand. 'My name is Taff Elias, I'm the Leading Hand of the ward.'

I told him my name and we shook hands. 'Well, Tommy Bach,' he said, with a slight sweeping gesture of his hand. 'This is a medical ward. Some patients with diabetes, others with dicky hearts.'

When he introduced me to the sister, I nearly had a heart attack myself. She was tall, and blonde with the bluest eyes I have ever seen.

'I am Sister Johannsen,' she said, with a pleasant Scandinavian accent. 'Familiarise yourself with the patients' bed-tickets. And please to ask any questions you like.' She then smiled, flashed a set of perfect white teeth and turned away. All eyes followed her as she walked down the ward.

'Gorgeous, isn't she?' remarked Taff with a sigh. 'Officer's meat only though. Even Sam couldn't get anywhere with her.'

'Is that the same Sam who runs the football team?'

'Yes,' replied Taff. 'And a randy bugger he is too.'

'I've got to report to him about soccer.'

'You'll find him on C Block. That's opposite to where we are. C3 is the female ward, you see.'

There were three other members of staff. One was a shy-looking first year nurse with freckles called Jean; another was tall with thick, wavy brown hair named Dave Jones. The last was Stan Major, the SBA I met in the mess. 'You'll be in the same watch as me then, Tom,' said Stan. We were in the galley having a mug of tea.

'This is a good ward for you to start,' said Dave. He paused, took a swig of tea, then grinned. 'The only thing we have to worry about is all the young doctors sniffing around Svenska. Mind you, I can't say I blame them.'

Blue Watch secured at 1300, so I decided to find PO Small.

In each corner of the grounds, masses of daffodils, arranged in neatly cultivated beds, added a touch of spring to the surroundings. As I walked across the pathway, two nurses, their blue capes billowing in the breeze, smiled as they passed.

Away to my right Trafalgar Block loomed high with its magnificent bell tower and clock. This was the administrative centre of the hospital. Where the two pathways met stood an ancient sundial. I paused and checked my watch. The time was a little after one o'clock. Much to my surprise all timepieces were correct. No excuses for being adrift in this place, I thought.

On my left were several imposing buildings. I found out these housed the Wardroom, Surgeon Rear Admiral and other senior officers. I looked around, remembering old Henry's words. No wonder the French copied the design. Everywhere looked symmetrical, compact and well organised.

Entering C block, I heard the sound of female laughter coming from the floor above. I walked up onto the landing and saw a tall, well-built flaxen-haired PO standing in the galley holding a cup. Close by stood four nurses. Whenever he spoke, they broke into peels of laughter. One of the nurses saw me, stopped laughing and said something to him.

He turned and looked at me. 'Hello, there,' he said, smiling. 'Who are you looking for?'

One of the nurses, a very attractive brunette, gave me a sly smile. 'If he's lost,' she said seductively, 'I'll take care of him.' The others looked at one another and giggled.

I felt my face redden. 'Er...the chief in the reg. office told me to report to you about football. You are PO Small, aren't you?'

'That's me,' replied the PO, handing his cup to a nurse. 'You haven't met my harem, have you?' This provoked more laughter and giggles. 'This here is Charlotte, Jean, Peggy and Sue.' As he spoke their names, he touched each one gently on their caps. With a false sigh, he shook his head, and said, 'You'll have to excuse me, girls, business to attend to. I'll see you all later. Be good, but if you can't be good, see the padre.' This provoked more laughter.

Once more the brunette gave me a smile. Sam looked at me, grinned. 'Steady lad, they belong to me.'

When we reached the colonnade, he said, 'Our left half has a broken leg and next Saturday we play Plympton Rovers. If we win or draw the league title is ours. Report for training on Wednesday evening. If you're on duty, don't worry. I'll get you off. OK?'

The staff quarters overlooked the football field and was surrounded by trees and a high wall. From the side of the building a sloping pathway led almost directly onto the pitch. Very handy, I thought, and walked down to get a feel of the turf.

I stood in the centre-circle. Away to my left, the staff-quarters rose like a huge grandstand. With people hanging out the windows cheering, it would be like playing in front of Liverpool's Spion Kop.

H2 ward was full of elderly ex-servicemen. I did as the sister suggested and learned as much as I could about each one.

One morning, during rounds, I quietly asked the MO, 'Why is Mr Parry's face so red, sir?'

The doctor, a pleasant young man in his thirties, replied, 'He has very high blood-pressure.'

'Aye, sir,' interrupted Stan, who was standing near me. 'And probably drinks lots of Bass. There's a few like that where I come from.'

The doctor gave him an odd look, and carried on along the ward.

Taff Elias showed me how to take blood pressure, and also the delicate art of withdrawing blood from a vein. First, he placed the inflatable cuff around the patient's upper arm. Then, after pumping it up, said, 'Always go into the vein from the side, like this.' He carefully inserted a needle into a vein, and withdrew some blood. He then, added, 'And always remember to loosen the cuff.' Just then, a line of blood spurted out onto his white gown. 'Or else, that will happen.'

'Bloody vampires,' growled the patient and slunk under the bedclothes.

That evening, Stan and I were on watch. The ward was warm and cosy. Supper was over and everything was quiet. 'Please. Come with me, Lightburn,' said Sister Johannsen. 'I will show you what medication each patient is on.' I needed no extra bidding and followed the sensual trail of her perfume. Before stopping at each bed, she explained which tablets a patient was on, administered the treatment then ticked their names in a book.

We stopped at Mr Parry's bed. He was sitting up, wearing hospital-issue pyjamas. His thick, grey hair was well groomed and he was reading the Plymouth *Evening Herald.* 'Haven't seen you here before,' he said in a thick Devon accent.

He swallowed his pills with a glass of water.

'SBA Lightburn is new on the ward, Mr Parry,' sain Sister Johnnsen with a smile.

'Is that so,' he replied, 'how are you getting on?' It was obvious Mr Parry wanted to chat to me, so the sister carried on moving around the ward.

'This is my first day, Mr Parry,' I said. 'How are you feeling?'

'I'd feel much better if Argyle would win for a change.' He gave a harsh cough, and I poured him more water. 'Thanks, son,' he said. As he spoke, I could hear his chest wheezing. 'That centre-half, Jack Chisolm, is right off his game.'

'Oh, really,' I replied. 'I support Liverpool. They're not doing too good either.'

With difficulty, Mr Parry reached into his locker drawer. 'Here, take a look at this.' He showed me an old, black and white photograph of a football team. 'That's me,' he said, handing it to me. 'Playing for the old *Dido,* in 1925.'

I didn't notice when he gave another cough.

'How old were you when this was taken?' I asked.

Mr Parry didn't reply. He lay with his newspaper resting on his chest. I noticed a trickle of spittle running down the corner of his mouth. His blue eyes were staring in front of him and his florid complexion was now greyish-white. Reaching down, I gently touched his shoulder. To my surprise he fell against me. I placed my arm around his shoulders to support him and his head slumped against my chest. I immediately panicked. 'Mr Parry!' I cried. 'Mr Parry, are you all right?'

'What's up, Tom?' said Stan, appearing by my side. 'What's all the shouting about?'

'There's something wrong with Mr Parry.' I cried. I still had his photograph in my hand. 'I was just talking about football. He showed me this photo. Is there anything wrong?'

Stan lifted Mr Parry's face then checked his pulse.

'He's brown bread,' replied Stan, as if nothing had happened. Good Lord, I thought. Dead! How could he be dead? I was just talking to him. I looked at him, hoping he would suddenly open his eyes. Instead, his warm body had gone completely limp and cold.

A feeling of sadness and shock welled up inside of me. A few moments ago this nice old man seemed so cheerful and happy. Now he was gone. At that moment, I discovered the fragile balance between life and death.

'Poor bugger,' I murmured, as we gently lowered him down in the bed. 'He told me about Argyle and I was telling him about Liverpool.'

Stan chuckled to himself. 'Bloody-hell, Tom,' he whispered, pulling the sheet over Mr Parry's ashen face. 'That's enough to give anyone a coronary.'

The next day I received a letter from Mum telling me everyone was fine. She went on, "Your Dad says to keep away from the Long Bar, and The Paramount – he says the steps there can be a bit tricky." I smiled, realising he was secretly passing me some valuable information.

'Guess what, lads?' I said, reading this out to Desperate and the others. 'I think we've found out where to go on our first run ashore.'

6

On Wednesday evening the football team met in the junior ratings'
bar prior to training. This consisted of a few laps of half-hearted
jogging, after which everyone returned to have a few more beers.

We were grouped around the bar. Every time Marlene, the
peroxide blonde barmaid, bent down to pick up a bottle of beer all
eyes stared down her cleavage.

Sam came in, dressed in a spotless, green tracksuit. 'Right, you
lot,' he said briskly, 'gather round. Keep your minds above your
navels and listen to my plan.'

'Oh, not the bloody off-side trap, again, Sam,' moaned Harry
Johnson, who, although he couldn't use his left foot, played on the
left wing.

'Shit in it, Harry,' chimed in Pete South, the team's stocky
centreforward. 'We've not done badly so far, have we?'

Brum Appleby, our centre-half, thrust a pint of beer in Sam's
hand.

All eyes watched as Sam downed half his beer in one gulp.
Then, licking the froth from his upper-lip, said, 'Defence, lads.
Defence.'

'Defence,' cried George Storey, his glass poised in the air.
George was the team captain and an ardent Coventry City supporter.
'That's crazy, Sam. They'll hammer hell out of us if we do that.'

One or two nodded in agreement, especially Tiny Baxendale, a
local born lad who kept goal. 'What if they score, Sam, my
handsome?' he asked. 'We won't be able to defend then, will we?'

Sam gave us all a cynical look. 'Now listen,' he said.
'Plympton Rangers have just signed Dick Bullock. He's had a trial
for Argyle and he's as fast as a whippet. George and newcomer,
Tom, here, will mark him. We'll keep Pete up field on his own. The
rest of you will fall back. Remember. We only need to draw to win
the championship. But,' he added, glancing around, 'if there's an
emergency, I have a master plan.'

Several heads preened forward. 'What master plan is that,
then, Sam?' asked several voices.

'Never you mind,' said Sam, with a mischievous glint in his
eye. 'Remember, when the conjurer pulls out a rabbit from his hat,

always look in his back pocket.'

With that, he finished his drink, winked at Marlene and left.

Later that evening, Lofty, Desperate, and I decided to go ashore and explore the infamous Union Street.

'From what your old man said in that letter,' said Lofty, polishing the brim of his cap, '"The Long Bar" and "The Paramount" sound great.'

'I've been told they have the best looking pro's in the country,' chuckled Desperate, as he buttoned up his uniform.

'Forget it, Des,' I said, giving my jacket a final brush down. 'You couldn't afford the price of their lipstick.'

'Ha,' retorted Desperate. 'It's not their lipstick I'm after.'

Lofty was preening himself in front of the mirror. 'I don't believe in paying for it,' he said, rather cockily. 'With looks like mine, they should pay me.'

Union Street stretched in a straight line from Stonehouse Creek to Plymouth City Centre.

As far as I could see, everywhere was crowded with service men. The neon signs and pale yellow street lighting almost turned night into day. Occasionally, matelots would stagger out of a pub, arms around each other, only to disappear into the next available bar. A few cars, double-decker buses and the occasional naval patrolwagon passed down the street. The noisy atmosphere set my pulse racing and I could not wait to get into the action.

We dived into a pub called 'The Standard,' and quickly downed a few pints of St Austell's best bitter. 'Where's the "Long Bar," my love?' enquired Desperate, ogling the pretty barmaid.

'Further down on your right, my lover, next to "The New Palace,"' she replied, blowing a large bubble of gum from her mouth and sucking it back in. 'Wouldn't go there though.' she added. 'It's a bit rough.'

After a pint in "The Robin Hood" we crossed over the street. In front of us was a large, Victorian theatre, built of dark green and yellow glazed bricks. On either end of the frontage was a mosaic of Drake defeating the Spanish Armada. A neon sign flickered above the box office announcing to the world that the great Arthur Askey, my fellow-Liverpudlian, was topping the bill.

'There's "The Long Bar,"' cried Desperate, pointing with a finger. 'Next to the theatre. Just like the girl said.'

I felt as if we were entering a saloon in Dodge City.

I pushed open the swing doors and was immediately hit by a blast of warm air and stale beer. A haze of blue tobacco smoke half hid the electric lights and the sound of high-pitched laughter and music filled the room.

In a corner, a man in a pale blue suit played *"Cruising Down the River"* on an out-of-tune piano. Several well-endowed barmaids served behind a bar that curved around the width of the room. Groups of servicemen sat at tables, drinking, and enjoying the company of seductively-dressed girls. Other men lounged against the bar, talking, while eyeing up the talent.

As soon as we walked in, two heavily rouged girls smiled and came at us like a pair of panthers on the prowl. One was blonde, dressed in a tight black skirt and yellow blouse. The other, thin-faced and dark, wore a coloured dress with a well exposed bosom.

'Hello, ducks,' said the blonde, fluttering a pair of eyelashes long enough to sweep a floor. 'Buy a girl a drink?' She spoke in a cockney accent and reeked of perfume. The dark one corralled Desperate, who welcomed her with open arms.

'Look you, Tom,' he said excitedly, trying to impress the girl. 'I'll get 'em in. What's you having, then, girls?'

'Pimms Number One with lemonade,' said the blonde, cuddling up to me. 'And the same for Mavis, here.' Her hair felt coarse against my face and her body odour was overpowering. I tried to move away, but she clung on to my arm. 'I sees you're medical men, then, darling,' she commented, glancing at the red cross on my arm. 'I say, Mave, we're in good hands here if we feel faint.'

Desperate flashed a fiver and paid for the drinks.

'You're right there, Annie,' replied Mavis. 'This one here can give me first aid anytime.' Both accepted drinks from Desperate, then burst out laughing. 'And the kiss of life.'

I had two pints in my hand. I looked around for Lofty. He was sitting at a table, talking to a buxom girl with red hair. Lofty had both elbows on the table and was staring into her eyes.

'Excuse me, love,' I said, carefully disengaging Annie's arm from mine. 'I'll be back in a minute.' I walked over and placed the beer in front of Lofty.

He looked like a man in a trance.

'Cheers,' he muttered, accepting the glass without turning his head. 'I'll be over in a minute.'

I shrugged my shoulders and returned to the bar where Mavis had both arms around Desperate's waist.

'How about another drink, Cedric?' Desperate's tongue had obviously been loosened. I shook my head and laughed.

I glanced across and saw that Lofty and his girl were gone. 'Hey, Des,' I cried, turning just in time to see Mavis planting a sticky kiss on Desperate's mouth. 'Lofty's taken a ball of chalk. He's disappeared.'

Desperate broke away, his mouth a smudged with lipstick. 'What did you say?' he stammered.

'Lofty's gone, I tell you.' I said. 'He was sitting over there with a red head. Now he's bloody vanished.'

The girls looked at on another and grinned. 'Don't worry about him, ducks,' said Mavis, giving Annie a sly wink. 'He will be OK, won't he, Annie?' Then she added, 'Now, Cedric, how's about that drink?'

It was a little after ten and the bar was crowded. I looked around hoping Lofty might appear. 'Looks like he's gone with that judy, Des,' I said. But Desperate didn't hear me. He was too busy stroking Mavis's bottom.

Abruptly, Mavis backed away from Desperate, opened her black handbag and took out a small mirror. 'Bloody hell,' she said, giving Annie a quick dig in her side. 'I look a soddin' mess. Come on, let's go to the ladies.'

'Don't worry, Cedric,' she said, giving him a re-assuring smile. 'We won't be a jiff.' Desperate gave Mavis's bottom another squeeze and they left.

After twenty minutes we began to get suspicious.

'They're a long time in the heads,' said Desperate, eagerly looking around.

'Yeah, you're right, Des,' I replied slowly, staring in the direction where the girls had gone. 'I think they've done a bunk, Des.'

The man in a pale blue suit, who had been playing the piano, appeared by our side. With a flourish of his hand, he produced a yellow handkerchief from his top pocket and gingerly patted his brow. 'If you lovelies are waiting for those two bitches,' he said, in a high-pitched voice, 'you are wasting your time.'

'What do you mean?' asked Desperate angrily. 'Wasting our

time?'

'They've scarpered, darling. Pissed off,' he replied, poking back his handkerchief, and placing a hand on Desperate's shoulder. 'But you can buy me a drink if you want, dearie. I'm going nowhere.'

Desperate's eyes nearly popped out of their sockets. 'Sorry, mate,' he stammered, glancing anxiously at me. 'We are going. Aren't we, Tom, lad?'

Feeling annoyed, we continued down Union Street looking for the Paramount. We stopped at a dingy entrance next to a Chinese restaurant.

'This is the place, all right.' I said, 'Look at all those bloody steps.'

'You're right there, Tom, lad,' replied Desperate, eyeing up the steps. 'Let's give it a go.'

At the top of the stairs stood a beefy bouncer badly in need of a shave. He wore a tight-fighting evening suit and stood with both hands on his hips. His gaze followed Des and I as our unsteady legs carried us upwards.

'Half a dollar each,' he grunted.

Desperate fumbled in his trouser pocket and after paying, dropped a few coins on the ground. All eyes watched as they clattered down the steps and rolled out of sight.

'Oh well,' burbled Desperate, shrugging his shoulders. 'Come easy. Go easy.'

A stout woman, with wire-wool hair and heavy eye make-up, sat in small kiosk. A cigarette dangled from the corner of her mouth. 'Leave your caps next door,' she said, 'it'll cost you a bob.'

'Bugger me,' whispered Desperate, checking in our caps. 'We've spent a bundle before we have had a few wets.'

"The Paramount" consisted of one long, smoke-filled room, a crowded bar and windows that hadn't seen soap and water since the Crimean War.

At the far end a man in red shirt sat at a piano playing "*Don't Fence Me In,*" Next to him, a fat man in a wrinkled suit accompanied him on the drums.

Around the edge of a beer-stained dancefloor were several crowded tables. The warm air reeked of cheap perfume. Heavily rouged women in gaudy clothes hovered around the bar, hoping to catch the eye of some unsuspecting serviceman.

Several couples shuffled around the dancefloor, more interested in each other's bodies than the music.

'My round, Tom lad,' garbled Desperate.

'About time you paid for something,' I grinned, and surveyed the scene.

Suddenly, I spotted our old friends, Annie and Mavis sitting with two Royal Marines.

I was just about to turn around and tell Desperate, when he let out a sudden cry. 'My wallet!' cried Desperate. 'I've lost me bloody wallet.'

I turned around. Desperate was frantically patting his uniform jacket. 'It's gone,' he cried. 'My bloody wallet's gone.' Several people crowded around him. One or two people stepped aside from the bar and glanced at the floor.

'Where did you have it last, Des?' I asked, moving my feet, and searching the floor.

Then I remembered.

'I know, Des.' I bellowed. 'You had it in "The Long Bar". That's when you bought those judies a drink.'

'Yeah,' replied Desperate, pursing his lips. 'You're right, Tom. You don't suppose...' his voice trailed off.

I indicated with my thumb to where the girls were sitting. 'They're over there, Des, why don't you go and ask them?'

'Where? Where?' he said, jerking his head around. 'Where are they?' He stared across the room and saw the girls. 'Right!' he said defiantly. 'If any of those bitches have taken my wallet, I'll smash their head in. It's got a picture of me Mam in it, so it has.'

Now Desperate was a big lad, well built, and no stranger to many a rugby scrimmage. He thrust out his chest, and stormed towards the girls.

Annie saw him coming and nudged her friend. What unfolded next was reminiscent of the Battle of Tower Hill.

Desperate stormed over and glared down at them. 'Which one of you bitches has got my wallet, then?' he boomed. 'Hand it over or you'll get what for, I can tell you.'

Both girls looked innocently at one another. 'What the 'ell's he talking about, Mave?' said Annie, patting her hair. 'If you ask me, I think he is a bit pissed.'

'Don't ask me, ducks,' replied Mavis, putting her arm around the marine sitting next to her. 'Never seen him before in me life.'

Desperate made a grab for Annie's handbag. In doing so he knocked a glass of beer all over Annie's lap. She let out a piercing scream and quickly stood up. With both hands flying, she grappled with Desperate, trying to prevent him opening the handbag.

'You lying bitch!' yelled Desperate, vainly trying to push her away. 'You've got my fucking wallet in there and I want it back.'

At that point, Mavis picked up a glass full of beer, stood up, and threw it over Desperate and myself. One of the marines also stood up. He was dressed in his best blues, collar undone and white belt slung casually over a chair. 'Why don't you sick bay tiffies fuck off,' he retorted, glaring at me. 'You are all arse-bandits anyway.'

That's when I let fly with a left hook that would have done Sugar Ray Robinson proud. Unfortunately, it missed and the marine hit me with a sledge hammer blow to the head. As I fell backwards, I grabbed hold of Mavis and pulled her over. We both fell, dragging down the table and spilling everything on the floor.

Both girls, clinging on to their handbags, began to scream.

Desperate and the other marine were yelling obscenities while grappling on the floor. A large crowd had gathered, cheering and yelling.

Then, the bouncers intervened.

One quickly put a half nelson around my neck and dragged me away from the marine. Two others held down Desperate.

'I'll kill the fucking bitch, and you with her,' he cried, both legs flying in the air. Meanwhile, the marines were also being restrained by another pair of gruesome-looking heavyweights.

The girls were huddled together, lines of black mascara running down their faces. 'Have any of you girls got his wallet?' growled one of the bouncers.

'No, we bleeding well haven't,' screamed Annie. 'We've never seen any of them before, have we, Mave? They started it,' pointing at Desperate and me. 'All we was doing was having a quiet drink with our friends. And they comes over an' begins fightin'. Aint that right, Mave?'

'Yes,' replied Mavis, nodding her head. 'Bleeding troublemakers, they are.'

The strong hands of the bouncers prevented me from moving. Desperate glanced at me with a look of anger. 'She's lying,' he snarled. 'We were with them in "The Long Bar" That's where they took my wallet.'

'He's the one that's lying' cried Mavis, pointing an accusing finger at Desperate. 'He's just trying to get us in bother.'

I felt the bouncer's grip tighten around my neck. I tried to back-heel him, but this seemed to make him more determined to choke me to death.

'Give them the boot, Charlie,' said the biggest of the bouncers. 'Go on, chuck the buggers out.'

Accompanied by burbled cries and drunken cheers we were bundled to the top of the stairs. With a feeling of great relief, the bouncer's vice-like grip around my neck was released. However, my heart leapt a mile as a hand pushed me down the steps.

Desperate followed directly behind me. We tumbled down, trying to grasp the side of the wall in an attempt to break our fall. After what seemed an eternity we arrived on the pavement, battered, bruised and somewhat bewildered.

As our caps bounced passed us a couple of matelots helped us to our feet.

'Are you all right, mate?' asked one of them, handing me my cap. I gave him a weak smile and nodded.

Our uniforms were covered in dust and our ties and shirt collars undone. 'Any bones broken, Des?' I asked, as we dusted ourselves down.

Desperate took a deep breath and tried to adjust his tie. 'No,' he replied with a grin. 'Takes more than a few Bootnecks to hurt me.'

We thanked the two sailors again, and started to walk down Union Street.

'You know, Tom, lad,' said Desperate, glancing at me. 'Your old man was bloody-well right. Those soddin' steps can be a bit tricky!'

A few hours later in the hospital, the sounds of men sleeping echoed around our darkened dormitory. Suddenly, I woke up. I poked my head over the bedclothes and saw Lofty. He was wrestling with his trousers, trying as best he could to undress in the dark.

'How much did she pay you, Lofts?' I whispered, still aching all over.

'Bollocks,' came his cryptic reply as he climbed into bed and covered himself up.

Saturday dawned cold, clear and sunny. A perfect day for playing football. The team gathered in one of the messes downstairs in the staff quarters. Our trainer, Mick Slaney, a small, freckle-face lad from Dublin, was handing out our kit from an old canvas holdall.

'Not green and white squares again?' grumbled Lofty Day, our gangly inside right. With a look of disdain, he held the shirt in front of him. 'We wore these last time and were beaten.'

'That's because you missed a few sitters,' cracked Harry Johnson. 'So belt up.'

'Forget about Lofty,' said Pete South defiantly. 'Just you give me the ball, and I'll do the bloody rest.'

Sam Small came in his usual green tracksuit. 'Everyone fit?' he asked, rubbing his hands. It was more a declaration than an enquiry about our health. 'Now don't forget, boys. *Defence.*'

One by one we trooped down the slope onto the football field. Plympton Rangers, clad in all blue, had arrived early and were practising at the far end of the ground.

'That's Bullock,' said George Storey, 'the one with red hair kicking the ball.'

'Bloody hell,' I replied. 'He's a big bugger, isn't he?'

A large crowd, including Bogey Knight and the matron, stood on the grassy bank overlooking the pitch. The open windows from the staff quarters gave many a grandstand view of the pitch. Sam and his harem dressed in their uniforms, stood near the touchline. The pretty brunette I met a few days earlier smiled and waved at me.

Almost as soon as the game started, Pete South was so surprised to find himself through on Plympton's goal he shot wide. 'Huh,' growled Brum Appleby.'Give you the ball and you'll do what…?'

For the rest of the half, Plympton lay siege to our goal. At half time the score was 0-0.

As soon as the second half started, Sam's harem began jumping up and down, chanting, 'Bullock, Bullock.'

During a lull in play while Mick used his magic sponge on an injured player, Harry Johnson turned to me, with a grin, said. 'Are they yelling bollocks, or Bullock?'

'Maybe they're describing the way we are playing,' I replied, as the game re-started.

The girls were especially vociferous whenever Bullock received the ball. At one point, he smiled back, mistiming his pass.

Suddenly, disaster struck.

A long ball found Bullock, who raced passed George and was clean through on goal. I tried in vain to catch him, but only succeeded in tripping him up. With both arms flapping in the wind, Bullock toppled over onto the ground. The referee immediately pointed to the penalty spot.

I felt sick and wished the ground would open up and swallow me.

Nobody seemed to notice as Sam's harem walked behind our goal.

Bullock carefully placed the ball on the spot, took a few paces backwards. All eyes watched as he turned to run at the ball. As he did so, Sam's harem raised their skirts, showing sets of shapely legs, black stockings and suspenders while attempting to do the Can-Can.

For a second Bullock hesitated before striking the ball.

As he ran up I covered my eyes with my hand. Suddenly a great roar burst forth from the crowd. I removed my hands and could hardly believe my eyes. Bullock was on his knees, pounding the turf with both hands. The girls behind the goal were jumping up and down, throwing the ball to one another. Bullock had shot wide!

I let out a sigh of relief and could have kissed the girls.

Our lads punched the air with delight and congratulated one another. Meanwhile, the girls made a quick exit before the matron could catch them.

Later, in the "Hospital Inn," Sam and his harem were given a hero's welcome. I went up to the one who had waved to me, and said, 'Thanks, love. You girls certainly saved my bacon. What'll you have?'

'A gin and tonic, if you please,' she replied giving me a smile that promised more than a goodnight kiss. 'And call me Charlotte.'

Meanwhile, Sam interrupted a chorus of "*This Old Hat of Mine.*"

With a grin as wide as the Mersey Tunnel, he stood in the middle of the room, his arms around two of the girls. 'Now,' he said, giving them a hug, 'you miserable bastards know what was in the conjurer's back pocket!'

7

One Saturday afternoon in early April, Simbo, Lofty and myself decided to go ashore to visit a tailor.

'Joe Feneck's in Union Street is the best place,' said Ginger Valentine,' 'the lads always deal with him. On the left-hand side going down, you can't miss it '

A headline outside a newsagents reported the death of Stalin, with photographs of him lying in state.

'Lost millions in the war, those Ruskies did,' commented Simbo.

'Don't know about them,' I replied. 'But there were hundreds killed in this city during the bombing.'

I remember Dad telling me how Plymouth was almost flattened in 1940. So it came as a pleasant surprise to see how modern the city centre was. Only the war-torn skeleton of Charles Cross Church, reminded everyone of those dark days during the Second World War.

Joe Feneck was a small, wiry, west-countryman who started up in business after the war. He was especially popular with the staff of the naval hospital. 'Hello, my 'andsomes,' he said as we entered the shop. 'And what can I do for you?'

'We've all made out allotments, to you, Joe,' I said. 'And we'd like to be measured up for our uniforms.'

'No problem, lads,' replied Joe, flicking his tape measure from around his neck. 'Blue serge for work, and Doeskin for number ones. All right?'

We agreed, and after being measured up, Joe assured us the uniforms would be ready in a week.

After a few pints in the "Antelope" we ambled up one of the steep roads which led onto Plymouth Hoe.

In sombre mood, we walked around the impressive, crescent-shaped war memorial. Now and then, one of us would stop and read a name. Nobody spoke. The countless names inscribed on the walls spoke for themselves.

The view from the Hoe was breathtaking. Smeaton's Tower, painted in red and white, stood tall against the clear, blue sky. Directly ahead, the waters of Plymouth Sound glistened like silver.

Lofty and Simbo stretched out on the grass, took off their caps and dozed off. I was far too interested in my surroundings. I stood admiring the statue of Sir Francis Drake, his right hand resting on the hilt of his sword, glaring defiantly across the English Channel.

A large crowd had gathered on the esplanade overlooking the harbour. Some women held children in their arms, others jumped excitedly up and down, waving and yelling. The object of their attention was a solitary, grey, destroyer sailing into Plymouth Sound. Her crew were fell in on the upper deck, no doubt impatient to join their loved ones ashore. From her mainmast a long, white, paying-off pennant fluttered lazily. It was a sight to stir the imagination of any young man.

I gazed in pure envy as the vessel passed Drake's Island on her way to Devonport Dockyard. How I yearned to serve in a ship like that. The prospect of being responsible for the medical welfare of over two hundred lives didn't worry me. I was confident that, given time, I would be ready.

The stories told by 'old salts' like Taff Elias had increased my enthusiasm. He had served in several small ships during the Second World War. 'The old *Stork,* were the best of 'em all,' boasted Taff, one day while we were serving dinners. 'Got a pier head jump to her, I did. Stationed in your home town too.'

'A pier head jump, Taff?' I asked with a frown. 'What's that?'

'It's when you're given a sudden draft to a ship. No leave. Nothing.'

'Bloody hell, Taff,' I replied, 'that must have been a bit rough.'

Taking a large gulp of custard from a ladle, he went on. 'Aye. It were a bit of a 'green rub', but I survived. 36th Escort Group we were Old 'Hookey' Walker were the flotilla captain. Great man, too.'

'But what did you have to do, Taff?' I asked, doling out a plate of rice pudding. 'And what's a 'green rub'?'

'A green rub is naval slang for "tough luck,"' said Taff. 'When you haven't got a doctor onboard, you do every bloody thing from diagnosing a case of appendicitis, to wiping vomit off the sick bay floor. Not to mention giving jabs for everything from Cholera to Gonorrhoea.' Helping himself to a slice of figgy-duff, he went on, 'Then, there's all the soddin' paperwork. There's the store account, the medical documents, not to mention the Medical Officer's

Journal. You are jack of all trades, mate, I can tell you.'

'Bugger me, Taff,' I replied. 'How the hell can I learn all that?'

'Nothing to it, boyo. You'll soon learn.' He handed me a soggy dishcloth. 'Here, Tommy bach, clean this trolley up. Some messy bugger's dropped bits of figgy-duff all over the place.'

The most interesting part of the day was morning rounds when I could watch the doctor and ask questions. The ward MO was Surgeon Lieutenant Ethrington, a tall, fair-haired man who was always willing to help the staff. One morning, everybody was grouped around the bed of Mr Henderson, a fresh case admitted earlier that day. Using his stethoscope, the doctor listened to the patient's chest. He removed the earpieces, stood up from the bed and passed the stethoscope to me. 'Here,' he said. 'You're new on the ward, listen to the left side of Mr Henderson's chest.' He smiled at the patient, and asked, 'Do you mind?'

Mr Henderson gave me a half-hearted smile. 'Help yersel,' he wheezed. 'I only hopes there's something to hear.'

I did as the doctor suggested, and asked Mr Henderson to breathe as best he could. As he exhaled, I could clearly hear a faint grating noise. I asked him to repeat his breathing. I quietly told the doctor what I heard.

He beamed at me, and, out of earshot of the patient, said. 'Well done. What you heard was a typical asthmatic's chest.' The doctor turned to the staff. 'He also had hypertension and will require regular physiotherapy and medication.'

'What's hypertension?' I whispered to Stan Major, as we moved on to the next patient.

Stan gave me a blank stare. 'High blood pressure. Didn't they teach you anything at Haslar?'

I studied bed-tickets of patients suffering from pneumonia, chronic bronchitis and heart problems, noting the treatments prescribed. In doing so, I also learnt a whole new vocabulary of Latin terms that would enable me to decipher doctor's prescriptions.

One morning Stan and I were in the ward heads. 'Here,' he said, holding a specimen bottle half full of yellow urine. 'I'm gong to show you the quick way to test for sugar. Now, watch carefully.'

He held the bottle in front of my eyes then quickly dipped his forefinger into the urine. Then, to my utter disgust, he appeared to place his finger into his mouth.

'Mm…' muttered Stan, licking his lips. 'Sugar. And lots of it too, Tom., lad.'

I could not believe my eyes. He had actually tasted the urine. I grimaced and turned away.

'Bloody hell, Stan,' I blurted. 'You filthy bugger. I hope you're sick to your teeth.'

Stan burst out laughing. 'Watch again.' To my disgust, he slowly repeated the 'test'. Suddenly, the penny dropped. He had, in fact, placed his forefinger in the urine, but put his third finger in his mouth, thus giving the impression he was tasting the urine. It was a great trick and we roared with laughter.

'Now, you know,' stuttered Stan, 'what taking the piss really means.'

One morning we admitted an elderly ex-serviceman named Mr Preston, suffering from chronic bronchitis. He had developed a chest infection and Doctor Ethrington had prescribed penicillin injections and physiotherapy. Mr Preston was a small man with a cherubic face who, despite his illness, had a keen sense of humour.

'I see you're from Liverpool,' he remarked, as I placed a cup of tea on the top of his locker.

'How do you know that, then?' I asked.

'All you Scousers talk the same. You all sound like bloody gangsters.'

'Oh, yes,' I replied, 'and where are you from, then?'

He gave a series of short, sharp coughs, before answering. 'God's own country,' he said, 'Somerset, where they makes the best cider in the world.'

I smiled, and carried on handing out cups of tea. When I had finished, Taff asked me to give the afternoon injections.

Much to my delight, Mr Preston's name was top of the list.

After sterilising everything, I washed my hands. Using a pair of forceps, I removed the metal plunger and syringe, fitted them together and attached a needle. I then cleaned the top of the penicillin bottle and withdrew the required amount. Carefully changing the needle, I placed the syringe in a kidney dish and moved in for the kill.

Mr Preston did not hear me coming. He was slumped against several pillows, engrossed in reading a detective magazine.

'OK, sweetheart, where do ya want it?' I said, mimicking

Humphrey Bogart, 'the thigh or arse?'

With a startled expression he looked up. His eyes widened as he focused on the needle.

'Is that for me?' he asked nervously, letting the magazine fall from his hands.

I held the syringe at eye level while tapping the barrel with my finger.

'It sure is, kid,' I drawled, then, with a gleam in my eye, added, 'Now, what was that you were saying about Scousers...?'

I decided to study for my Leading Rate. One morning, I went to the regulating office and handed in my application to do so. After reading it, the chief pursed his lips. 'Heaven's above, Lightburn,' he said. 'You've only been in the navy a dog-watch.' He signed the form and added, 'but I admire your spirit. The next exam's in July. And the best of luck.'

When Jock and the others followed suit, he must have thought we had gone mad.

Time seemed to fly by. Finally, Easter leave arrived. Once again, Scouse Wilson and I travelled together, arriving at Lime Street.

Everyone was there to meet me. Alma jumped up and down waving frantically, Mum stood with tears in her eyes, Dad beamed with joy and Joe gave me his famous Tommy Steele grin.

After hugs, kisses and handshakes, I introduced them to Scouse. 'Have a good leave, Tom, lad,' he said, before leaving. 'I'll see you in two weeks.'

We then caught the bus to the Pier Head and boarded the ferry boat

'You look a bit thin, love,' remarked Mum. 'Are you getting enough to eat?'

'It's all that rum,' quipped Joe. 'He's living on a liquid diet.'

A few hours later, Joe and I were having a pint in the "King's Arms." 'By the way, Bud,' he said, passing me a cigarette, 'I met Monica and Jessie last week at the "Grosvenor." They asked when you were coming home.'

My eyes lit up. 'Oh, aye,' I replied, pouring the remains of the bottle of brown into my beer. 'When are we meeting them, then?'

'To-morrow night at the "Grosvenor,"' replied Joe rubbing his hands together. 'And guess what? Their old girl's away in North

Wales visiting her brother. She'll be away all week.'

'Now that's what I call looking after the troops,' I replied.

'Talking about troops,' said, Joe, 'I'll be going into the army early next year. I hope to get into the Cheshires, then transfer to the Paras.'

'The what!' I exclaimed. 'The Paras. What d' you want to do that for, mate? Only a crazy person would want to jump out of a perfectly good aeroplane.'

The next evening Joe and I met Phil Leatham and Reg McKnight. Reg was a steward, serving in HMS *Newfoundland*. He was small and stocky, with wavy fair hair and a ready smile.

Phil was built like a middle-weight with brown hair. 'I'm joining HMS *Eagle* when I've done a gunnery course at Whale Island.'

Joe glanced at Phil. 'What's this Whale Island?' Joe was the only civilian in the group. 'They don't have whales there, do they?'

Phil laughed. 'No, Joe,' he replied, 'It's a gunnery school, where everybody runs around like banshees. And believe you me, mate, the discipline is tough.'

'Talking of running,' I said, finishing my drink, 'I think it's about time we got our skates on, or all the talent will be taken.'

Ernie Hignet's quartet playing *Rock Around The Clock.* hit us as we entered the "Grosvenor." The floor was packed with couples, some jiving, others keeping to a strict tempo.

'Ok, lads,' said Joe. 'It's every man for himself. And we meet here after each dance.'

Joe eagerly glanced around. 'There they are,' he cried, nudging me in the ribs. 'Our targets for to-night.'

The girls were sitting in a café, separated from the main hall by a glass partition, drinking milk shakes. Monica wore a yellow dress and Jessie had on a white blouse and dark skirt. Monica saw us and waved. 'Come on, Bud,' said Joe. 'This could be our lucky night.'

How right he was. Dawn was breaking when we left the girls.

Things were going fine until the spectre of Tony appeared. One afternoon, while Mum was shopping, Dad, as he always did, opened a letter addressed to Mum. Alama was at school and I was ironing a shirt.

I immediately sensed something was wrong. With a scowl, he threw the letter onto the kitchen table. 'She's been sending him money.' His voice was loud and sharp. 'Money I've turned to in all weather to earn. Well, the bugger's gonna get no more. I'll tell you that for nothing. '

Shortly afterwards, Mum came into the living room, pulling a heavy shopping bag on wheels. 'Whew!' she gasped, sitting down on the settee. 'That queue in the co-op gets longer every day.' She lit a cigarette, and, with a tired sigh, exhaled a stream of blue smoke. 'What's the matter with your face?' she said, looking at Dad. 'Your horses gone down again?'

Dad, his face flushed with anger, flung the letter at her. Mum read it. 'Well,' she replied defiantly. 'What if I am? It's my bloody money. I work too, don't forget.'

'Aye, that's as maybe,' said Dad facing her.

For a moment I thought he might hit her. I immediately sprang up from my chair. 'Does anyone want a cup of tea?' I said, trying to diffuse the situation.

Mum shook her head, and Dad ignored me.

'But not enough for the food and ciggies he wants in that letter,' snapped Dad. 'It's my money what pays for that. Well, you can take a run up my backside for next week's housekeeping.'

Mum stood up, pushed Dad out of the way and emptied her handbag on the table. A few coins, a small bottle and bits and pieces fell out. She then unzipped the top of the food bag, and tipped its contents on the floor. 'There!' she yelled. 'That's where your precious money goes.' Suddenly, she gave a gasp, clasped a hand to her chest, and fell against the door.

'Mum,' I yelled, and caught her just as she was falling. Dad also gave support, and between us, we helped her onto the settee. 'What's the matter, Mum?' I placed an arm around her shoulders. 'Are you all right?'

Her face was covered with perspiration and she had difficulty in breathing.

'My pills,' she wheezed, clutching her chest. 'In my bag on the table.' I immediately grabbed the bottle, read the label which said 'Ephidrine. Two tablets, prn' – meaning whenever necessary.

'Get some water, Dad, and a damp towel.' Dad quickly brought a cup of water. I supported Mum's head while she swallowed the tablets. I gently wiped her face, unbuttoned her coat and laid her head back onto the settee. Dad sat looking at her, concern etched in his eyes.

'It's my asthma,' she gasped, tapping her chest. As she looked at me, her soft brown eyes began to water. 'Don't worry, son. I'll be OK.' Christ, I thought, she is worrying about *me*.

I remembered how the physiotherapist administered breathing exercises to the asthma patients on H2 ward. Placing my hand over Mum's lower abdomen, I said. 'Breathe out and gently push up on my hand, it will help you to relax.' She did this and gradually began to breathe easier.

She smiled and placed a warm, shaking hand, over mine. 'Thanks, love,' she said.' I feel a bit better, now.'

Dad suddenly came to life. 'I'll make some tea, love,' he said. By the time Dad returned, she was sitting upright, her breathing almost normal. 'How are you feeling now, Cora?' he asked. His manner was quiet. All his anger was gone.

'Better, now,' she replied, sipping her tea. 'Thanks to doctor Lightburn, here.'

'Promise me, you'll go and see the doctor before I go back, Mum,' I said. With a smile, she patted my hand and agreed.

A few days later, she kept her promise. It was a little after two o'clock when we arrived outside the doctor's surgery. Before going inside, she said, 'I'm going to visit Tony to-morrow. Your Dad's at work, so, would you...?' Her voice trailed away.

'OK, Mum,' I replied, cheerfully. 'Don't worry. I'll keep you company.'

After a quick kiss on the cheek, I met Joe and Jock in the "King's Arms." They already knew about the trouble between Tony and Dad. 'He comes out in five months,' I said to them, as we stood at the bar. 'Christ only knows what will happen then.'

'I never got on with my old man,' said Jock, taking a packet of Panatelas out of his pocket. 'Try one of these,' he said, then went on, 'In the end, things got so bad, I went and lived with my Aunt Doris in Birkenhead.'

I gave him a quizzical glance. 'Jock, my son,' I said, putting my arm around his shoulder, 'you have just given me an idea...have another pint.'

For supper that evening we had thick, greasy chips, fried eggs and beans. Dad was slurping tea from his mug while Alma was fiddling with her knife and fork. 'What did the doctor say, Mum?' I asked, cutting a slice of bread. 'Did he give you anything?'

'No,' replied Mum. 'He said I had...er. Hyper, something or

117

other. I can't pronounce these big medical words.'

'Hypertension,' I said, with an air of authority.

'Right little quack, is our Tom, isn't he Alma?' said Dad, making a chip sandwich.

Alma, egg-yolk running down the side of her mouth, simply nodded.

'Well,' said Mum. 'What's wrong with me, then, doctor?'

'Oh, just a bit of high blood pressure,' I replied, trying not to sound too dramatic. 'What else did he say?'

She stood holding a frying pan in her hand. 'Oh, just to take more exercise and keep off greasy food. More chips anyone?'

The large room looked even more depressing than last time. The guards hovered around as if expecting a mass breakout and someone in a nearby cubicle began to cry. With both hands in his pockets, Tony sauntered towards us. 'Got any fags? 'he Mumbled, and sat down.

'I've brought what I can, Tony,' said Mum, wringing her hands. 'It's a bit difficult.' She glanced anxiously at me, and did not go on.

'Anyway,' said Tony, sitting back in his chair, 'I'll be out in a few more months, so you can get my room ready.'

'Do you think that's a good idea, son?' Mum's voice faltered as she spoke. She was clearly frightened. 'You know… what Eddie is like.'

'Bugger him,' snorted Tony, leaning towards Mum. 'He doesn't worry me.'

Suddenly, I'd heard enough. 'No.' I interrupted. 'But Mum has to live with him.' I pleaded. 'How about going to stay with Auntie Lottie? You and her always got on well. What do you say, Tone?'

He looked at Mum a suspiciously. 'I'd have to pay her for me keep, wouldn't I?'

I quickly shot a glance at Mum. 'No, no,' I replied. 'It wouldn't cost you anything. '

Mum did not reply straight away. She looked a bit startled. 'Er…no, Tony,' she spluttered.

'And you could come and go as you liked,' I added quickly.

Tony's expression changed to a sly grin. 'Well,' he said, standing up, and stretching his arms. 'We'll see. It doesn't sound a bad idea, at that.'

When we left, Mum still appeared to be confused.

'What was all that about, then?' she asked, on the way home. 'Him staying at Lottie's? Whose idea was that, then? And where's the money coming from?'

'Don't worry,' I replied. 'I'm going for promotion. I'll increase your allowance, and you can pay Aunt Lottie. That's if she'll have him.'

'Well,' she sighed. 'I only hope you are right, son, and thanks for thinking about it.' I smiled, making a mental note to buy Jock a packet of his favourite Panatelas.

The morning after I returned to the hospital a crowd gathered around the main notice board.

'Bloody hell,' I cried, turning to Dave Jones. 'I've been moved to A1.' Lofty Small, who worked there, was always going on about how busy they were.

'It's the main surgical ward. We never stop – appendicectomies, hernia repairs, not to mention head injuries. You name it. We've got it.'

A Block was at the bottom of the far colonnade, opposite B1 the main orthopaedic ward. Lofty and I arrived just in time to help carry an unconscious patient from an ambulance, into the ward. 'First bed, over there,' said the sister. Lofty, another SBA and myself wheeled him inside and gently placed the patient onto a bed. A nurse immediately placed screens around the bedside. Doctor Fulford, the ward medical officer, appeared. He was tall, fair and a member of the teaching faculty. From his top pocket he produced a small torch. Gently lifting each of the patient's eyelids, he shone a small light into each eye. 'M'mm,' he said, glancing up at the sister. 'His left pupil is dilated - probably a fracture somewhere. Call the mobile x-ray unit.'

'I already have, doctor,' said the sister. 'They'll be here soon.' After completing his examination, he glanced at me. 'Have a look at his pupils,' he said, handing me his torch. 'Dilated pupils are diagnostic of a fractured skull.' I did as he asked. The man's pupil looked like a large, black disc. It was a valuable lesson I would not forget.

The rest of the day staff had arrived, and I introduced myself to Johnny Halligan, the leading hand of the ward. 'That mad Cornishman,' he said, nodding towards a tall, ruddy-faced SBA taking a patient's temperature, 'is Dickie Vellacot.' Harry Johnson, was also there. They both gave me a friendly wave'

'You'll be sorry.' said Dickie, giving a thermometer a wristy flick. 'No long stand easies here, Tom.'

From behind came a female voice.

'Hello, tall dark and ugly.' I turned and saw the pretty brunette I had met earlier. She was holding a tray containing a tin of powder and a bottle of spirit.

'I see you've met Charlotte the harlot,' said Johnny, jokingly.

'Pay no attention, to him,' replied Charlotte, giving Johnny a playful push.

'See you two later,' said Johnny, and carried on along the ward.

'I see you are going to do some pressure areas?' I asked, nodding at the tray.

This was a procedure carried out to prevent bed-sores.

'Yes, that's right,' she replied with a mischievous glint in her eyes. 'Get your gown on, and you can give me a hand, so to speak. It'll be a good way to meet the patients.'

The ward was almost full. Most were recovering from a variety operations ranging from partial removal of their stomachs to hernia repairs. I placed screens around each bed, as Charlotte joked with patients while applying spirit and powder to shoulders, buttocks and heels. 'Watching you do that,' I said, holding the tray, 'it's almost worthwhile being a patient.'

Charlotte gave me a wicked smile. 'You never know, I might give you one for free.'

We came to a man propped up in bed wearing blue pyjamas. A few strands of sparse, grey hair lay loosely over his balding head. His eyes were closed, and his pale skin was stretched tight over the bones of his thin face. We stopped some distance away. 'This is Mr Ricketts,' whispered Charlottte. 'He came in for a hernia operation, but it was discovered that he had Hodgkin's disease.'

I frowned, and stared at her, 'What's that?'

'Cancer of the lymph glands,' she replied. Her voice took on a tone of deep concern. 'He hasn't long – has four lovely children and his wife's really nice. I feel terribly sorry for them. They visit him every day.'

On the top of his bed-locker next to a few books, stood the finest model of a ship I have ever seen.

Mr Ricketts sensed our presence. He slowly opened his eyes and his tired face broke into a gentle smile. 'Hello,' he murmured. His pale lips were dry and slightly cracked. 'My favourite nurse.'

'And how is *my* favourite patient, today?' came Charlotte's cheerful reply. 'This is Tom. He's new on the ward.'

'Nice to meet you, Mr Ricketts.' I said, noticing how weak he looked.

I supported him, while Charlotte gave him a good rub, and applied glycerine to his lips. Afterwards, I combed his hair and made him comfortable. 'That's a smashing model, Mr Ricketts.' I said.

'Pick it up if you like, son,' he said.

With great care I did so. The hull was painted black with red below the water line. Her rigging and masts were perfect with tiny uniformed men on the bridge and deck. Small lifebelts lay next to wooden seats and from derricks hung several lifeboats. I rolled the ship up and down, as if it were cutting through the sea. As I did so, her four buff-coloured funnels glistened in the morning sunlight. On her stern, neatly printed in white, were the words, *Titanic*. Liverpool.

'Did you make it?' I asked, replacing the ship. 'She really is a beaut.'

Mr Rickets turned his head, and looked at me. 'Yes' he said, slowly turning his head towards his locker. 'I made it at home, before all this happened to me. Reminds me of when I went to sea.' All the talk and attention was making him feel tired. I could almost see the strength draining from him. He began to blink, before slowly closing his eyes.

We moved on. From within a small, side cubicle, came a hissing sound. I looked through the glass partition and saw Harry and Dickie holding a frail-looking young man on his side An intravenous drip of clear fluid ended with a needle taped into the man's a vein. 'This is Stephen Connolly. RTA (Road Traffic Acident). He's on a glucose and saline drip,' whispered Charlotte. 'He has a severly fractured skull and has been unconscious since was brought in a week ago.'

'What's that hissing noise?' I asked.

'He's had a tracheotomy, and has a tube in his throat,' said Charlotte. 'The sound you hear comes from that machine by his bed. When his airway is cleared with a suction tube, the sound increases.'

When Charlotte had finished, Harry and I rolled Stephen onto his back. His body felt warm, limp and feeble. Dickie and Charlotte gently sponged him down. Stephen's eye flickered, and for a moment, I thought he was about to open them. Instead, he went into a paroxysm of coughing. Harry immediately placed the narrow rubber tube into the tracheotomy tube. The sucking noise increased as the airway was cleared. Charlotte carefully mopped the patient's brow and wiped his face. I watched, and realised this was what nursing was all about: tender care, compassion and burning desire to help your fellow man.

During the weeks that followed, I learned more about the practical aspect of nursing than any textbook could tell me. I learnt to prepare sterile trays for lumbar punctures, remove stitches, take blood pressure and record eye charts on patients requiring special watch. There was so much to learn. Dickie Vellacott was right – there was no time for long stand easies.

Of course, on some occasions, we had a laugh. This was necessary or I am sure we would have cracked up. A young sailor came in with appendicitis. Charlotte and I were detailed to shave him in preparation for surgery. I brought a tray containing warm water, shaving-soap, a small brush, spirit and a cutthroat razor. Charlotte stood at foot of his bed examining the razor.

'Aren't you going to give me any anaesthetic?' cried the startled patient. Charlotte gave him a mock glare, and slowly shook her head. 'My God,' he whimpered. 'The lads told me you were all butchers, and they were right!'

'I'll cut,' she said to me, whipping back the bedclothes. 'You sew.'

The poor lad looked terrified.

I could not contain myself, and burst out laughing.

'Relax, pal,' I said. 'We are just going to shave you.'

'But I had one earlier on,' he replied, his eyes fixed on Charlotte.

'Not like the one we are going to give you now,' she said.

I had never been in the company of a girl and a half-naked man before and felt slightly embarrassed. It didn't bother Charlotte, I expect she had seen it all before.

The young man gave a gasp as I covered his genital region

with a soapy lather. 'No don't,' cried the man as Charlotte, using her forefinger and thumb, gingerly lifted up the man's limp member. With her other hand she made a small scrape, and removed a tuft of pubic hair.

'There, there,' she said reprovingly. 'What a lot of fuss over such a little thing.'

One evening we were handing out meals. Mr Ricketts shook his head at the chicken soup I placed before him.

'No thanks, Tom,' his head deep in the pillows. 'Just a cuppa will do.'

As usual, I gave the *Titanic* more than an admiring glance. 'It must have been really something to have sailed in a ship like that,' Noticing the books on his locker, I added, 'I see you've read a lot about her.'

With what seemed a tremendous effort, he turned his head and gave me a smile. 'Aye, that I have.' His white tongue flickered across his dry lips. With my hand under his head, I supported him while he took a sip of tea. Then, I gently rested his head back onto the pillows.

He raised his eyebrows and tried to smile. 'When she sank,' he said, 'there were 20, 000 bottles of beer onboard, at 6d each.'

'Crikey,' I replied with a grin. 'What a waste, eh?'

With a tremendous effort, he raised himself slightly, and in a hoarse whisper, said, 'Remember, Tom, in a way, we are all on the *Titanic*. And like her passengers, there is no escape.'

Before going off duty I gave him a wave. He lifted a weak hand in recognition.

He died later that night.

When I returned next morning I stood for a minute or so, looking at his empty bed.

'The sister wants to see you, Tom,' said Johnny Halligan. 'She's in her office.'

I did not reply.

After knocking, I entered her cabin. She asked me to sit down. My gaze instantly fell on Mr Rickett's model on her desk. 'As you know, Mr Ricketts died yesterday.' I looked at her and nodded. She opened a desk drawer, and took out a piece of white paper, folded in two. 'The ward-master found this in his drawer,' she went on. 'It's addressed to you.' She handed it to me.

The letter was dated two days ago, and the handwriting was thin and spidery. It must have taken him quite some time to write. He wrote about my admiration for his model, and wished me to have it. "Something to remember me by," he wrote. When I finished reading, I looked at the *Titanic,* but as I tried to make out its details, my eyes became blurred with tears.

One morning, Charlotte and I were making beds and cleaning lockers. 'Don't you think it is about time you asked me out?' she said. For a moment I was taken aback.

'But, what about you and Sam?' I asked. The last thing I wanted to do was upset our illustrious manager.

'Oh, never mind him,' she replied. 'He's away on weekend leave.'

'Er... Ok,' I replied. 'Do you fancy, 'Annie Get Your Gun,' at "The Drake," on Saturday?'

'Yes,' she replied, looking at me with those gorgeous hazel eyes. 'That sounds fine.'

We arranged to meet outside the cinema at six o'clock. That, I thought, will give us time for a quick drink and, afterwards, if I was lucky...

Junior ratings were not allowed to go ashore in civilian clothes. However, for a packet of blue-liners, Dot, the owner of a café close to the hospital in Union Street, let us use a back room to change into civvies.

Dot was a stout lady with a vocabulary that would make a stoker blush. 'Mind you bugger's are back 'ere before midnight,' she would say. 'Else the fucking doors will be locked.'

Charlotte was on time. She wore a short blue coat over a skirt and blouse. 'My goodness,' she said, looking me up and down. 'You look so different. I hardly recognised you in that dark brown suit. You look so smart.'

'So do you,' I replied, giving her hand a squeeze. 'You look even better in civvies.'

I took her to "The Continental Hotel," a rather up-market hotel near the Hoe. When she removed her coat, her well-developed figure attracted more than a passing glance from a few men at the bar.

'Listen, Tom,' she said cautiously. 'When Sam comes back, it might be a good idea not to mention this. All right?'

I always suspected Sam fancied her, and told her so. 'I know,' she replied, sipping her port and lemon. 'But I don't fancy him.'

How odd, I thought, Sam and her always looked so friendly together. Nevertheless, I agreed and we finished our drinks.

While Betty Hutton and Howard Keel belted out a series of popular songs, we sat, holding hands. Then, taking my hand, Charlotte placed it on her knee. A surge of excitement ran through me as I felt myself becoming aroused. She cuddled closer and I put my other arm around her. As the pair on the screen sang "*Anything You Can Do, I Can Do Better,*" I slid my hand further up onto the softness of her thigh...

Later, on Plymouth Hoe we couldn't keep our hands off one another. Charlotte had the most wonderful, soft lips of any girl I had known. Afterwards, my own were sore from kissing her. Later, we lay quietly, silently smoking and staring at the stars.

Suddenly, the spell was broken. Charlotte turned her head, and said. 'Unfortunately, I have to go on nights next week.' She paused and took a drag of her cigarette. 'I'm on C3 ward. It's not busy so why not come up and see me? About midnight, after sister has done her rounds. I'll give you ...a cup of tea.'

On Monday, I finished duty at eight in the evening. I had a few pints with Desperate and the others. We then returned to the mess to study for our higher rate examinations next week. 'This bloody dispensing is a mystery to me,' groaned Lofty to no-one in particular. 'What use is it to us in a hospital?'

'It's for when you go on board ship, you daft bugger,' said Ginger Valentine. 'You have to make up your own medicines.'

'It's still a bloody mystery to me,' Mumbled Lofty, throwing his book down and lighting a cigarette.

By eleven fifty the mess was in partial darkness and everyone was asleep. I quietly slipped on my plimsolls and tiptoed out of the mess.

Everything was quiet as I crept up the sloping area leading to the colonnade. Away to my right a few lights were still on in the officers' ward. The yellow, colonnade lighting cast eerie shadows on the ground as I made my way to C Block. The sudden squeak of a door penetrated the silence. I darted behind a pillar. Then, like a thief in the night, I slowly peered around and saw the night-duty sister – her cloak flapping like a vampire – hurrying towards A

Block. I knew I was breaking the hospital regulations, but as Joe once told me, 'Your dick will drag you further than dynamite will blow you.'

I quietly pushed open the door and padded up two flights of stairs. I stopped on the landing, and listened. Suddenly, the ward door opened. I quickly withdrew down a few steps, but when I looked up I saw Charlotte. She had removed her starched white apron, and only wore her pale-blue uniform and cap. In one hand she carried a cup and saucer.

'Charlotte,' I whispered. She turned around, saw me and smiled. 'Is the coast clear?' I asked.

'Yes,' she replied, beckoning me up with her hand. 'The sister and the duty chief have been, so don't worry.'

I breathed a sigh of relief and tiptoed towards her.

'Wait here in the galley.' She reached up and gave me a quick kiss. 'I'll just check on the patients. We only have four and one of them is RFD (Referred For Duty) to-morrow.' She smiled and left, leaving behind the aromatic smell of antiseptic and talcum powder.

After a several minutes, she returned. The fresh perfume she wore acted upon me like a lightning conductor. We leaned against the galley sink and kissed. Those lips were still warm and soft and I felt myself rising to the occasion. Both her hands were behind my neck, pulling me onto her. She pressed herself hard against me. The gasps of her breath came fast and the warmth of her cheek told me its own story. As my hand sought the softness of her breast, the sound of a male voice suddenly broke the spell.

'And just what do you two think you're doing?'

Charlotte and I froze with fear. Standing a few yards away was the tall figure of Sam Small. 'You know you are not supposed to be here, don't you, Lightburn?' he snapped.

'Yes, PO,' I replied, feeling my throat dry up. I glanced at Charlotte. To my surprise I saw she was grinning.

'Right,' replied Sam, baring a row of even white teeth. 'On you way, Lightburn. I'll deal with you in the morning.'

As I left Charlotte gave me a weak smile, but when I reached the lower floor I stopped. It suddenly occurred to me that Sam wasn't supposed to be duty. I opened the door and closed it, giving the impression that I had left the building. I then crept silently up the first flight of stairs, and looked across the landing. Sam and Charlotte stood silhouetted against the light in the galley. She was looking up at him. With a sly smile playing around his mouth, I heard him say, 'Now, Nurse Hughes. You have a choice. You can have Matron's punishment in the morning. Or,' he paused, and pulled her towards him, 'you can have mine. Which is it to be?'

Charlotte cocked her head to one side, smiled seductively, and in a husky voice, replied, 'I'll take yours, Sam, anytime.'

'Good,' replied Sam. He then removed his hands from Charlotte's waist, and undid his flies. Charlotte gave a gasp and her eyes lit up. 'Oh, Sam!' she exclaimed, kneeling down. 'It's so b...' He turned and blocked my view, but Sam's reaction told me exactly what was happening.

At breakfast next morning, the headlines on my *Daily Express,* read, "All This and Everest Too!" with a photograph of our smiling queen-to-be. To this was added the exciting news of Hilary and Tenzing's conquest of Mount Everest.

'Pity we have to work,' remarked Desperate. 'I have a mate in the army, I bet he and the pongos in Aldershot get a make-and-mend for the Coronation.'

'Mount Everest, Coronation Day or whatever, it doesn't matter,' said Lofty. 'Patients still need treatment.'

'Maybe we can listen to it on the wireless,' said Jock. 'David Dimbleby's doing the commentary.'

'Pity we have not got one of those new television sets,' I replied. 'We could have watched it.'

Later, walking with Lofty down the colonnade, my heart missed a beat. There was Sam, a smirk on his face, approaching us.

'Good morning, Tom,' he said as he passed. 'Sleep well?'

'What was that all about, then?' asked Lofty, glancing at me.

'Oh, nothing,' I replied, breathing a sigh of relief. 'We have a mutual friend, that's all.'

I never saw Charlotte again. Two weeks later, when she came off night-duty, she was sent on draft to HMS *Raleigh,* a training base in Cornwall. This was just as well. After what I saw, I never wanted to kiss those lips again.

During the next few weeks we burned the midnight oil. The examination was basically the same as when we passed out, except that we had to gain higher marks.

A week later, the results were posted on the main noticeboard. Much to our joy, we all passed. With the extra money this would

bring, I would be able to increase Mum's weekly allowance –
providing Tony agreed to live with Aunt Lottie. Much to my relief a
letter arrived telling me he had agreed to do so. However, I still
dreaded to think what would happen if Dad and Tony met again.

The next few months past quickly. Everyone was excited when
a small, black and white television was installed in the mess.
Whenever we could, we sat glued to the magic box, watching
Coronation Street or Hancock's Half Hour. But it was sport that
really held our interest. We cheered when the swashbuckling
Brylcreem boy, Denis Compton, hit the winning run against
Australia. And when Len Hutton raised up the small metal urn
containing the famous ashes, we cheered even louder.

'Pity we didn't have television last month,' I commented to
nobody in particular. 'We could have watched the Cup Final.'

'You are right there, Tom lad,' said Scouse. 'Old Stanley
Mattews beat Bolton almost on his own. 4-3 wasn't it? With only
seconds to go. What a game, eh?'

By the time summer leave arrived I had nursed every surgical
condition from partial gastrectomies to laparotomy (exploration of
the abdomen.) I even managed to cope with my emotions when a
patient died. This was the sharp end of nursing, and I was learning
fast.

Once again I travelled home with Scouse Wilson.

A police restriction order preventing Tony from visiting our
house was placed on him. 'If he breaks this,' said Mum to me on the
way to the prisonm, 'he will end up back in prison.'

'Are you're sure I won't have to pay Lottie?' asked Tony, on
the bus to New Brighton.

'Just you try and behave, son,' replied Mum. 'And keep off the
drink.'

Aunt Lottie opened the front door and greeted us. She was
small, with steely grey hair, dark brown eyes and a sharp, Scottish
accent. Uncle George was slightly built and almost bald. They
married late and were childless.

'Thanks for doing this, Lottie,' said Mum, embracing her
sister. 'I don't know how to thank you.'

'Och, stop your blethering, Cora, and come in,' replied my

aunt. 'George has just put the kettle on, and I've baked a few scones.'

Uncle George shook my hand. 'Hello, Tom,' he said. 'How's the navy treating you, then?'

'OK,' I replied. He then turned and shook Tony's hand.

'Come in, Tony,' he said, smiling. 'Good to see you. Your room is ready and we hope you'll be comfortable.'

I heard Tony mutter a few words of thanks as we went into the small lounge and sat down.

Before saying goodbye, Mum warned Tony again. 'Don't forget, be on your best behaviour or you know what will happen.'

But she was wasting her breath.

Two nights later, I was awakened by the sound of someone thumping on the front door. I instinctively knew who it was. I got up and carefully drew back the curtains. Down below I saw Tony kicking the front door. 'Come out, you bastard, come out and face me.' His speech was slurred and he staggered backwards. More obscenities followed. Lights from bedrooms across the road suddenly came on.

The banging woke everyone in our house. 'What the bloody-hell's going on?' Dad cried from the next room. 'It's that bugger, Cora,' he said. 'It's after one, for Christ's sake. This time, I'll fix him good and proper.' I heard the dull thud as his feet hit the floor. This was exactly what Mum and I had dreaded.

'Oh, leave him, Eddie,' came Mum's tired voice. 'He'll go away.'

'I'll make the sod go away,' snorted Dad. 'He's waking the whole friggin' road.'

With mounting fear, I flung back the bedclothes, and quickly slipped on a sweater and trousers. As I left the room, Dad wearing dungarees over his long-johns hurried downstairs.

The banging on the front door continued. 'Open the door, you coward,' ranted Tony. 'Come on you bastard. Let's finish it.'

Alma slept in the small room next to mine. The noise woke her up and she cried, 'Mum, there's somebody shouting.'

I met Mum on the landing. 'It's all right, Alma,' she said. 'Go back to sleep, love.' Mum was in her dressing gown, her hair a tousled mess. 'Jesus, Mary and Joseph,' she cried. 'They'll kill each other. Tom, call the police.'

The front door opened and I heard a series of obscenities from both Dad and Tony. I dashed downstairs just as Tony caught Dad a glancing blow to the side of his head. Dad fell sideways against me, and we both fell onto the wooden fence into the garden.

'I'll kill the get!' shouted Dad, jumping to his feet. I leapt up but was too late to prevent Dad hitting Tony in the face. With an animal cry, Tony came at Dad and they both tumbled back, flattening the rose bush.

'Stop, for God's sake,' cried Mum. She tried to pull them apart but Tony pushed her away. Suddenly, I saw a brick in Tony's hand and grabbed his arm.

'Look out, Dad.' I yelled. 'He's got something in his hand.' But I was too late, Tony's raised his arm. Screaming at the top of her voice, Mum flung herself at Tony, knocking his hand away before he hit Dad. By this time, we were all grappling in a heap. Mum and I grabbed Tony by his coat in an effort to pull them apart, but it was no use.

At that moment a police car pulled up outside. I learnt later Mrs Hislop, next door, had thankfully called them. Most of the nearby house lights were on, with everyone peeking through curtains. Two burly policemen leapt out and dragged Tony and Dad apart.

'It's you again, Scala,' said a policeman, pinning Tony's arms behind his back. 'Don't worry, Mrs Lightburn,' said the sergeant. 'We'll take it from here,' and he forced Tony, still shouting obscenities, into the car.

Dad was bruised, but soon recovered. Tony was remanded in custody, and later sent to Pentonville prison for a further two years.

'London's a long way,' sobbed Mum, shortly before I was due back off leave. 'But blood is thicker than water. Promise you won't turn out like him, son.'

So ended yet another leave.

At the end of November, Johnny Halligan and I were detailed off for night duty on A1. 'Bloody hell, John,' I cried. 'Nights for a whole month. What is it like?'

Johnny was a one-badge killick, and knew the ropes. He gave me a wink. 'Piece of piss,' he replied, with the confidence of a veteran. 'We know the patients, so there will be no problems.'

There was something unnatural about night-duty. As darkness fell, a quiet, almost surreal atmosphere took over from the hustle and bustle of hospital life. The noise from the city gradually died away, leaving lights glimmering and the ghostly sound of footsteps echoing around the hospital.

At seven-thirty each evening, we would report to the receiving room. We were informed of any serious cases that required special watches. The duty chief then issued eggs, tins of beans or whatever, for out mid-night meal.

Jock McBride held an egg between his forefinger and thumb. 'Och,' he grumbled, 'this wouldna feed a mouse, let alone a grown lad, like me.' The chief simply gave him a jaundiced look.

'If you're not satisfied, Jock, slap in to see the padre. Now, piss off.'

My first job was keeping special watch on a patient who had part of his stomach removed. He was on a blood drip and a thin rubber tube led from his nose into his stomach.

Much to my delight the night duty sister was Svenska. 'Quarter hourly pulse, BP and regular aspirations,' she said, giving me a smile. 'Any problems, Lightburn, call me.'

This ward was quiet and everything seemed under control until I noticed the patient's blood pressure falling. He turned pale and his pulse became weak. I quickly told Johnny.

'Christ,' he whispered. 'There's something wrong here.' He immediately telephoned the receiving room, who contacted the duty medical officer and the sister.

'He's bleeding internally,' said the doctor. As the duty OT staff wheeled the chief away, the sister turned to Johnny, and said, 'Well spotted, Halligan.'

'I wasn't me, sister,' said Johnny. 'It were SBA Lightburn, here. He called me.'

Once again she gave me a lovely smile. 'Well, good work, especially you, Lightburn.'

As I was fully occupied, Johnny was on his own, scurrying around with bowls of warm water, making beds, giving treatments. He even had to collect the breakfast trolley. 'Next time,' he said, when the day staff came on duty, 'I'll to do the special watch, and you can do the donkey work.'

'You know, Johnny,' I said jokingly on our way to breakfast, 'I think Sister Johannsen fancies me.'

Johnny gave a loud laugh. 'Forget it, Tom,' he said. 'Officers and rating mixing is against the law. Pete Davey, an old mate of mine, was seen in town with one of the sisters. Next thing he knew he had a pier head jump to Hong Kong. Bogey Knight had struck.'

Sometimes we went for a few pints in the "Hospital Inn," before going to bed. However, one sunny morning, I suggested a leisurely stroll into the city centre. The other two declined, so I went by myself.

A recent AFO (Admiralty Fleet Order,) allowed us to wear civilian clothes. So, courtesy of Joe Feneck, I wore a brand new, dark blue blazer, white shirt, naval tie and grey trousers.

By the time I reached the bottom of Union Street, I felt thirsty. However, I did not feel like a beer. I remembered Charlotte telling me *Dingles,* Plymouth's biggest department store, sold the best coffee in town.

Dingles stands at the bottom of Royal Parade, a wide boulevard built, like so much of Plymouth, after the Second World War.

I followed the sharp smell of roasted coffee beans and found myself upstairs in a spacious café. The warm aroma of food and the hubbub of conversation filtered through the air. The snorting sound of the frothy coffee machine echoed around as I sat down at a table. A waitress, primly dressed in black with a white apron, smiled. I ordered coffee and cakes then glanced around. The clientele was mainly elderly women, catching up with latest gossip before going shopping. I opened my *Daily Sketch* and relaxed.

The coffee lived up to its reputation, as did the famous Devon cream-cakes. I was about to order more when, to my amazement I saw Sister Johannsen. She was sitting on the far side of the room, reading *The Times.* Dressed in a dark green costume with her honey-blonde hair tumbling down over her shoulders, she looked strikingly beautiful. I found myself staring as she turned over a page. She lowered her newspaper, and reached for her cup. Just then, she looked up and saw me. To my surprise, she smiled and beckoned me over.

I nervously folded my paper, picked up my coffee and walked towards her. As I did so, the steady gaze of her pale-blue eyes made my legs feel like jelly. 'Good morning, sister,' I managed to say.

'How nice to see you, Lightburn,' she replied. Her thinly applied make-up and well-defined features enhanced her good looks. 'Please will you sit?'

'Thank you,' I answered. 'A bit of a surprise, seeing you here.'

'Oh, it was too nice to stay in,' she replied, taking a sip of coffee. 'And you. You come here every morning. Yes?'

I gave a nervous laugh. 'No...No,' I said. 'This is a bit up-market for me. But the coffee is good.' I offered her a cigarette, but she declined.

'No thank you,' she said. 'I do not like smoking. You are from the North. Yes?'

'Aye. Wallasey, near Liverpool,' I replied, hastily putting my cigarettes away.

'I am from Sweden. And my name is *not* Svenska, as you say.' At this, she laughed, displaying teeth that would have done justice to a Colgate advert. 'It is Anita.'

'As in Eckberg,' I replied, inferring that she was named after the Swedish film star, Anita Eckberg. Again she laughed. 'Yes, I suppose so,' she said. 'I know what your second name is, but, tell me. What is your first name?'

Her question caught me unawares. After all, she was an officer, and I a lowly medic. There was an awkward silence, before I plucked up enough courage to tell her.

She sensed my embarrassment, and said, 'I shall call you Thomas – and there is no need to worry. I shall not tell anyone.'

Nobody ever called me Thomas, but I was not about to complain. I looked across at her and said, 'You...you look so different in civvies. Really nice.'

'Thank you, Thomas,' she replied. 'And you also, so smart. A real gentleman.' I felt my face redden. 'It shall be our secret. Yes?'

We ordered another coffee, and she told me that she was once engaged. She spoke quietly, with a far away look in her eyes. I had the feeling that she was unburdening herself. 'He was a pilot in the Fleet Air Arm,' she said, glancing at the well-manicured fingers on one of her hands. 'He was on the HMS *Ocean*..' Her voice faltered slightly. 'His 'plane was shot down in Korea, and he was killed.'

'I am sorry,' was all I could think of to say.

She suddenly smiled, as if trying to hide behind a mask of pain. 'And you. You are married. Yes?'

'No,' I replied, shaking my head.. 'I nearly became engaged, but it did not work out.'

She finished her coffee. 'What a pity for you,' she replied, standing up, and smoothing her skirt down. 'You are very good listener, Thomas. I must go, now. See you tonight, on duty. Yes?'

she said, picking up a small brown hand-bag. 'Goodbye for now.'

Remembering my manners, I stood up. and watched, as she glided over the thickly carpeted floor. When she was gone I sat down. All that remained were the lipstick stains on her coffee cup and the smell of her perfume.

We did not meet until she did her mid-night rounds. Somehow, I felt ill at ease. With Johnny in attendance, she silently walked around the ward, checking blood drips and bed-charts. Her smile, before she left, put me at ease.

A few days later, I told the others that I was going to Joe Feneck's to be measured up for a suit. Instead I headed for *Dingles*

I saw her as soon as I walked in the café. This time, she wore her hair in a chignon and was dressed in a cool, pale-blue dress that matched the colour of her eyes. 'Hello, Thomas,' she said, inviting me to sit down. 'We meet again, yes?'

I still felt somewhat ill at ease and replied, 'Yes, so we do.'

Once again I ordered coffee and cream cakes.

'Very fattening,' she chided, as I removed a small blob of cream from the corner of my mouth with a finger.

'That is something you will never have to worry about, sister,' I said. 'You're nice and slim,' I felt I was pushing my luck, remembering who she was.

'Why thank you, Thomas.' she replied, taking a sip of coffee. 'What are you going to do on your day off? Going out with your friends?' Today was Tuesday and on Thursday we had a twenty-four hour break. I had no idea what I was going to do, and told her so.

'Don't know really. Probably go to the pictures, and have a few drinks,' I replied. 'I am not sure.'

She sat back in her chair, and with a curious look in her eyes, asked, 'What film would you go and see?'

For a moment I said nothing. Then quickly replied, 'Gene Kelly in *Singin' in the Rain,* most probably. It's on at "The Drake."'

'How lovely,' she cried, giving a little girl laugh. 'Maybe we could go together. I love Gene Kelly. He is very popular in Sweden.' I could not believe my ears. Here was this beautiful, slightly older woman, asking me for a date. As she smiled, her naïvety was obvious. I suddenly felt a pang of guilt.

'It might be difficult,' I said, stirring my coffee. 'You are an officer. And, well…' My voice trailed off. I wasn't sure what to say.

'I know all about the navy's silly rules,' she replied dismissively. 'And I do not care.'

Fair enough, I thought. I have warned her. And anyway, I told myself, we are only going to the pictures, not eloping to Gretna Green. 'All right,' I replied. 'If you are sure. We could go to the matinee. The programme begins at two o'clock.'

'Good,' she said, with a satisfied smile. 'We will meet outside at, say, ten minutes to two. Thirteen-fifty hours, as the navy says. Yes?'

'OK,' I answered. 'But Mum's the word.'

'What does this 'Mum,' mean?'

I pursed my lips, before answering. 'It means we have to keep this quiet. Or we will both be in hot water!'

Every time I saw her at work, she gave me a smile. I could not help but wonder what she saw in me. Perhaps she was lonely. After all, she had lost a fiancé and was a long way from home.

When Thursday arrived, Lofty, Scouse and Ginger wanted to visit Drake's Island. I pulled the blankets over me pleading a heavy cold. 'You lot go without me,' I said forlornly. 'I'm knackered. I think I've got 'flu.'

As soon as they left, I leapt out of bed, shaved, and splashed on a gallon of Old Spice. The time was one thirty and as I walked down Union Street, my heart beat faster with every step.

Once outside the cinema, remembering Anita's dislike of smoking, I decided to have quick drag before she arrived. I only had time for a few puffs before I saw her coming towards me. Dressed casually in a light brown skirt, a baby-blue sweater with a fawn handbag over a short suede jacket, she looked fantastic.

I hurriedly stubbed my cigarette out. 'Hello, sister,' I said. 'You're on time.'

'Thank you,' she replied. 'We Swedes are always punctual. Can we go in now?'

'Yes,' I replied nervously. 'The film does not begin till after the news. '

We went in the three-shilling, back stalls. She tried to give me a ten bob note, but I refused.

'In England, the man always pays,' I said. 'But I'll let you buy the ice-creams.'

The cinema was almost empty. Her perfume almost anaesthetised me. I was so preoccupied with her presence I hardly noticed the Gaumont British News commentator telling of the forthcoming armistice in Korea. For a while we sat in silence, eating our tubs of Walls icecream. When she had finished, I quickly handed her a clean, white handkerchief.

'Thank you, Thomas,' she said, dabbing the corner of her mouth. 'That was very gentlemanly of you.' For some reason, that seemed to relax us. We roared with laughter when Tom and Jerry came on. At one time, she squeezed my hand, crying, 'Oh, Thomas, they are so funny. Do you not think so?'

During the big film, she tapped her hand on her thigh in time to the music and gasped with delight when Gene Kelly did his famous dance in the rain. At the end, when the lights went up, she lent back in her seat and exclaimed, 'That was wonderful, Thomas! I did so enjoy it.' Suddenly, she lent across, and placing a hand on the side of my face, kissed me on the mouth. Her lips were moist and soft. 'Thank you for bringing me,' she said. 'Now, I think we must go. Yes?'

'Yes,' I sheepishly replied. 'I think so.'

The glare from the daylight hurt my eyes as we arrived outside. For a while I could not distinguish things clearly. 'I had better leave, now, Thomas,' she said. 'Thank you again.'

'No, sister,' I said, blinking my eyes. 'Thank you for coming.' Just then, she took out a small, lace handkerchief, and wiped my lips.

'You have my lipstick on you,' she laughed. 'And that will never do, will it?'

We said goodbye again. As she walked down Union Street, her blonde hair became tousled by the breeze. However, I was not the only one watching her. I turned, and was about to light a cigarette, when I saw Wardmaster Lieutenant Knight standing a few yards away. He didn't speak. Instead, he quickly turned and strode away.

A week later, I was told to report to the regulating officer.

As usual, Chief McKenzie was sitting behind his desk. As I entered, he sat back and his face broke into a smirk. 'Well, Lightburn,' he said, sarcastically. 'What have you been up to, eh?' He did not wait for me to answer. Instead he said. 'You are on draft, me boyo.'

My heart missed a beat. 'What ship, chief?' I asked excitedly. 'Is it a destroyer?'

The chief laughed. 'No,' he replied, sitting forward and

drumming his fingers on his desk. 'After Christmas leave, you are going to HMS *Seahawk,* a Royal Naval Air Station at Culdrose.'

'A naval air station,' I said dejectedly. 'I wanted a ship. Where the hell is Culdrose?'

The chief glared at me. 'It's near Helston, in Cornwall. And you want to thank your lucky stars it isn't in the Antarctic.' He nodded his head towards the wardmaster lieutenant's door. 'The boss isn't too pleased with you.'

'What do you mean, chief?'

Once again he fixed me with a steely glare. Then, his expression abruptly changed. With a glimmer of a smile playing around his mouth, he replied, 'Ratings and nursing sisters don't mix.'

Suddenly, I knew what he meant.

Shortly afterwards, Sister Johannsen was re-appointed to the Royal Naval Hospital at Bighi, Malta.

Bogey Knight had struck again!

8

As usual, leave seemed to fly by. Just before midnight on New Year's Eve, everyone went to "The Brighton". This was the local opposite the Town Hall in King Street. Alma stayed next door with Jean, the nine- year-old daughter of Mr and Mrs Hislop.

At closing time, we sang our way to Seacombe Ferry. This was a traditional venue where crowds gathered to welcome the New Year. When twelve o'clock struck everyone kissed, cheered and joining hands, sang *Auld Lang syne*

The ships in port sounded sirens, whistles and foghorns. Fireworks burst high in the air, their brilliant colours turning night into day. It reminded me of the Blitz.

'This is the only way to see in the New Year, Bud,' burbled Joe, after kissing some girl.

'You're right there, Woods,' I replied, grabbing the nearest girl and doing the same.

Dad passed around a bottle of whiskey. 'Get this down you,' he shouted as we shook hands. 'And all the best to yer.'

Joe and I hugged Mum and we did a quick jig, singing at the top of our voices.

'Happy New Year,' I said, giving Mum a kiss. 'And remember what Doctor Rettie said, eh?'

Her breath smelt strongly of gin and her voice was slightly slurred. 'I will, son, don't worry. And I hope next year is better than the last one.'

'So do I, Mum,' I replied, giving her a kiss. 'So do I.'

Joe shook my hand. 'All the best, Bud,' he said with an uncharacteristic sigh. 'God knows where I'll be this time next year.'

After the celebrations were over we ambled home. Kicking a tangled heap of coloured streamers, I glanced at Joe singing his head off, and I too wondered what the next twelve months would bring.

'I'm really fed up, Dad,' I muttered, before taking a good swig of beer. 'I was hoping to be drafted to a ship instead of some poxy place in the wilds of Cornwall.'

We were sitting in "The Brighton". Outside, the bitter January wind battered sleet against the stained glass windows. People entered, wet and cold, rubbing their hands together and breathing streams of vaporised air.

Dad's head was buried in the racing section of *The Daily Express.*

Suddenly he looked up. 'Now, what was that you said?'

I lit a Woodbine, and passed one to Dad. 'Culdrose, Dad,' I said. 'I wanted a ship. Not a bloody air station. '

Joe arrived, soaked to the skin. He took out a handkerchief, wiped his face, and looked at our empty glasses. 'I see you two are well ahead.'

Dad grinned. 'You're just in time to get them in,' he said, passing both glasses to him.

Joe returned with the drinks and sat down.

'This lad, here,' said Dad, looking at Joe, 'can't wait to get to sea. But there is one thing he's forgotten.'

'What's that then, Pop?' asked Joe, lighting a cigarette.

'Experience,' replied Dad, glancing across at me. 'He's only been in just over a year. No bloody use going on a ship if he's not experienced. My oath, it's not.'

'I've had lots of experience in RNH,' I replied, feeling rather hurt at his remark.

'Just pipe down a minute,' said Dad. 'And I'll give you an education.'

Here we go again, I thought.

Dad took a good mouthful of beer and sat back in his chair. 'It were 1943. We were off the coast of Sicily, sweeping ready for the invasion.' His voice was quiet and he licked his lips before carrying on. 'There were five minesweepers. Converted trawlers they were. They called us *The Sparrows. '*

'Why did they call you that, Dad?'

'We were HO's, you see. Hostilities Only,' Dad smiled. 'The regular navy lads called us that because the ships bobbed up and down in the sea like small birds.'

Dad finished his beer and lit a cigarette. Joe left and returned with three rums. I had a feeling this was going to be a long afternoon.

Dad took a sip and continued, 'We had one leading SBA to look after all of the five of us, you see. And he were onboard the senior ship. During a sweep, one of the ABs, a big lad from

Newcastle – Chats Harris his name was - split his head open on a hatchway. There was blood everywhere. The cook tied a white apron around his head, but it didn't stop the bleeding.' Dad paused and stubbed his cigarette out.

'Who did the medical work onboard, then, Dad?'

'The coxswain,' replied Dad. 'But this were too much for him. So our skipper, Lieutenant Peter Reid, had a message flashed across for medical help.'

'Were you in the middle of a sweep?' asked Joe.

'My oath, we were,' said Dad, finishing off his rum. 'But we had to stop. Now, that were dangerous. You see there were U Boats and Jerry aircraft about. And for a while we were sitting ducks.'

By this time, Joe and I were a captive audience. We even forgot to drink our rum.

'Well, the LSBA climbed onboard carrying a brown canvas bag called, err…'

I quickly interrupted him. 'A first aid valise.'

'Aye,' answered Dad. 'That were it. Had a big red cross on it. Anyway, the ship was rolling and the LSBA put twelve stitches in old Harris's nut.'

'Bloody hell,' I gasped. 'Twelve stitches.'

'That's right. And we were bobbing up and down like a cork in a bath. Old Harris was doped up with rum.' Dad lent back, pursed his lips and went on. 'That LSBA's name was Paddy Murphy. He came from Belfast and knew his stuff, all right. Gave him a real good going over. Put each stitch in with the up roll. '

'Was Harris all right, Dad?'

Dad took a deep breath and lit another cigarette. The dimples faded away as he spoke.

'Oh aye, Harris was OK. Paddy stayed onboard for a few days. Kept on looking in Harris's eyes with a torch. But Paddy had to return to the senior ship as someone else had been hurt.'

Dad went quiet, stroked his chin again and carried on talking. 'We went on sweeping. I was on the wheel. We were doing four knots, keeping line abreast with the others.' He paused. 'That's when there was this bloody great explosion. The senior ship on our starboard beam went up in a sheet of flame. I was flung against the bulkhead. Ours was hit buy the blast and nearly capsized. When I looked across, all that was left of the ship was a cloud of black smoke and bits of…' his voice trailed off and he frowned.

'Did...did anyone survive?' asked Joe.

Dad shook his head. 'No,' he replied in a hoarse voice. 'The only thing we found was that medical bag. Floating amongst the bodies, it were.'

'Bloody-hell, Dad,' I muttered. 'That must have been terrible.'

'Aye, son, it was,' said Dad.

I had never heard Dad talk about the war like this. Not once had he mentioned danger or people getting killed. Joe and I sat in silence.

'You see,' said Dad, looking at me. 'Paddy Murphy was an old hand. The poor bugger got himself killed, but he knew his job. Not many medics could have put twelve stitches in a man's head in a rolling sea. That's what I mean by experience, son.'

I returned to Plymouth early on a cold Sunday evening. Desperate and the others gave me a good send off.

'Watch out for those Cornish folk,' joked Ginger Valentine, handing me my umpteenth pint of bitter. 'They are nowt but a crowd of sheep-shaggers,'

'Och, he's right, man,' chimed in Jock. 'And that's only the lassies.'

Dickie Vellacot glared at them. 'Hey, you buggers,' he said. 'Pack it in. You're talking about God's country. The place where they sell the best scrumpy in the world.'

When Marlene called last orders, I looked around at their faces wondering when, or, indeed, if we would ever meet again. As we shook hands the expression in their eyes said the same.

'Take care of yourself, Tom,' said Lofty, with a humorous glint in his eye. 'And if they have any nursing sisters at Culdrose, keep it in your trousers.'

This, of course, brought forth peels of laughter.

'So long, you miserable Sassanach,' muttered Jock. 'And stay away from that scrumpy Dickie mentioned. It will rot your balls off.'

Desperate, who had been quiet, took out a small brown parcel from his pocket. 'Thought you might like a few toffees to eat on the train,' he said, handing the package to me. 'Look after yourself, Tommy Bach.'

A lump the size of an egg came into my throat – it was worse than saying goodbye to my parents.

The cigarette I was smoking tasted like seaweed and my head ached. The jostling of the train did nothing to ease my king-size hangover.

My destination was the small town of Helston, situated on the Lizard Peninsula in Cornwall. From here I would be met and taken to the naval air station.

The train, leading into Cornwall, slowly rumbled across the suspension bridge, built by Brunel in 1859.

Away to my left, silhouetted against the morning sky, the houses of Plymouth slanted down towards the dockyard. Below, the waters of the River Tamar stretched like a strip of molten silver towards the open sea.

Towering cranes looking like giant pelicans dotted the skyline, but it was the grey shapes of the destroyers and frigates that caught my eye. How I wished I were joining one of them instead of some isolated naval air base in the heart of no-man's land.

My thoughts were rudely awakened as the train, bellowing clouds of steam, slowly shunted to a halt. I looked out the window. A sign read, 'Saltash, You Have Now Entered Cornwall.'

Suddenly the countryside changed. On either side I could see huge waves of steep, rolling hills covered in frost. Flocks of sheep shivered in the biting wind as they sought shelter behind high hedges.

Far below, a tiny tributary of the Tamar splashed over rocks before disappearing around the base of yet another steep hill. Thick, wintry, pine forests, covered in shiny particles of frost, stretched away on my right. It was a scene that would have graced any Christmas card.

My fingers felt icy cold against the window as I wiped away cloudy condensation. I gazed outside remembering the words of Dickie Vellacot. Perhaps he was right. Maybe this was God's own country.

The train slowly rattled on. The acrid smell of steam irritated my nostrils and the compartment felt warm and muggy. About an hour after watching the tall spire of Truro cathedral disappear in the distance, we finally arrived at Helston.

I was the only person to leave the train. After collecting my kitbag from the guard's van, I looked around. The station was deserted except for an elderly stationmaster and a matelot wearing a greatcoat. The stationmaster shot me an inquisitive glance before disappearing into a small, red-bricked building. The matelot gave me a half-hearted wave. His face was pale and the end of his nose was red. 'Are you the new Doc for the base?' he asked.

'Yes,' I answered, putting down my suitcase. 'SBA Lightburn.'

'Thank fuck for that,' he replied, stamping his feet. 'I'm freezing my bollocks off.' Wearing blue woollen mittens with the fingers showing, he picked up my case. 'I've been waiting here for half an hour. Bring your gear and follow me.'

Outside the station was a blue naval utilicon van – tilly, for short. 'Not many people around, is there?' I said, climbing inside.

'No,' replied, the matelot, starting the engine. 'I think they all hibernate in the winter.'

We drove down a steep hill and turned left into what looked like a main street. I caught a glimpse of shops and old houses with overhanging bay windows. Several people, bent against the cold wind, hurried along well worn, stone pavements. An old box Ford trundled past, sprouting streams of exhaust fumes. The driver, an old white-haired man, gave us a toothy grin and a wave.

On the right, we passed a large, white Georgian building called the "Bell".

'At least they've got a pub here,' I commented.

'One of many,' replied the matelot. 'You'll get to know them all in time.'

Then I remembered the rum ration. 'Do you get your tot at the base?'

'Too true, mate,' exploded the driver. 'You sick bay tiffies draw it in one of the naval airmen's messes.'

Thank goodness for that, I thought, as streaks of sleet splattered against the tilly window.

'Is the weather always this bad?' I asked.

'Ha!' laughed the driver. 'This is nothing, mate. Last year we were snowed in for a month.'

The road, curving away, was bordered on the right by a grassy verge and wall made of tumbledown masonry. In the distance stretched the frost-covered hills of the Cornish countryside. Away to our right I saw the tops of several large buildings.

'Is that the base?' I asked.

'Aye,' replied the driver. 'The biggest building is the admin block. Next is the wardroom and the officers' quarters.'

On the left side I could just make out the dark shapes of hangars and what I assumed was the control tower.

'What are those?' I asked, looking up in the air at numerous pylons dotted at varying intervals around the landscape.

'Oh, those. They're homing beacons,' replied the driver. 'They light up to help guide in aircraft at night or during emergencies.'

'I see,' I replied, glancing at the sky. 'Not much flying at the moment.'

'No,' replied the driver. 'Won't be for a sometime. Ice on the runways.'

On either side of the main gate was a high, barbed wire fence. Nearby was a wide sign in bold silver lettering which read, HMS *Seahawk*. Behind this, mounted high on a tripod, was a full sized replica of a fighter poised as if in a steep dive. It was painted light blue with RAF roundels on each wing. It took me by surprise and for a fleeting moment, I thought it might take off.

'Bugger me,' I cried. 'Is…is that a Seahawk? It's fantastic.'

'Sorry to disappoint you, mate,' said the driver as we were waved through. 'It's a Seafire. F17. Don't ask me why.'

The sight of more huts surrounded by barbed wire reminded me of one of those concentration camps I saw in the pictures.

'That's the Wren's quarters. Off limits to you and me,' laughed the driver. 'Officer's meat only, mate.'

Now, where have I heard that before, I said to myself.

After we drove past a rectangular parade ground, a tall, white building caught my eye.

'What's that? A drill shed?'

The driver laughed. 'No, Doc. That's where we show the camp films, and hold a dance every Saturday. And over there,' he pointed to other wooden huts near the parade ground, 'is the NAAFI and dining hall.'

We passed more huts before driving through an open gate into a wide compound. We stopped outside a long, flat-topped brick building. The window-frames and double doors were painted green.

'Your home from home,' said the driver. 'This is the sick bay.'

I slid back the door of the tilly and climbed out. A biting wind hit me in the face. Even though it was a little after two o'clock in the afternoon, there was nobody about.

'That's the morgue, over there,' he said, pointing to a small building away to my right. 'It's empty at the moment.'

Thank God for that, I thought, as he drove away.

At that moment the sick bay door opened and a stocky, grey-haired chief petty officer appeared. His uniform jacket hung open revealing a white shirt covering a portly abdomen. With both hands thrust deep into his trouser pockets, he gave me a toothy grin. 'I see you made it then?' he said. Without waiting for a reply, he shouted, 'Vinson, get your arse out here and give us a hand.' His voice was gruff, but his accent was that of a Liverpudlian.

At that moment a member of staff appeared. He was tall, pale and did not have a jacket on. .

'Lend a hand here,' growled the chief.' Show, er…Lightburn isn't it?'

'Yes, Chief,' I replied, picking up my suitcase. 'Tom Lightburn.'

'Ah, yes,' he said, hastily buttoning his jacket. 'Your name was on the signal. Show Lightburn here, where the mess is, Vince.'

'Report to me when you've settled in,' grumbled the chief, as he limped down a corridor. 'These bleedin' Cornish winters play havoc with me arthritis.'

The mess was not too dissimilar to those at *Collingwood.* The central heating was the same, but instead of thirty beds, there were only four on either side of a wide, well polished floor.

Vince deposited my suitcase by a bed near the door. 'This is yours,' he said.'

I sat down on the bed and lit a cigarette. 'By the way,' I said, 'when do we get our rum issue?'

'Bugger me,' said Vinson, his face wrinkling with laughter. 'Another bloody rum-rat. We draw it at midday. As you're ship's company, we mess with the airy-fairies.'

Ship's company meant you were permanent staff. Those attached to squadrons moved regularly to aircraft carriers and other air stations.

Walking towards the door, Vince said, 'I'm on duty today. When you've stowed your gear, report to the chief. He'll be in the office just on your right as you came in.'

I looked around. Four armchairs were scattered close to a table. On one bedside table was a record player with several records stacked nearby. At the end of the room in a corner stood another table and a wireless. Above this was a shelf with an odd assortment of books. A few framed photographs stood on bedside tables and at the opposite end of the mess was a single door which I later learned was kept closed to prevent cows and sheep from wandering in and out.

Half an hour later I retraced my steps down the corridor. The first person I met was a petty officer. He was tall and stood outside what looked like a dispensary. His hair was light brown and combed straight back. His firm, clean-shaven features were set in a scowl and for a moment I thought he was going to bite my head off. Instead he nodded and his pale blue eyes lit up into a sheepish grin.

'Ah,' he bellowed, thrusting out a hand. 'You must be the esteemed Lightburn. Yes?'

He spoke with a distinct West Country burr and I noticed he wore Korean War medal ribbons.

'Er…yes, PO,' I replied, wondering what 'esteemed' meant, and took his hand.

'Welcome to the mad house. I'm Petty Officer Bill Manley. The chief is in the office, second on your left. See you later.' He began to hum and sat down at a desk cluttered with papers.

The main part of the sick bay consisted of a long corridor with various offices on either side.

The chief was sitting at his desk reading yesterday's *News of the World*. I nervously walked in and stood with my arms by my side.

'Come in, lad,' he said, 'no need to stand to attention. This isn't Victoria Barracks.'

His humorous, bluff manner instantly made me feel at ease. He put down his newspaper. 'I'm Chief Elsworth,' he announced. 'And I take it you're from Liverpool. Right?'

Like Bill Manley he also wore Korean medals and several others from the Second World War.

'No, chief,' I replied. 'I'm from Wallasey.'

He rolled his eyes upwards and lent forward. 'Bloody hell, not another one. ' He turned his head to one side. 'Dutch,' he shouted, 'there's a townee of yours here. You'd better come and meet him.'

A slightly built lad with glasses and a mop of wavy fair hair came into the office.

'What's up, chief?' he said, looking at me.

'Lightburn here is joining us. And guess what?' His voice took on a sarcastic quality. 'He's from your neck of the woods. Another bloody toff from across the river.'

'Pay no attention to the chief,' said Dutch, shaking my hand. 'He's jealous because we're all rich in Cheshire. I'm Trevor Holland – Dutch to you.'

A hatchway behind the chief's desk snapped open and a fresh-faced young man appeared. 'What's all the noise, then?' he asked.

'Calm down, Ross,' said Dutch. 'This is Tom Lightburn.' Dutch glanced at me. 'This lecherous sod is Harry Rosser. He works next door in the admin section.'

'Get back to work, you lazy bugger,' growled the chief, and whipped the hatchway closed.

'See you later, Tom,' came a muffled reply from the next room.

The chief stood up. He seemed bigger than when we first met, with hands as like dinner plates.

'Can you type?' he asked, taking down a cardboard box-file from a shelf.

I felt my mouth drop open. Type, I thought to myself. I haven't come all the way here to bloody type.

'Er... no, chief,' I replied, 'I can't.'

The chief pursed his lips, and looked up at me. 'We'll see about that. Report to me in the morning.'

Dutch beckoned me outside.

I gave him an apprehensive glance. 'What did he mean by that?'

Dutch gave me a cynical smile. 'Don't worry, Tom,' he said. 'You'll soon find out. Come on. I'll introduce you to the other inmates.'

The lights were on as it was getting dark. A couple of ratings in overcoats walked past and, after knocking, went into a room opposite the chief's office. Dutch and I followed on behind them.

'This is the treatment room,' said Dutch. 'You'll be working here at some stage.'

The room was quite large and had a familiar smell of antiseptic. One on side were shelves, lined with bottles containing various coloured lotions. In the middle was a leather examination couch. Nearby, stood two glass cabinets full of various surgical instruments. On a trolley lay a kidney dish, a few bottles, an assortment of bandages and plasters plus a large pair of scissors. The brown linoleum on the floor was marked with dark smudges made by muddy boots. In a corner was a large sink. Under this was

147

a green disposable-dressing bucket with a foot-pedal. White neon lighting lit the room and two frosted windows were closed tight.

Vince was bandaging a rating's leg. The other, a small, rotund SBA with a sparse black hair, was busy painting some obscure red dye onto a man's feet. Both SBA's glanced up at us as we entered the room.

'You've met Vince,' said Dutch. 'This is his oppo, Robbie Roberts. Don't bend down in the shower. They're both Cornishmen from Truro.'

'Nice to meet you, my bird,' said Robbie, grinning. 'One of these days we'll have our independence from you foreigners. Just you buggers wait.'

Dutch introduced me to Fred Smith, a stocky Welshman from Wrexham, whom I learned, fancied himself as another Caruso. I then met another Cornishman, Jan Colliver. Jan worked with Ross and was sitting at a desk, flicking through filing cards. He was tall, with red hair and a rolling gait any sailor would have been proud of.

'Nice to meet you, Tom,' he said, standing up. His outstretched hand held mine in a vice-like grip. 'Do you play rugby, by any chance?'

'Sorry, mate,' I replied. 'Soccer's my game.'

He rolled up his eyes in disgust. 'Bloody party's game,' he said in disgust, and sat down.

Finally, there was Paddy Brophy. Like Dutch, Paddy was a leading hand. He was quiet-spoken, with a typical Irish sense of humour.

'Pleased to meet you, Tom,' he said, grasping my hand. 'To be sure, your life will change from now on. You see, we're all round the bend here.'

I had a feeling he would be proven right.

I was briefly introduced to two doctors. One of them, a stocky, broad-shouldered man with fair hair, vigorously shook my hand. 'Hope you like scrumpy, old son,' he said with a wild look in his eyes. 'That's all this bloody place is good for.'

'That's Surgeon Lieutenant Phillips. He's as mad as a hatter,' whispered Dutch, as we left his surgery. 'From South Africa. Fought with Monty in the desert, then became a doctor. And a damn good one too.'

The other medical officer was Surgeon Lieutenant KM Coia, a small, dark-haired man, recently qualified. I also met Sister

McDonald, a stout lady with freckles and a warm smile. 'Nice to meet you,' she said in a soft Scottish accent. She glanced at Dutch, and added, 'Don't you be leading this laddie astray, now Holland.'

No chance in this dead-end place, I thought.

Then there was Surgeon Commander Lawrence Young from New Zealand. Every time I went into his surgery he was always busy studying to become a member of the Royal College of Surgeons.

He was tall, slim with serious brown eyes. His greeting was curt. No handshake, only a furtive glance. 'Work hard, lad, and make sure my desk is kept clean,' he said, and carried on making notes from a book.

Three Wrens, wrapped up in dark blue greatcoats, came out of a room further down the corridor. All of them were laughing nosily. When they saw Dutch and me, they stopped. The tallest gave us a quick wave.

'Hello,' growled Dutch out of the corner of his mouth. 'Here comes trouble.'

'Who are they?' I asked.

'They're our nurses,' replied Dutch. 'The tall one is Julie, the dental assistant, the other is Iris and the smallest is Margaret. '

Julie was a stunner. Wisps of blonde hair curled from under her cap and the bulge under her overcoat suggested a more than ample figure.

'Hi,' said Dutch as they approached us. 'Just going off duty, then?'

'No,' replied Margaret. 'We're off to Timbuktu.'

I had the distinct feeling that she and Dutch did not see eye to eye.

Dutch introduced me. 'This here is Tom Lightburn. He joined us today.'

Iris smiled and held out her hand. 'Welcome, Tom. We could do with some new blood around here,' she said, 'couldn't we, Marg?'

Margaret glared at Dutch. 'You're not kidding. The men around here are all half - dead.'

Julie did not speak. She simply smiled demurely while rummaging in her shoulder bag. She brought out a small, lace handkerchief and dabbed her nose. 'Nice to meet you, Tom,' she said in a refined voice. 'We'll no doubt see each other again when you do your joining routine.'

Before I could reply, a car pulled up outside.

'Come on, girls,' said Iris. 'That'll be our transport back to the Wrenery'

A blast of cold air hit us as they opened the door and left

When they had gone, we returned to the mess.

'By the way, Tom,' said Dutch, throwing himself on his bed, 'the only person you haven't met is the boss, Surgeon Commander Boyd-Martin. He is the Principal Medical Officer. Be on your guard. He can be a bit of a bastard.'

That's all I need, I thought. A dodgy boss and a typewriter I can't use.

Just after four o'clock, everyone except Vinson came into the mess. Dutch and the others took out small medicine bottles full of brown liquid. Suddenly the air was saturated with the unmistakable spicy smell of rum.

'Tot time,' cried Ross, handing me his bottle. 'Sippers, mind. Not gulpers.'

I glanced at Dutch. 'I thought rum issue was at twelve?'

Dutch grinned. 'It is, but during the week, we bottle it and have it when we secure at 1600. That way, if there's an emergency, we are all alert instead of being half pissed.'

The smell was stronger than its civilian counterpart. After taking a sip, I felt a surge of heat slowly descend through my body.

'Mm…' I said, running my tongue over my lips. 'It's tastes great.'

'It's called two and one,' said Robby. 'The buggers put two parts of water to one of rum for us junior rates. The chiefs and POs get it neat.'

I felt drowsy and lay down on my bed. The next thing I knew, Dutch was shaking me. 'Wake up, jack,' he was saying. 'Do you want to buy a battleship?'

I opened my eyes and blinked. My mouth felt like a vulture's crutch and my head was aching. I sat up and looked around. The others were standing nearby with wide grins.

'You flaked out, Tom,' said Jan Colliver. In his hand be held a mug. 'You soccer players can't take it, you see.'

'Come on,' said Robby. 'We'll show you where the dining-hall is.'

As we left the sick bay, the cold air helped to clear my head.

'It's big place, is this, Dutch,' I said, huddling into my greatcoat. 'Was it built during the war?'

'No,' replied Dutch, clouds of hot air coming from his mouth. 'Just after, in 1947. It's the biggest operational naval air base in Great Britain.'

I was glad when we reached the warmth of the dining hall.

'What happens when there's a crash?' I asked Vince. We were standing in line, holding our wooden trays, waiting to be served.

One or two heads turned around as I spoke.

'Don't worry, Tom,' he said, accepting a mound of mashed potatoes onto his plate 'you'll find out soon enough.'

9

The following morning I woke up to the ear-splitting strains of Glen Miller's *American Patrol*. I sat up in bed, rubbed my eyes, then peered around the room. 'What the hell' going on?' I yawned.

'You better get used it,' said Jan Colliver, climbing out of bed. 'That mad bugger wakes us up with it every morning.' With that, he threw back the bedclothes, stomped into the heads and slammed the bathroom door.

The music stopped and I saw Dutch remove an LP from a red Dansette record player on his bedside table. He placed the disc inside a coloured sleeve and put it among several others on a shelf above his bed. 'Don't forget *Moonlight Seranade,'* he said, 'I play that last thing at night, they love it.'

'Like hell we do,' grumbled Ross, rubbing his eyes. 'Gives me a fucking headache.'

'Give me Doris Day anytime,' yawned Colliver. 'She reminds me of me missus.'

'Rubbish,' replied Roberts, lighting a cigarette. 'I've seen your Ethel. She looks more like Margaret Rutherford.'

'Glen Miller doesn't do much for me, either,' said Vince, breaking wind. 'Good for the system, though.'

The others laughed.

Anyway, it was better than *The Tennesse Waltz*.

The chief was slouched in his chair, holding a mug of steaming hot coffee. He carefully took a sip and looked up at me. His blood-shot eyes told me he had downed more than a few rums the previous night.

'Morning, Chief,' I said, shuffling my feet nervously. 'I was wondering. Er...can you tell me why I have to learn to type?'

The Chief grunted and placed his mug on his desk. He squeezed his eyes together and yawned. 'Ah... yes. Typing.' he sighed, sitting back in his chair. 'According to your documents, you worked in an office before you joined up. Is that right?'

'Yes, Chief,' I answered weakly. 'But I didn't do typing.'

'Well, you will here,' he replied. 'You'll be working next door with Rosser. You'll have to type out medical reports and so on. See that?'

I turned and looked behind and saw a heavy-looking Imperial typewriter on a desk.

'It's all yours,' he said.

He reached across and scribbled something on a signal pad and handed it to me. On it was written, 'Now is the time for all good friends to come to the aid of the party.'

'Sit down and practice this.'

The chief stood up and moved behind me. 'Shift lock and key for capitals. Press here to start a new line. Space bar here to begin a new word. Got it?'

After inserting a sheet of A4 paper, I began – two fingers at a time. Ocassionally, one or two of the lads popped their heads around the door.

'Don't let him overwork you, Tom,' laughed Dutch. 'He'll have you typing out his betting slips next.'

Shortly after nine o'clock, the PMO sent for me.

Surgeon Commander Boyd-Martin was sitting behind a highly-polished oak desk. His face was tanned and his thick, greying hair curled up at the base of his neck. He had wide shoulders and a chest full of medal ribbons. In front of him was an open folder. He spoke without looking up. 'Just wait,' he said. His voice sounded like a BBC announcer on the wireless.'I'll be with you in a minute.'

I glanced around the room.

On each corner of his desk were two metal trays full of papers. A shining brass lighter lay next to an open packet of Senior Service cigarettes. Behind him were shelves of medical textbooks, and on the wall, next to a window was a framed photograph of the queen. Nearby stood a red-leather examination couch and a small trolley containing various instruments. A cigarette smouldered in an ashtray, sending a thin line of smoke into the air.

With a quick movement he reached across, took a deep drag of the cigarette.

'Mm...' he murmured, piercing me with a pair of pale blue eyes. 'I see you've passed for leading hand,' he said, turning over a page of what I assumed to be my service documents.

'Yes, sir,' I replied, standing loosely to attention.

'Well, you'll have to prove your worth to me before I rate you up. You've not been in long and need experience.'

Bugger me, I thought. There's that word experience, again.

'Yes sir,' I replied, glancing down at him. 'I hope to get some here.'

'You will,' he replied, stubbing his cigarette out. 'What do know about the Fleet Air Arm?' He sat back in his chair and steepled his fingers on his chest..

'Not a lot, sir,' I replied.

'I see...' he slowly replied. 'Well, young man. 'This is a frontline station. There are nearly a thousand men here. We have 849 squadron with Douglas Sky raiders; 766 squadron with Fairey Fireflys, not to mention 847 with Gannetts. Then there are Grumman Avengers and several Sea Princes.' He paused and leant forward.

I had never heard of any of these aeroplanes. 'Er..., where are the Seahawks, sir,' I asked.

'They are here in 856 Squadron. I expect they'll be going to *Eagle* soon.'

He stood up, and I was surprised to discover he was quite small. 'Get to know the crash drill,' he said in a stern voice,' and the next time you come in here, make sure you are properly dressed. Your top button is undone. Carry on.'

When I returned to my shirt clung to me and I was covered in perspiration.

My last stop after doing my joining routine was the dental department.

'When did you last have a check up?' muttered the dental officer, probing away at my teeth. 'You need a filling.'

Normally I hated dentists. But seeing Julie again was worth it. Later, as I was typing, I suddenly felt a stinging blow across my head.

'Hey, what the bloody-hell...?' I yelled, quickly looking up.

Chief Elsworth was standing over me. In his hand he held a piece of A4 paper. 'You've made four mistakes,' he barked. 'Start again.'

The faces of Robby, Vince and Dutch appeared around the door. They all laughed. 'We told you you'd soon find out,' they said in unison, and quickly disappeared.

Twelve o'clock arrived and I braced myself for my first full tot of rum.

Rum issue was a daily ritual in the Royal Navy.

Under the eagle eye of the Master-at-Arms and Officer of the

Day, the rum is measured out and taken to the mess in an aluminium fanny. Here, it is carefully meted out by duty 'rum bosun.'

As the duty rating came in carrying the rum, ratings quickly stopped what they were doing and gathered around the table. They watched impatiently as a container was dipped into the fanny and poured into a tumbler.

As each person received his tot, he gave 'sippers,' to the rum bosun. If any was left it was referred to as 'The Queen's,' and was shared out.

Standing in line, I said to Dutch, 'It's a pity the rum has to be watered. Whose idea was that?'

A rating standing close gave loud grunt. 'It was bloody Admiral Vernon's fault, that's who.'

I gave him a quizzical glance, 'Who the hell was he?'

The rating laughed. 'Hey, Schooly,' he shouted.

A dark haired man wearing spectacles was lying nearby on a bed reading. With a frown he placed his book on his chest and looked up.

'What the devil do you want, Dusty?'

'The new Doc here wants to know about Admiral Vernon and the rum.' Dusty turned to me and added, 'This is Coder Humphrey Browning – Smyth. Humph to you and me. He helps the instructor lieutenant. When he finishes his National Serviceman he's off to Oxford, aren't you Humph?'

'You damn matelots are all ignorant sods,' said Humph, sitting on the end of his bed. He peered at me over his spectacles. 'In 1655, we captured Jamaica from the French. As an act of gratitude, the Jamaicans granted rum to the navy.' He stood up, placed his book on the bed and looked at me. 'However, the jolly jack tars, like these you see before you, were continually pissed. So, in 1740, Admiral Vernon ordered water to be added. The sailors nicknamed the admiral, 'Old Grog.' Now, if you don't mind, I'd like to finish my book.'

When my turn came, Dutch told everyone I was drawing my tot for the first time.

'Sippers all round for the new Doc,' someone cried.

I glanced nervously at Dutch. 'What shall I do?' I said. 'I have to work this afternoon.'

'Forget it, Tom,' he replied. 'The chief isn't stupid. He knows the routine.'

155

We drew our rum, and after taking a small sip, bottled the rest.

On the way to the dining hall the fresh air made me feel slightly giddy, and I staggered against Vince.

'Steady on, matey,' he said, grabbing hold of me. 'It's just as well you didn't have your full tot.'

Once again, I woke up with a mouth like sandpaper and a head like Birkenhead.

A few days later, after listening to *Hancock's Half Hour*, I was lying on my bed reading a Mickey Spillane thriller. The weather remained icy cold and the windows were steamed up.

Colliver was on duty. Robby and Vince were in the bathroom washing some clothes. Fred Smith was doing his Caruso act in the bathroom and the others had gone to the NAAFI. 'Come on,' Tom said Dutch, climbing from his bed. 'I'd better show you the crash gear, and explain the routine. This bloody weather won't last forever.'

Inside the main entrance was a room containing several pieces of medical equipment.

We were joined by Jan Colliver and Bill Manley.

'When there's flying,' said Dutch, 'there are two ambulances called Red Cross One and Two. One ambulance is on stand-by, and the other is permanently manned by a driver.'

'When the ambulances arrive, we load all this,' said Dutch, nodding towards the equipment. 'These are Neil Robertson stretchers. Go on, pick one up.'

I did as he asked. They were made of canvas and bamboo with straps. At each end was a metal loop attached to a length of rope.

'Anyone encased in one of these is completely immobile,' said Bill. Standing it on end, he added. 'They're particularly useful moving injured people onboard ship. Go on, find out for yourself.'

He was right. When I was strapped in, I could hardly breath.

'Bloody hell,' I cried. 'Now I know how an Egyptian Mummy feels. Get me out before I suffocate.'

The rest of the equipment consisted of dull green army stretchers, boxes of splints, bandages, tourniquets, first field dressings and two large maps covered in Perspex. There were also four wrinkled overalls made of grey material. Bill picked one up. 'These,' he explained, 'are called 'Fear Naught' asbestos suits.' He handed one to me. They were heavy and rather cumbersome.

'When do we have to wear these?' I asked, holding it in front of me.

Colliver was the first to answer. 'They're to protect against fire,' he said. 'So far we haven't had to use them. The firefighters usually get to a crash first.'

Suddenly, I caught sight of a brown medical valise. On each side was a Red Cross on a circular white background. I took hold of one of the straps and picked it up. 'I think I have a good idea what's in this,' I said quietly.

'Look inside and see,' said Bill.

Inside were several compartments stuffed with metal tubes full of various tablets. As I expected, there were syringes, needles, sutures and an assortment of surgical instruments.

'Quite a lot of stuff, here, isn't there?' I said. 'What's this one for?' I removed a surgical instrument that looked like a sophisticated pair of pliers.

'Needle-holding forceps,' said Dutch. 'Have you ever done any stitching?'

'Not yet,' I answered.

'You will, don't worry,' commented Colliver.

Then something occurred to me. I looked at Bill, and said, 'Where's the morphia?'

'The MO carries that,' he replied.

I nodded and closed the valise. 'What exactly actually happens when there's a crash?' I asked.

'The claxon sounds,' replied Dutch, 'and the nearest person mans the ambulance.'

'Then everyone,' interrupted Bill, 'no matter where you are in the sick bay, drops everything and turns too.'

'Once in the ambulance,' Dutch went on, 'you put on the earphones which are already plugged in. You then call, 'Red Cross One, Red Cross One'. The control tower will give you a grid reference. You look this up on those Perspex maps and tell the driver.' Dutch paused to pass around cigarettes. We lit up and he continued, 'You really have to concentrate and at the same time guide the driver. It can be a bit tricky.'

'Crickey,' I replied, picking up one of the maps. 'That's quite a drill. Looks like I'll have to study those maps all right.'

'Well,' said Bill, glancing at the ice-covered windows, 'you'll have plenty of time. This frost is likely to go on for days.'

157

Everyone left the room and went into the chief's office. The desks had been tidied up and everywhere looked spic-and-span. Bill told me that, besides doing the five o'clock treatments, tidying up the sick bay was part of my duty. 'If you have any dental cases,' he added, 'telephone the dentist or give them a painkiller till morning.'

I sat down on the edge of the chief's desk. 'What's the worst crash you've had recently?'

They glanced at one another.

'The Firefly crash,' said Colliver.'

The other three nodded in agreement.

'About two months ago a Firefly crashed in a field not very far from here,' said Jan. 'We ran out of road and had to barge through hedges and fences.' He stopped talking and shook his head. 'What a bloody mess. The only bits of the pilot we could find were a few fingers and an arm. At least we brought back something for Frank Strike.'

'Who's he?' I asked

'The undertaker in Helston,' replied Bill. 'Nice bloke. Always supplies lead-lined coffins.'

Bill excused himself saying he had letters to write. Dutch then showed me a small room situated in the corridor near the entrance.

'This is the duty room,' he said. 'Cosy, isn't it?'

I could hardly believe my eyes. All the walls were painted black with a solitary light bulb hanging from the ceiling. A bed with a telephone resting on a table stood under which was a window.

I grimaced and looked around. 'Christ,' I gasped. 'It looks more like a cell in Walton Prison than a duty room.'

'I know,' echoed Colliver. 'It gives me the creeps.'

'Whose idea was it to paint it black?' I asked, glancing around.

'The boss,' interrupted Colliver, trying to disguise a smile.

'It used to be cream and green,' said Dutch, grinning, 'until Rosser was caught in there with a Wren by one of the doctors.'

'What happened to Ross?' I asked.

They grinned. 'He got off lightly with a ticking off. It was Doc Phillips who caught him. If it had been the boss, he'd have been for the high jump.'

After supper we decided to go to the camp cinema to see Ava Gardner in *The Barefoot Contessa*. The bitter westerly wind cut through our greatcoats as we huddled across the parade ground.

'The Saturday night hops are held here as well,' said Robby.

'A lot of the local fanny comes. Not bad are they, Ross?'

Apparently Rosser was an expert on the local talent. He dug his hands deeper in his coat pockets. 'The parties are all right,' he grunted. 'But they all talk like country yokels.'

Colliver, Vince and Dutch burst out laughing.

'What do you expect, you silly bugger,' said Colliver. 'That's because they are country yokels.'

The large hall was crowded and full of tobacco smoke. Facing us was a big white screen. Above the hub of conversation a record belted out Bill Halley's *Rock Around The Clock.*

'What is it like here in the summer?' I asked Robby, who was sitting next to me. His balding head glistened in the dull light and when he blinked, he reminded me of an oversize owl.

'Helston's all right, m' dear,' he said, offering me a cigarette, then passing them around. 'But Penzance is much better. More talent and dances, see.'

'I likes Porthleven,' commented Jan Collver, who was next to Robby. 'Small fishing village not far from here. Best sea bass and haddock around. The beer's good as well.'

Suddenly, the lights dimmed and I noticed Julie, the blonde dental Wren. She was sitting a few rows in front, next to one of the nurses. Just as the Gaumont British New began, she turned and looked at me.

Officer's meat only, eh? I said to myself. We'll see about that.

One morning I was helping in the treatment room. Suddenly, the door burst open and in came a rating holding a first field dressing on his head. He looked pale and was in a state of collapse. Another rating supported him as we lay the injured man on an examination couch.

'Raise the end of the couch,' said Dutch, 'he's suffering from shock and cover him up with a blanket.'

Colliver and I did as he ordered.

'When someone's in shock,' said Dutch. 'The blood drains from the upper body. Always raise his legs to redress the balance. And keep him warm'

In a short while, the colour returned to the rating's face.

Doctor Phillips arrived and removed the field dressing revealing a gaping laceration almost four inches long. 'You've got yourself a nasty cut there, lad,' he said, using a pad of gauze to stem the bleeding.'I'm afraid it will need a few little stitches'

After examining the man, he scrubbed up while Colliver cleaned the wound.

'Just lie back and close your eyes. This won't take long,' said the doctor. Colliver then tied a operating mask around the doctor's mouth.

I watched as the doctor bent over and carefully removed a patch of hair around the wound. Using the needle-holders, he inserted a stitch. After doing so, he gently dabbed the area with a piece of gauze to stop any bleeding.

The doctor then stood up, removed his mask, and beckoned me to one side.

'This is a good time for you to try your hand,' he whispered. 'There aren't many nerve ending in this part of his scalp, so take your time.'

I quickly put on a mask and scrubbed up. The MO handed me the forceps complete with needle and suture.

My hand started to shake slightly as I bent over the rating. A bead of perspiration was about to run down my face. Colliver caught it in time with a pad of gauze, and gave me sly wink.

I looked down at the partially-closed wound and took a deep breath.

Holding the lip of the skin with a pair of forceps, I carefully pushed the needle through both edges before drawing them together. After pulling slightly upwards to ensure the suture was secure, I tied the wound.

'Well done,' whispered the doctor in my ear. 'Now put in another one.'

After I had put in two more stitches, the rating opened his eyes and looked up at me. 'Didn't feel a thing,' he lied, and gave me a toothy grin.

With glowing pride I stood back and examined my handiwork. At long last I was getting that experience Dad had told me about. However, I was about to get more than I bargained for.

Next day was Friday and everything was quiet. The atmosphere was relaxed and the staff stood around talking and smoking.

Paddy Brophy and I were duty over the weekend. Jan Vinson and Robby were looking forward to a few days in Truro.

'I hopes this frost don't stop the trains, Vince,' said Robby, wiping his horn-rimmed spectacles with a piece of gauze. 'Else we'll have to walk home.'

'What's the matter?' replied Vince. 'You on a promise, or something? Do you bloody good. Get some of that fat off you.'

The fair-haired figure of Doctor Phillips appeared. 'Is it always so bloody cold in this country?' he said. 'Back in J'borg you can fry eggs on the sidewalk at this time of year.'

'Stop complaining,' said the chief, standing up and reaching for his greatcoat. 'In a week or so we'll all be snowed in.' He turned to Bill Manley. 'Keep it quiet Bill, I'm going—'

Suddenly, the crash alarm sounded.

For a few seconds everyone froze.

The telephone rang and the chief instantly picked it up. A look of horror slowly came over his face. I held my breath as he replaced the telephone.

'There's Britannia 175 with one engine out of action,' he paused to swallow, 'coming in for an emergency landing.'

I felt the blood drain from my face and heard myself say, 'How many onboard?'

'Nearly two hundred,' he said hoarsely.

At that moment the PMO came into the office. He was quickly joined by the two doctors.

The chief quickly explained what was happening. 'The ambulances are on their way, sir.'

The PMO immediately took charge. 'Holland,' he snapped, 'you and Lightburn, go in Red Cross One with Doctor Phillips.'

The sound of my name sent adrenaline pumping through my body. Pictures of torn aircraft shown on the newsreels during the war flashed through my mind. And as for all those passengers, well...

The PMO's strident voice interrupted my thoughts. 'Alert RCI, Chief. (Royal Cornwall Infirmary, Truro.) Tell them we'll keep them informed.'

He took out a packet of cigarettes and lit one. 'Doctor Young, you take Vinson and Roberts in Red Cross Two.'

'Bang goes our weekend,' whispered Vinson to his mate.

The sister and nurses arrived. The PMO told the sister what was happening and ordered her to prepare for any emergency. 'PO Manley and the others will help you. Chief, you stay by the telephone. How long have we got?'

The chief glanced at his watch. 'Just under an hour, sir.'

'Right,' replied the PMO, taking a deep breath. 'Let's get to it.'

We quickly loaded the ambulances. Rosser handed us our greatcoats. Dutch and I joined the driver in the front seat of the ambulance while Doctor Phillips checked the gear.

The wheels of the ambulance crunched as we drove towards the main gate. It was just after five and darkness was rapidly falling.

I quickly put on the earphones and called the control tower. A sharp voice replied, 'Red Cross One, proceed to the Control Tower, and await further instructions. Over.'

My God, I thought. This was the real thing. Not some war film with John Wayne at the wheel of a bomber in distress, but a life or death situation.

Keeping the earphones on, I passed the information to the MO and Dutch.

The control tower was mass of lights. It was smaller than I expected, with a wireless mast and several tall antennae. In the distance the approach lights on the pylons pierced the night sky. On either side of the runway lines of lights lit up the tarmac.

The driver stopped the ambulance behind the fire tenders. Red Cross Two drove up alongside us.

Doctor Phillips left the ambulance. He was joined by the tall figure of Doctor Young. Both stopped and talked to another officer. I saw Doctor Phillips slowly shake his head. He then came back to the ambulance and climbed back in. 'According to the pilot,' he said, nervously licking his lips, 'the outboard starboard engine's packed in, and the port one doesn't sound too good.'

'Bloody hell,' I gasped. 'How many engines has the plane got?'

'Four turboprops,' was Doctor Phillips curt reply. 'Back home we used them regularly.'

Suddenly, I heard the crackle of the earphones and a voice telling Red Cross One and Two to follow behind the fire-engines.

All eyes strained upwards. By this time it was dark as pitch. A few stars glittered weakly, and the cold wind made me catch my breath. I adjusted the earphones and waited.

'There it is,' someone shouted. 'Away over on the right.'

All eyes and faces quickly turned in that direction.

'Yes, I can see her,' shouted someone else. 'She's starting her approach now.'

The voice from the control tower crackled through the earphones. 'Red Cross One and Two. Aircraft approaching. ETA fifteen minutes.'

Tension was etched over everyone's faces. Suddenly, out of the sky came the dark shape of the stricken aeroplane. The only visible lights came from her port and starboard wings. A flurry of white sparks belched from one of her engines. I watched transfixed, as the aircraft slowly banked to starboard and began its descent.

'Christ Almighty,' I heard Dutch shout. 'Another engine has packed in. She'll never make it.'

'My God,' I cried. 'Do you think it'll crash?'

'It depends on how good the pilot is,' said Doctor Phillips.

I glanced at him and realised he had probably been through worse than this during the war. He then added, 'And hope another engine doesn't wrap in.'

'Jesus, Dutch,' I murmured, 'I wish there was something we could do.'

He turned his head. The lights of the control tower reflected in his spectacles. 'There is,' he said. 'Pray.'

'Stand by, all emergency services,' came the voice from the tower.

All of a sudden, its dark, cigar-shape appeared closer. The flaps and undercarriage were down, and as she came in to land, her wings wavered slightly. I held my breath. A small blizzard of white sparks belched into the air as the wheels hit the frosty tarmac.

Suddenly, I remembered those onboard. I imagined masses of bodies being scattered all over the frosty tarmac and began to tremble. I clenched my fists, and prayed.

With mounting tension I watched the runway lights flicker on the pale blue fuselage. All at once there was a sickening, screeching noise. More sparks flew in the air as the huge bird swung off the tarmac.

'Christ!' yelled Harry, the driver. 'She's heading for the control tower.'

'Don't wait for instructions, move in closer,' yelled Doctor Phillips.

The ambulance started up. Red Cross Two followed suit.

Like a gigantic predator, the aircraft moved imperceptibly forwards. Several figures emerged from the building, running for dear life.

'Oh, no,' I heard myself cry, 'for God's sake, no.'

'All emergency services, close in,' came the voice from the tower. 'Engage when necessary.'

The four fire tenders whined into action. The harsh clanging of bells rent the air as they moved towards the crippled 'plane. The two ambulances followed.

Meanwhile, we watched, horrified, as the aircraft bounced towards the tower. Then, with only a few yards to spare, it swerved, slowed down and came to a shuddering stop.

Relief poured from my body. I sat back in my seat. The tension drained slowly away and despite the cold, I was bathed in sweat.

'Thank the Lord for that,' I gasped.

'You can say that again,' came Dutch's laconic reply. 'Someone up there must have heard your prayers.'

I watched as the yellow-coated figures dragged out equipment and covered the engines with fire-retardant foam.

'Get everyone off as soon as possible,' barked an officer. 'I don't want it going up and blowing us to kingdom come.'

'That's a happy thought,' said Harry. 'Very reassuring indeed.'

From then, everything happened at once.

White chute-like aprons emerged from three hatchways and unfolded onto the tarmac. With commendable calmness, stewardesses re-assured passengers and helped them onto the chutes. One by one they slid down into the waiting arms of several ratings. Wrens placed warm blankets around white-faced passengers and assisted them on board coaches. I learned later they were taken to the main hall, given hot drinks. After collecting their luggage, they were taken to a hotel in Truro to await onward passage.

An officer hurriedly arrived. 'There's a man injured inside,' he said. 'The crew have given him first aid, and are going to lower him down in a stretcher.'

From the doorway of the aircraft two of the crew carefully lowered a Neil Robertson stretcher down the chute. A man's head swathed in bandages protruded from the top.

'Come on,' barked Doctor Phillips.' Let's give them a hand. One of you fetch the valise.'

We rushed over and helped to place the stretcher onto the tarmac.

The man in the stretcher was wrapped in a blanket with blood oozing through a dressing. His eyes were closed and his face ashen.

The four of us lifted the stretcher and placed it in the back of the ambulance.

The two doctors climbed in. Vince and Robby undid the stretcher's harness.

Doctor Young bent over and examined the man. He was unconscious and did not move. Under the dressing was a large, blood - stained swelling.

Doctor Young straightened up and looked at his colleague. 'We had better get him to RCI as soon as possible,' he said. 'He might have internal injuries.'

He turned to Vince and Robby. 'Keep him still and warm, and nil by mouth.'

A tall, dark-haired officer with a handlebar moustache appeared. He wore a pale blue uniform and a row of medal ribbons.

'John Anderson, the pilot,' he said, shaking hands with Doctor Young. 'Anything I can do? The stewardess told me he has serious injuries.'

'Yes, he has,' replied Doctor Young. 'We're taking him to hospital. You did a fine job landing that 'plane.'

'Not at all,' was the pilot's modest reply. 'I only hope the man's all right.'

Robby whispered to Vince, 'Do you suppose Doc Young could drop us off home when we leave the hospital? I don't live far from RCI.'

Much to their surprise, they were allowed to do just that.

'Bugger me, Dutch,' I sighed, on the way back to the sick bay. 'That was some night. It's a miracle nobody was killed.'

'Good experience for you, Tom,' replied Dutch, with a grin. 'It's what they call "on the job" training.'

10

After the *Britannia* incident we were galvanised into action once again. Shortly after nine o'clock on Monday morning the telephone rang in the chief's office. I was busy next door, but the connecting hatchway was open and I could hear everything.

'ADLS beginning at 1000. Very good sir, the ambulance will be there at nine forty-five,' came Chief Elsworth's curt reply.

After informing the PMO and the doctors, the chief returned to his office.

Dutch and the others came into the office.

'Something exciting in the wind?' he asked.

The chief told everyone what was happening.

'What the hell's are ADLs, Chief?' I asked.

The chief unbuttoned his jacket and sat down. 'Assimilated Deck Landings,' he said. 'The 'planes touch down and then take off again. Good training for landing on carriers.'

'And very dodgy, too,' muttered Bill. 'As I recall, there were two belly-landings last time.'

I looked aghast at Bill. 'Bloody-hell,' I gasped. 'Anyone killed?'

'Yes, there were,' replied Bill. 'And several 'planes were a write off also.'

'Take Tom with you in Red Cross One, Dutch,' beamed the chief. 'It's about time he saw the airfield.'

'What 'planes are flying, Chief,' asked Bill. .

'Fireflies from 766 Squadron,' answered the chief. 'Number seven runway And remember. Nobody leaves the sick bay until flying finishes.'

I sat next to Harry, the driver. Overhead the sky was eggshell blue with only a few scattered white clouds.

The control tower loomed up with its white façade and double railed balconies. I could see several uniformed figures inside. An officer stood with both hands resting on the balcony, a pair of binoculars around his neck. On the roof of the tower, sandwiched between several antennae was a box-like structure displaying the duty runway number.

The landing area was clear of snow and the airfield was

bristling with activity. Recovery cranes stood in readiness next to fire engines. Away to my right, a couple of tenders were busy fuelling two strange-looking aircraft.

'Those monsters over there,' Dutch shouted, pointing across the tarmac, 'are Skyraiders. That dome you see, under the fuselage, is used for radar detection. They belong to 778 Squadron,' he gave a laugh, and nudged me.' Look like big black ducks, don't they?'

I nodded in agreement.

However, my attention was drawn to six aircraft lined up at the end of the runway. Each was pale grey with red, white and blue roundels on both wings and fuselage. Even at this distance I could clearly see the whizzing circle of the propellers and hear the roar the engines.

'They're Fireflies,' said Dutch, then went on. 'These ADLs can be rather tricky and we've lost quite a few pilots recently. People who should know better say the Cold War hasn't killed anyone. They ought to come here and take a look.'

Please God, not today I prayed.

'They will accelerate, then take off one by one,' said Dutch. 'Watch what happens. It can be quite hair-raising.'

He was right. Each aircraft roared down the runway, increasing speed until it was airborne. The undercarriage retracted as they gained height and circled around the airfield. As they soared upwards, the sun glinted on their wings and fuselage. It was an exhilarating sight, but danger was not far away.

One by one, each aircraft lowered its undercarriage and came in as if it were going to land. Then, just as the wheels touched the tarmac, the pilot revved the engine and accelerated into the air.

'Bloody hell, Dutch,' I cried, 'that's fantastic. I bet that takes some doing.'

Dutch grinned at me. 'The pilot's call them dummy landings. Imagine what it would be like on the rolling deck of an aircraft carrier.'

My heart was in my mouth as each aircraft repeated the exercise. Each did two sorties before coming into land. One or two aircraft bounced slightly before coming to a halt - others made perfect three-point landings. Then, ground staff waving what looked like oversized table-tennis bats guided each aircraft away from the landing area. Finally, the last one made its approach.

'This one's in trouble,' cried Dutch. 'It's coming in too high.'

Suddenly, the earphones crackled and Dutch hurriedly put them on. 'Christ Almighty,' gasped Dutch, looking at me. 'He can't get the wheels down, and there's smoke in his cockpit.'

He then flicked the switch and replied, 'Call sick bay. Send Red Cross Two and the MO.'

All eyes focussed on the stricken aeroplane.

The fire engines moved along the edge of the runway. We followed behind.

My stomach churned with a mixture of fear and apprehension as the aircraft slowly made its descent.

Still the wheels did not come down.

With a mighty roar the Firefly came in low and pulled up.

'Jesus,' cried Harry, clasping his hand to his cheek. 'He'll have to go round again.'

I held my breath. All eyes concentrated on the aircraft silhouetted against the clear blue sky. When it turned we could clearly see the black smoke in the cockpit. Slowly it turned and came in low.

Without moving my head, I cried 'Bloody hell, Dutch, do you think it'll crash?'

'He is going to attempt a belly-landing,' replied Dutch, his voice quivering slightly. 'He'll make it all right. A few months ago these pilots were shooting down MIGs in Korea. He knows what he is doing.'

I clenched my fists and felt my heart pounding as the Firefly cut its engine. With a shattering roar it slithered along the tarmac. In the cockpit, the pilot's head and shoulders were an indistinguishable dark mass. Sparks flew out from under the fuselage as it swerved awkwardly before completing a two hundred and eighty-degree turn. The tips of the propellers broke off and flew into the air like pieces of matchwood. The stricken aircraft then came to a shuddering halt.

'Keep back!' yelled one of the firemen. 'There might be an explosion.'

Harry immediately backed the ambulance off the tarmac some distance away on the muddy grass.

Without considering the dangers, a yellow-clad firefighter leapt from a tender onto the wing and opened the cockpit canopy. As he did so, a black cloud bellowed into the air. Another firefighter joined in and together they helped the pilot out.

Meanwhile, other firemen covered the engine and surrounding parts with foam.

With a sigh of relief, I watched as the pilot walked away from the wrecked craft. By this time, Red Cross Two arrived.

Two firefighters accompanied the pilot as they hurried from the stricken aircraft. Doctor Phillips left the ambulance and walked towards them.

Dutch and I joined them.

I stared, open-mouthed at the pilot. With his flying suit, May West and face blackened by smoke, he looked the epitome of a fighter ace. He grinned at Doctor Phillips. 'I'm fine, Doc,' he said, running a gloved hand through his flaxen hair. 'A small problem with the engine. Couldn't seem to get the damn undercarriage down. Bad show really. Anyone got a cigarette?'

As he spoke he dusted himself down. The letters on the left side of his flying suit read F. Findlay. Lt. RN.

He was quickly surrounded by the ground crew and two naval officers.

'That's your third prang this year, Freddy,' said one of the officers, handing the pilot a cigarette. 'Are you sure you're all right?'

'Fit as fiddle, Peter, old boy,' he replied, his blue eyes crinkling with laughter. 'Nothing to it. Just pure good luck, I guess.'

On the way back to the sick bay, Dutch grinned and said 'One of these day Firefly Fred's luck is going to run out. You never know, maybe he'll give you a flight.

'Never in a million years,' I replied.

One Saturday afternoon I was lying on my bed thinking about home. In her last letter, Mum informed me she had to see a specialist and it worried me.

The Cornish lads were on weekend leave, Rosser had a date in Falmouth and Paddy Brophy was duty watch. The atmosphere was relaxed and lazy.

Fred was sitting up in bed reading the *Daily Express.* "I see this Colonel Nasser has become Prime Minister of Egypt,' stated Fred, turning over the pages of his newspaper.

'So what?' replied Dutch, putting on a Frankie Laine LP. 'What's that got to do with anything?'

'It says here,' said Fred, 'the bugger wants to take over the

Middle East, oil and all.'

I was still thinking about Mum, and paid no attention.

'Rubbish,' replied Dutch. 'We've got too many troops in the Canal Zone for that to ever happen.'

Suddenly, Dutch sprang off his bed. 'Come on, Fred,' said Dutch, turning off the record. 'It's about time we introduced Tom to Big Aggie.'

The mention of my name made me look up. 'Who the hell is Big Aggie?' I asked.

'You'll find out,' said Dutch. 'What do you say, Fred? How about a run ashore in Helston?'

'Sound like a bloody good idea, Dutch,' replied Fred. 'I fancy a few pints of special.'

A book I found was quite informative about the town. Apparently Helston is mentioned in the Domesday Survey in 1088 and a castle had once stood on the local bowling green. In 1305 King Richard made Helston a coinage town and it was granted a special charter. The money was assayed in the Coinage Hall. This was renamed Coinagehall Street, which to my delight, contained many of the town's pubs.

Puffing like racehorses, we trudged along a narrow, muddy pathway that curved towards Helston. The four spires of the local church dominated a skyline surrounded by chimneys and leafless trees.

'This is Meneage Road,' said Dutch, hunching up against the wind. 'And that road,' he added, pointing to his right, 'leads to Penzance.'

On either side of a narrow, cobbled street, stood Georgian and Edwardian buildings. Many of these still retained their old fronts and overhanging gallery windows. Gas lamps dotted the well-worn pavements. It looked like a scene straight out of a Dicken's novel.

We stopped outside a Tudor-style pub.

'Ah, The dear old "Bell",' sighed Fred, looking up at the sign. 'Time for a pint, and it's your round, Tom.'

After a few pints, we moved on and arrived at an impressive Georgian building.

'That's the Guildhall,' said Dutch. 'Dates back from 1576, re-built in 1826,' said Dutch.

I stared at him. 'Bloody-hell, Dutch. You seem to know a lot about this place.'

Dutch grinned at me. 'Simple, mate,' he replied. 'It's all in the local guide book.'

We came to a corner and stopped. 'Up there,' said Dutch, pointing to his right, 'is Wendron Street. That's where Bob Fitzsimmons was born – he was heavyweight champion of the world in 1897.'

I was suitably impressed.

We turned left into a wide street that sloped gently downhill.

'This is Coinagehall Street,' said Fred. 'And watch out for the drains. They've bust many a leg after closing time.'

On the right was a pub called "The Regent". Then came the "Alpha Hotel". Opposite was the "Seven Stars" and "The Star Hotel".

'Bugger me,' I gasped. 'There's more pubs here than in Union Street.'

'There used to be fourteen, a hundred years ago,' said Dutch. 'But the locals have slowed down a bit since then. Now, there is only about a dozen.'

We continued down Coinagehall Street and arrived outside yet another pub called 'The Blue Anchor.'

Fred turned to me and with a gleam in his eye, announced, 'Now, we're going to introduce you to Big Aggie.'

'About bloody time, too,' I replied. 'I'm dying of thirst.'

Inside was a bar running the length of the room. Several locals were there, laughing and talking. A few sailors sat at tables listening to Lita Roza singing *How Much is that Doggy in the Window.*

Behind the bar, a thin woman was busy wiping down the counter. As she moved strands of limp, black hair moved from side to side. She was flatchested and her face had more lines than the Great Western railway. From under a long-sleeved blouse poked a pair of boney hands, one of which held a damp cloth. When she saw us, she stopped work.

'Hello, Dutch, my bird,' she cried, raising her arms in the air. 'How are you? I sees you 'ave a newcomer.' She smiled at me, displaying a row of yellow teeth. 'And what might your name be, my pretty?'

'Tom,' I said hesitatingly. 'Tom Lightburn. '

She gave Dutch and Fred a cunning look. 'Does he know the rules?'

Both grinned and shook their heads.

'What bloody rules?' I asked, staring at them. 'You never said anything about rules.'

Dutch took off his cap, and scratched his head. 'Well, you see it's like this, Tom,' he said warily. 'Before any newcomer can order a drink, he has to arm wrestle.'

'Arm wrestle,' I exploded. 'Who do I have to arm wrestle?'

Big Aggie leaned forward on the bar. 'Me!' she bellowed. 'And so far, my handsome, I've never been beaten.'

I blinked in astonishment. The only time I had arm wrestled was with Joe – and he won.

I stared at her. She looked undernourished and weak. How on earth, I asked myself, could someone like this arm wrestle?

'And, if you win,' she said, running her lips over her tongue, 'you gets free ale for all the time you're at Culdrose'

Free ale, I thought. This sounds too good to be true. 'Right,' I said emphatically. 'You are on.'

The word soon got around and a crowd gathered near the bar.

'Half a crown on Aggie,' cried one of the locals.

'You are on,' replied Fred.

'I'll take two bob on Tom,' chimed in Dutch. 'This lad's a Scouser. He's as strong as an ox.'

Then came my greatest surprise. Big Aggie stood up and slowly rolled up the right sleeve of her blouse. To my amazement I saw an arm that would have done justice to an all-in wrestler.

She gave me a steely smile, and flexed her biceps. 'Nice aint they?' she said. 'Care to feel?'

I swallowed and shook my head.

'Come on,' I said, taking off my jacket and rolling up both sleeves. 'Anything for free beer.'

Amid cheers and jeers we took up our positions. Big Aggie lent forward and placed her elbow on the bar. I handed my jacket to Dutch and did the same.

'No cheating, mind,' she said. 'Left arm behind your back, now.'

We clenched hands. Her grip was firm and tight. I felt her exert pressure as she tried to lever my arm downwards. Summoning all my strength, I resisted and pushed, but her arm did no move.

More cheers came from the crowd.

Fred shouted in my ear, 'Come on, Tom, lad. We've got money riding on you.'

My heart was pounding and I could feel sweat breaking out on my forehead. She was surprisingly strong, and I could feel myself weakening. My God, I thought, if I am beaten, I'll never live it down.

We looked at one another. Big Aggie gave me a toothy grin.

My arm was aching and I could hardly feel my fingers. Gritting my teeth I made one last effort. Slowly, I managed to force her arm over. The crowd continued to cheer. This stirred me on. I summoned all my strength and put in a final effort. It was no use. My arm went numb as she gradually levered it over and onto the bar counter.

Sweat poured down my brow. My arms and back ached and my fingers felt like last week's sausages.

'There you are, my beauty,' cried Big Aggie, standing back behind the bar. 'Still unbeaten, I am. Anyone else wants a try?'

I took a deep breath and looked at Dutch and Fred. 'Sorry lads,' I muttered, rolling down my sleeves. 'She was too good for me'

Big Aggie burst out into peels of laughter. She thumped the top of the counter, looked at me and said, 'and I was too good for your mates, as well. Weren't I Dutch?'

'Aye, you were that, Aggie,' replied Dutch.

Big Aggie reached over the bar and ruffled my hair. 'Come on now, Tom,' she said,. 'Let me buys you a drink. What will you have?'

After a cursory glance at the other two, I leant across the bar and felt Aggie's biceps. 'Whatever you drink, love,' I said with a grin. 'I'll have a double.'

One evening, when I was duty, a rating came in with pains in his stomach. Luckily Doctor Young was at hand to examine him in his surgery.

At first, the doctor asked him how long he had had the pain and if he had been sick or constipated.

The man's pulse was racing and his temperature raised.

I watched as the doctor gently used both hands to palpate the rating's stomach. Beginning on the left side, he slowly moved across to the right.

'That's the spot, sir,' said the rating, tensing up. 'That's where it hurts.'

The doctor pursed his lips and glanced at me. 'Do you know the name of this area?' he asked, touching the man on his right side.

Remebering my anatomy, I replied, 'Yes, sir. The right illiac fossa.'

'Good man. Now watch closely.' He gently pressed the area, then suddenly removed his hand.

The rating gave a sharp gasp of pain.

'That is called "rebound tenderness",' he said. 'Note how he tenses up afterwards. This is called "guarding".'

The doctor then performed a rectal examination. He turned the man on his left side and, using a surgical glove smeared with petroleum jelly, inserted a finger into the man's rectum.

'Ouch,' cried the unfortunate rating. 'That hurts, sir.'

'I'm afraid you probably have appendicitis, young man,' said the doctor. 'It's off to hospital with you.'

I was learning something new each day.

When we found out it was Jan Colliver's birthday, everyone except Paddy, who was on duty, adjourned to the NAAFI. Later on, after crashing out for the afternoon, everyone woke up feeling worse for wear. 'Christ, I've got a mouth like a vulture's crutch,' moaned Colliver, climbing off his bed. 'Anyone got an asprin?'

At that moment Bill came in.

In one hand Bill held a tumbler containing a white, effervescent concoction. 'Here you are, young Colliver,' he said, stirring up the liquid with a teaspoon. 'This will fix you good and proper.'

'What's in it, Bill?' croaked Colliver, taking the glass from Bill.

'Never you mind. Drink it down quickly. All in one.'

Colliver, a pained expression on his face, did as he was told. The result was an instantaneous belch.

'Good,' exclaimed Bill with an air of satisfaction. 'It has worked. You'll be right in no time.'

The rest, including myself, drank some. 'It tastes like Alka Seltzer,' I said. 'What's in it?'

'A special recipe,' replied Bill with a smug look on his face. 'A mixture of citric acid, magnesium tricillicate, soluble asprin and water.' He narrowed his eyes, and added, 'Given to me by a herb specialist in the Far East.'

We didn't believe him, but the concoction seemed to work.

Shortly afterwards, I wrote the recipe down. It was to come in handy much later on.

A few nights later Dutch and I decided to go to the camp pictures to see Frank Sinatra and Doris Day in *The Tender Trap.* The others didn't fancy it. 'Can't stand that skinny bugger,' said Fred. 'I don't know what Ava Gardner sees in him.'

'You're only jealous,' said Vinson. 'He's probably got a bigger dick than you.'

As usual, the hall was packed and once again I spotted Julie. She was sitting with Iris and when she saw me, she smiled and waved. However, my joy was short-lived when a man in plain clothes sat next to her. Dutch saw me looking at her. 'Forget it Tom, that's an officer in civvies. You've got no chance there.'

When the film finished, Iris came over to me. She had brown hair, hazel eyes and a good figure. 'It's dark outside,' she said coyly. 'How about walking me back to the Wrenery?'

Any port in a storm, I suppose, I said to myself, grinned at Dutch and walked away.

'Enjoy the film?' said Iris, as we made our way to her quarters. 'Not bad,' I replied.

Just then an MG sped past. Sitting beside the same man was Julie. 'Lucky cow,' said Iris with a touch of jealousy. 'She's been invited to the wardroom for a drink. Personally, I can't stand officers.'

We stopped outside her gate. Immediately, she pressed herself against me and gave me a long, lingering kiss. When we broke away, she looked up and whispered. 'You know, Tom Lightburn, even though I'm engaged, I still fancy you.'

This came as a surprise. 'Who are you engaged to?' I asked.

'Malcolm Tennant,' she replied. 'He's a PO Telegrapher on the *Albion.* He's away in the Far East at the moment.'

'Is he, by God?' I replied, and kissed her again.

A few days later I was on duty. Everything was quiet. I lay on the bed listening to *Round The Horn* . Without any warning, a knock came at the door and in came a rating, holding his jaw. 'It's me tooth, he moaned. I've lost a filing and it's killing me. Any chance of a codeine, or something?'

I put my book down, and stood up. I didn't know much about

175

teeth and couldn't ask any of the others as they were all at the NAAFI. Perhaps, he was right, I told myself. All he needed was a couple of painkillers. Then, he could see the dentist in the morning. However, I decided to take a look. To my horror I saw a large dark cavity on the back row of his teeth.

Then, I had an idea - perhaps Julie could help.

I telephoned the Wren's quarters. After a brief wait, I heard a familiar female voice.

'Hello,' I said. 'Is that you Julie?'

'Yes,' she replied. 'Who is this?'

'It's Tom, from the sick bay.'

At first she thought it was a social call. Then, when I explained the problem she sounded disappointed.

'Oh, all right,' she said curtly. 'I'll come down and see him.'

I told the rating what I had done. 'She'll fix you up, don't worry,' I said, trying to comfort him. He simply muttered under his breath and held his jaw.

Julie arrived ten minutes later. She looked just as gorgeous as ever.

'Well. Where is he?' she said, fiddling with the key of the dental surgery.

I ushered the suffering rating into the surgery and she abruptly closed the door.

Twenty minutes passed and the rating came out. He had a smile on his face. Before he left, he muttered. 'That feels much better. Thanks very much.'

I was extremely impressed. 'That was great. What did you do?'

Julie removed her jacket. 'Oh I simply used a mixture of oil of cloves and zinc oxide. It numbs the pain and acts as a temporary filling. Lasts for days.'

I didn't reply. I was too busy staring at the black brassière clearly visible under her white shirt.

'Got any coffee?' she asked, walking into the duty room.

'Yes,' I eagerly replied, and filled the electric kettle with water.

'Nice and cosy,' she commented, making herself comfortable on the bed. As she did so, her blue serge skirt slowly slid up her legs, revealing a flash of white thigh and suspenders.

She looked directly at me. On the small bedside table, the

kettle was boiling, and so was I.

I made two cups and handed her one.

She patted her hand by her side. 'Come and sit down,' she said in a husky voice. 'You look nervous standing there.'

'Oh, right,' I replied hoarsely. The bed creaked as I sat down. Licking my lips, I turned and said. 'How is your coffee?'

'Too hot,' she replied, her blue eyes penetrating deep into mine. 'Put it on the table and let it cool off.'

That was not the only thing that needed cooling off, I thought. Suddenly she reached up and pulled me down to her. When we kissed, her tongue immediately darted into my mouth. One of my hands slid up the taut material of her shirt and cupped her breast. As she moved down the bed her skirt rode higher. Using one hand she quickly removed her panties. From that moment on everything happened quickly.

When it was over I lay by her side, my shirt open to the waist.

She looked into my eyes and smiled. 'Have you got a cigarette?'

Just then I heard the crunch of footsteps approaching the main door.

'Quick,' I cried. 'There's someone coming.'

In a flash I was off the bed, tucking in my shirt. Luckily I still had my shoes on, but my tie hung around my neck like a noose. Behind me, Julie was hurriedly putting on her shoes.

The door opened and there stood the burly figure of Surgeon Commander Boyd-Martin. My stomach hit the ground and I felt shell-shocked.

For a few seconds, he did not speak. Instead, he bayoneted me a with a rheumy stare.

Finally he spoke. 'What's going on here? Who is on duty?'

I tried to swallow, but my mouth had dried up. 'Me sir,' I managed to say. Glancing across at Julie, I added. 'I...I asked Wren Marsh here to see a rating who had lost a filing.'

The PMO frowned and stared at Julie.

'Is this true, Marsh?'

'Yes, sir,' she replied, her face flushed with embarrassment.

The PMO gave a cough. 'A likely story,' he muttered. 'Return to your quarters, Marsh.'

'Yes, sir,' came Julie's weak reply, as she hurriedly collected her jacket and bag.

'As for you, Lightburn. I'll see you in my office in the morning.'

Once again, I swallowed before answering. 'Yes, sir,' I said. 'But Wren Marsh did see a patient. He will be seeing the dentist in the morning.'

'And so will she,' he replied. His gaze suddenly focussed on a crumpled mass of pink near the side of the bed. He glared at Julie, and said. 'And I suggest you take those with you. '

Julie's face went a brighter shade of red. 'Oh my God,' she cried. In one quick movement, she bent down, picked up her panties and ran out.

The PMO gave me a final stare then strode down the corridor.

Later, when the lads returned from the NAAFI, I told them what had happened.

'Not the old man?' cried Fred. 'He'll do his fuckin' nut.'

'We were only sitting on the bed,' I said to Bill. 'We were not actually doing anything.'

Bill shook his head. 'I'm afraid you are in the mire, old son,' he said. 'I wonder what the chief will say?'

That night I did not sleep. This time to-morrow, I told myself, I could be back in Plymouth. Desperate and Jock would probably have a good laugh. My promotion prospects would be finished, as would my naval career. And worst of all, how could I explain all this to my parents.

Next morning, standing in front of the chief's desk, I felt my world was about to collapse. My stomach had rebelled against breakfast and my legs felt weak. There were just the two of us. The others kept out of the way.

'Good God, lad,' cried the chief. 'What the hell were you thinking of, eh?'

I shrugged my shoulders in despair and said nothing.

'You'd better learn to keep it in your trousers,' he said. 'Or one day you'll really be in trouble.'

My God, I thought. Surely I couldn't be in worse trouble than this.

The chief lit a cigarette and sat back in his chair. He took a long drag and exhaled a jet of blue smoke. 'Well,' he sighed. 'I'll do what I can for you, son. But I can't promise anything.'

Just then a rating dressed in a greatcoat came in. 'Morning, Chief,' he said cheerfully. 'Do you have an SBA Lightburn?'

The chief nodded. 'That's him there, why?'

The rating withdrew a yellow envelope from his pocket and handed it to me. 'A telegram for you,' he said. 'Came a short while ago.'

It was the first telegram I had ever received. For a while I looked at it. Then I remembered something about telegrams always bringing bad news.

The staff had gathered in the office.

'Open the bloody thing up, then,' shouted the chief. 'You might have won the pools.'

I ripped open the envelope. As I read its contents my heart sank. I looked up at the chief. 'It's my Mum,' I murmured, hardly able to speak. 'She's been taken to hospital. Dad wants me to get leave.'

I passed the telegram to the chief. After reading it, he quickly stood up. 'I'll show this to the PMO when he comes in. Easter leave begins next week, so we'll get you away early.'

'What's going on here, chief?' came the distinctive voice of the PMO.

Everyone had been so concerned about me they had not noticed him.

'A telegram for Lightburn, sir,' said the chief. 'May I see you in your surgery.'

Clutching my telegram, the chief followed the PMO. A few minutes later he returned. 'I'm going to try and get you a flight,' he said, picking up the telephone. 'Go and pack your gear.'

My mind was racing. I told myself, it must be something serious for Dad to send a telegram. Could it be her heart, her chest or what? I quickly threw a few things in my small Pusser's brown case.

Dutch, Rosser and Robby came bursting into the mess.

'Chop, chop, Tom, my handsome,' said Dutch. 'The chief's got you a flight.'

When I arrived at the control tower, an officer ushered me into a large room. In the middle was a long, shiny oak table, and around the walls were metal lockers on which names and ranks of pilots were printed.

A petty officer came into the room. 'You SBA Lightburn?' His voice was sharp and crisp.

I gave a brief nod. 'Yes, PO,' I replied.

'Here,' he said, handing me a mustard-coloured flying suit. 'Slip this on over your rig, and put these boots on.' I did as he asked. The boots were fur-lined and the suit was a snug fit. The PO then gave me a pilot's cap to which was fitted a mouthpiece. Then came the Mae West. This hung around my neck like a crinkly, yellow garland.

'If you go in the drink, it will automatically inflate,' said the PO with a sardonic grin. 'But I don't think you'll need it.'

I gave him a anxious look. 'I bloody-well hope you're right.'

While admiring myself in a full-length mirror, thoughts of home were momentarily dispelled. My spine tingled with excitement. Staring me in the face was the image of a fully-fledged fighter ace.

At that moment a door opened.

My heart suddenly sank to my boots.

Standing before me, grinning like a Cheshire Cat, was Firefly Fred!

11

Lieutenant Freddie Finlay was dressed in a yellow flying suit. In one hand he carried his goggles and mouthpiece.

'Right,' he said. 'Have you ever flown before?'

'No, sir,' I replied.

'Nothing to it, old boy,' he said. 'It's like falling off a log.'

The sky was slightly overcast and threatened rain. I watched as a Skyraider took off.

Not far away were the portly shapes of several Fairey Gannets belonging to 796 Squadron. However, it was the solitary Firefly that caught my eye.

Resting on a small tail wheel with two larger ones under each wing, the aircraft sloped upwards like a bird of prey. The words 'Royal Navy' stood out against the pale blue of the fuselage and on the tail were the letters CU.

'That's our crate,' said Freddie. 'They've finished fuelling, and she's ready to go.'

During the war, I remember watching vapour trails high in the sky left by Spitfires and Hurricanes. I watched in awe, marvelling at their aerobatics and wondering how they managed to stay in the air. I was about to find out

My Boy's Own thoughts were interrupted by the voice of a naval airman.

'Here you are, Doc,' he said. 'This is for you.'

As he helped me into a parachute, I thought about Joe. If he could see me now, he'd be green with envy.

'This,' said the rating, indicating a small metal handle, 'is the rip-cord. Just in case...'

I nodded meekly.

'Well,' he whispered, 'you never know with Firefly Fred!'

Using the toeholds, I nervously climbed up into the cockpit, stowed my case between my legs and was strapped in.

'You press that red button on the dashboard if you want to eject your canopy,' said a naval airman. 'And when you fasten your mask,' he went on, 'just flip the switch at the side if you want to talk to the pilot. OK?'

The last item he gave me was a folded brown paper bag. 'And

I don't have to tell you what this is for, do I?'

Except for a small dashboard, a pint-sized collapsible table, and the all-important ejector button, the cockpit was surprisingly empty. Where was the joystick and deadly machine-gun button?

I asked the rating about this.

'The Battle of Britain's over, matey,' laughed the rating. 'Besides, this is the Observer's compartment.'

Another rating plugged in my oxygen lead. 'The pilot will tell you when to turn it on,' he said, indicating a small switch. He then pulled the canopy over my head, and gave me the traditional thumbs up. My mouth felt like sandpaper and I could hear the blood pounding in my head.

Fred's voice crackled in my ears. 'All right behind?' he said.

I quickly replied, 'Yes, sir. I'm OK.'

'Hold tight, here we go.'

After what sounded like a series of harsh coughs, the engine spluttered into action and we began to move. I glanced at my watch. The time was a little after ten.

My line of vision was restricted to each side. I could not see the propeller or the nose. As we began to taxi along the runway, I licked my lips and braced myself.

At first, the aircraft bounced slightly, then, with an ear-splitting roar, accelerated. My body was thrust back into the seat and the straps tightened around my body. Then, as if lifted by an unknown hand, the ground fell away, everything felt weightless and we were airborne.

In a matter of seconds, fields, farms and hedgerows became a patchwork quilt of greens and browns. Helston shrunk into a toy town with cars moving on pencil-thin roads. It was a beautiful, awe-inspiring sight, making me feel I was sitting on top of the world.

I swallowed, causing my ears to pop. Abruptly, the engines became louder.

'How are you doing, Doc?' said Fred through the intercom. His voice sounded nasal and more pronounced.

'It's fantastic,' I replied. 'Really great.'

'Good man,' he replied. 'We are only at five thousand feet. I am gong to level out at ten for the next hour.'

'How long before we reach *Blackcap*, sir,'

HMS *Blackcap* was a naval air base near Warrington.

'Three hours, at the most,' he replied. 'So sit back and enjoy the trip.'

Soon we were enveloped in diaphanous clouds billowing against the canopy like puffs of steam.

All of a sudden, we broke into an umbrella of breath-taking blue. Below, separating us from mother earth, stretched a fleecy, undulating, wilderness of white.

I began to relax, and for the first time since take-off, thought of Mum. My experience on the medical wards told me heart problems were a complication of asthma. I began to panic, trying not to think of the worst.

Just then, Fred's voice broke into my self-inflicted torment.

'We're just over the Bristol Channel,' he said. We had flown into thick, dark grey clouds. 'I am going down to try and get out of this bloody pea soup.'

As we descended, streaks of cloud swept past. My ears began to pop and rain began to batter the canopy.

I held my breath as the force of our dive pinned me to the back of my seat. Suddenly, as we broke cloud a ship's mast came into view.

The aircraft immediately rose into the air and I caught a glimpse of infinity. Once more my body was forced back. By this time my head was spinning. When we finally levelled out, I was not sure if I was on my arse or my elbow!

'Sorry about that,' came Fred's voice. He sounded quite unperturbed. 'Could have been a bit dicey. Nothing to worry about, though. How are you?'

Trying not to sound too terrified, I replied, 'Oh… all right, sir. Still in one piece.'

'Good show, old boy, glad to hear it,' came his cheerful reply.

Down below, the Bristol Channel shone like a mill-pond. One or two vessels cut through the sea, leaving behind a thin, white wake.

Quite abruptly, the sun broke through the murkiness. The glare hurt my eyes and I slipped my goggles on. Then, as if by sorcery, a hand reached out and pushed the sun behind a black cloud. The scene instantly changed, casting a dark, silent shadow over the waters.

After a while, the scene changed yet again. Scattered villages and Lilliputian towns appeared and quickly disappeared.

Then, the nightmare began.

Just as I felt myself dozing off, Fred's voice came through the intercom. 'A spot of dicey weather ahead,' he said. 'It's an electric storm and I can't fly round it.'

As he spoke, we flew into a morass of black, cumulo-nimbus clouds. 'An electric storm,' I cried. 'What's that?'

'Nothing to worry about, old boy,' he said. 'Just hold on.'

Hold on to what? There was nothing to hold on to, except the straps of my harness!

'Roger,' I weakly replied and said a silent prayer.

At that moment, we were instantly engulfed in total darkness. Vivid white flashes exploded in the sky, followed by a rumbling noise that sounded like an earthquake. More flashes occurred, only these were closer, momentarily lighting up both wings.

The Firefly began to shake with each rumble of thunder.

'I'm going to dive and try and get us clear,' said Fred.

Once again I was pinned to the back of the seat. But it was no use. We broke cloud and were confronted by a scene from Dante's Inferno. Flashes of forked lightning rattled around the sky like flack.

A dagger of white light streaked passed the aircraft and for a terrifying second I thought the 'plane might disintegrate. The aircraft began to weave awkwardly from side to side. My bowels felt like bursting and I thought we were going to crash.

Above the cacophony came Fred's calm voice. 'I say, you do know about that red button, don't you?'

My heart nearly stopped.

Now, I was sure we were going to crash.

I was almost too scared to speak. 'Y... yes, sir,' I managed to say.

'Well, don't bloody-well touch it,' he replied. 'Because we'll be out of this in a jiffy.'

His calmness did nothing to re-assure me. When we finally broke clear my face was wet with sweat and I felt sick.

'You'll be home soon, old boy,' said Fred. 'In time for a pint at your local.'

Suddenly all my fears disappeared. Even my bowels began to behave.

The dots below gradually increased in size, becoming a town, which, in turn, changed to a widespread city.

'Warrington below,' said Fred. 'We'll be landing in about fifteen minutes.'

Once again my ears began to pop again as we descended. The ground rushed up to meet us, and after a few bumps, Firefly Fred made a perfect three-point landing.

My whole body seemed to tremble as Fred helped me out of the cockpit.

He looked at me with a sly grin. 'I bet that shook you up a bit,' he said, offering me a welcome cigarette.

'Not half, sir,' I replied, taking a drag. The effect of the tobacco smoke penetrated deeply into my lungs. 'Christ,' I sighed. 'I bloody-well needed that.'

'There is a tilly waiting to take you home,' said Fred. He offered me his hand. 'Good luck, and I sincerely hope your mother is all right.'

Glancing over my shoulder, I took a last look at the Firefly. Standing alone on the tarmac, it looked proud and defiant. It was hard to believe a short while ago this metal creature had carried me though the air, giving me the most exhilarating experience of my life

Firefly Fred was right. I arrived home just in time for last orders. But there were more important things on my mind than beer.

'How is she?' I cried as I burst into the living room.

Dad looked up from his newspaper, a startled look in his eyes. He could see how worried I was. 'Calm down, son,' he replied, his weather-beaten face breaking into a grin. 'Your old girl's going to be OK. She's in the Central.'

Although it was not official visiting hours, the sister, seeing my uniform, allowed me into the ward. Mum was in the end bed on my right. She was resting against a mound of pillows and draped around her shoulders was a white woollen shawl. When she saw me her pallid features immediately broke into a smile.

A film of tears covered my eyes as we held one another. For a while neither of us could speak.

Finally, I managed to ask her how she was.

'Och, I am OK,' she said, blowing her nose. She took both my hands in hers. 'It's good to see you, son. Are you on leave, then?'

I did not mention Dad's telegram.

'Yes, two weeks,' I replied.

'Oh, that's lovely, son,' said Mum. 'I'll be home well before then. The doctor said it's just a touch of asthma. Nothing for you or your Dad to worry about.'

But she was wrong. Next day, the policeman came and told us Mum's condition was worse.

Mrs Hislop, my mother's next door neighbour had 'phoned a taxi.

My heart stood still when I saw her frail face encased in a polythene oxygen tent. Her breathing was shallow and she appeared to be asleep.

Dad stood in silence, cap in hand, looking down at her.

'How is she, sister?' I asked.

'Holding her own,' she quietly replied. 'The specialist is seeing her shortly, so you can't stay long.'

Her arms were outside the tent.

With tears in his eyes, Dad gently took hold of her hand. 'Cora,' he whispered. 'How are you, love?'

She must have heard him. Slowly her eyes opened. A weak smile played around her mouth as she looked at both of us and mouthed, 'OK.'

Her hand gave his a squeeze and she closed her eyes. My heart jumped and for one terrible second I thought the worst. Thankfully the sister interrupted my thoughts.

'She is asleep, now,' she said. 'You'll have to leave.'

During the next two weeks, Mum's condition improved, and a few days before I was due back off leave she was discharged.

However, the sister's parting words to Mum rang in my ears as the taxi left the hospital. 'You will have to take it easy, Mrs Lightburn,' she had said. 'No strenuous work. And try not to worry about things. That strapping sailor son of yours can look after himself.'

Of course, both Dad and I knew it was not me she worried about. Tony was still in Pentonville, but with good behaviour, he would be eligible for parole in a year.

'You do realise the charges you face are very serious?' Leave was over. Mum had been discharged a few days before I was due back. Now, standing before the PMO, I awaited the worst.

'Yes, sir,' I nervously replied, wondering what my fate might be.

'You have broken all my standing orders,' he went on, 'and I could have you removed from the station.'

Oh God, I said to myself. Here it comes.

The PMO lit a cigarette and lent back in his chair. 'However, because the chief has spoken highly of you, I'm going to withhold your B13 for three months. Understand?'

A B13 was a form issued by the navy when someone was due for higher rate. I had forgotten about it.

'Yes, sir,' I said, breathing a sigh of relief.

'But make no mistake,' went on the PMO. 'Another episode like the last one, and you'll be returned to RNH. Understand?'

'Yes sir,' I replied. 'Thank you, sir.'

After 'stand easy', I met Julie as she came out of the dental surgery.

'Don't you dare speak to me,' she hissed, her blue eyes dark with anger. 'I was the laughing stock of the camp. I never want to see you again.' She then turned abruptly on her heels, went into the surgery and slammed the door.

Bill poked his head around the dispensary door. 'Hell hath no fury like a woman scorned,' he laughed and disappeared.

It was the same with Margaret and Iris. Passing me on the way to dinner, they turned up their noses and ignored me.

'Pay no attention, Tom,' said Vinson. 'There's more fish in the sea.'

'I know,' I replied. 'But the last one got all my bait!'

12

The summer of 1954 was particularly hot. We watched as the local band marched through Helston celebrating Flora Day, after which we attempted to drink the town dry. There was an outbreak of myxomatosis, Oxford won the boat race and wartime rationing finally ended. As yet, the continental package tour was not in vogue and people flocked in droves to Billy Butlins, Blackpool and Bournemouth.

Abroad, an uneasy peace existed between North and South Korea. The Cold War continued while in Egypt, Colonel Jamal Abdul Nasser came to power. The irony of his promise that all British troops would leave the Canal Zone by 1956 would become all too apparent in due course.

Meanwhile at Culdrose, the fine weather meant perfect flying conditions.

In the third week of July, Culdrose held its annual Air Day. The warm weather brought people from all around. But, for the medical staff, pilots and ground crews, it was business as usual

Doctor Phillips, Paddy and myself, were on duty in Red Cross One near the main runway. All ratings, including ourselves were in half blues.

From midday till six in the evening, the airfield thronged with excited crowds. Girls in bright coloured dresses sauntered around, trying to catch the eager eyes of the naval airmen. Schoolchildren, eating ice creams and candy floss, gazed excitedly at the aircraft on display.

These included the ubiquitous Firefly, the chunky Douglas Skyraider and a group of Sea Hawks, their wings folded like giant bats. There were Avengers, Gannets and the odd-looking Supermarine Sea Otter with its engine situated centrally in the upper wing. Close by, the silver fuselage of the Meteor sparkled in the afternoon sun. This was a jet fighter and attracted lots of attention.

'What are they, over there, Paddy?' I asked, pointing to four, twin-engined aircraft lined up outside a hangar.

'They are Sea Princes,' he replied. 'Used for ferrying personnel about. '

Dr Phillips climbed out of the ambulance, stretched his arms outwards, and yawned. 'Those bloody wardroom parties, my head is killing me.'

I gave him a side-ways grin. 'Been on the piss again, sir?' I said.

He gave me a dirty look. 'Cheeky Pom,' he replied, handing me a pound note. 'Go over to one of those stalls and get us all some coffee. And make mine strong.'

I did as he asked.

When I returned with the coffee, Iris and Margaret were having a joke with Dutch. Iris and I were now on speaking terms. Her well-formed breasts, supported by a white brassière, strained against the thin material of her uniform blouse.

'Where's ours, then?' chirped Margaret

Straight away, Dutch offered to go and fetch them a drink.

'I'll go with you,' said Margaret, giving him a comely smile.

Harry was in the ambulance and Dr Phillips was talking to an officer. Suddenly, Iris and myself were left alone.

'Have you been to Penzance, yet, Tom?' she asked, smiling at me.

'No,' I replied. 'Not as yet. Why?'

'Well,' she said, slowly running her finger around the rim of her polystyrene cup. 'I was thinking. I'm off next weekend. How about coming there with me?'

I looked at her. As she spoke a smile played around her mouth.

'Penzance? Sounds good to me,' I replied with a puzzled expression. 'But we'd have to catch the last bus back.'

'Why come back,' she said.

Just as I was about to ask exactly what she meant, Dutch and Margaret returned.

The day's activities ended with a fly-past by a formation of Sea Hawks followed by a solitary Tiger Moth.

On the way back to the sick quarters, we dropped the girls off at the Wrenery.

'See you tomorrow, Tom,' she whispered before climbing down from the ambulance. 'Don't forget our date. Penzance, next Saturday.'

Gradually, the implications of what this meant dawned on me. This was 1954 and moral codes were strict. Surely Iris knew this, I told myself. Perhaps she had done this sort of thing before. After all, she was engaged, and, well, you never know...

It was pointless trying to keep my date with Iris a secret from the lads. There was no way I could escape on Saturday without someone smelling a rat. I therefore, decided to tell them.

We had finished supper and were in the mess.

'You dirty, lucky bastard!' exclaimed Rosser. 'You mean to say it was her idea?'

'Don't forget to take plenty of johnnies,' said Dutch.

'I shouldn't bother,' snorted Robbie. 'Go bareback. They like it that way.'

'Aye,' said Vinson. 'And end up putting her up the duff.'

His comment reminded me of Cynthia, and I made a mental note to take Dutch's advice.

'We want to know all the sordid details,' chimed in Vinson, taking hold of a dart and throwing at the board. 'Every time you get a bull's eye. Don't we lads?'

'You bet,' said Dutch. 'We want to know how many pubic hairs she has, and if she shaves under her armpits.'

Glancing pleadingly at them, I said. 'Look fellers, keep it to yourselves. If it leaks out, Iris might get in the rattle.'

'Don't you worry, Tom, my handsome,' said Robby, making his way to the heads. 'We will keep your secret. Who knows, she might fancy a dirty weekend with me.'

The next day I met Iris in the corridor. 'Where will we stay?' I whispered, glancing about.

'Don't worry about that,' she said 'There is a place called the Trelawny Hotel. A few of the Wrens have stayed there. It's along the sea front, not far from where the bus drops us off.'

After tot-time on Saturday I packed my civvies and carefully slipped several condoms in my trouser pocket.

We had arranged to meet at the Meneage Street bus stop.

Feeling as if every eye was watching me, I quickly left the sick bay. Clutching the canvas grip, I made my way to the main gate.

'Have a good week-end, Doc,' shouted the rating on duty.

Bloody-hell, I thought - every bugger in the camp knows!

By the time I reached Helston, my shirt was sticking to my back.

Along with several people, Iris was standing at the bus stop. She looked even more attractive out of uniform. Her brown hair was tied in a short ponytail. She wore a pale blue dress, a matching belt and flat-soled shoes. In her hand was a canvas grip similar to mine.

I gave her a sheepish grin, and went to the back of the queue.

She smiled and joined me. 'Hi' she said, 'for a minute I thought you had changed your mind.'

Overhearing her, one or two people gave us suspicious looks.

'Ha,' I replied weakly, quickly glancing around. 'No danger.'

Penzance is roughly fourteen miles from Helston. We passed through a small town with typical grey granite houses. 'This is Marazion,' said Iris, 'and that, over there, to your left is St Michael's Mount, lovely, isn't it?'

'Yeah,' I replied. 'By the way,' I added, hastily changing the subject. 'How is this fiancée of yours - Malcolm something or other?'

'Oh, don't worry about him,' answered Iris, throwing her head back. 'He's still onboard *Albion,* in the far east.'

The Trelawney Hotel was a converted Edwardian building on the sea front. Walking into the foyer, I felt my stomach churn over.

Behind a counter stood an elderly woman. She had wire wool hair, thick make-up and an expression of a camel about to spit.

'Yes,' she asked in an exaggerated, posh accent. 'And what can I do for you, pray?'

Iris poked me in the back. I removed my cap, took out my handkerchief from my trouser pocket, and mopped my brow. 'A room. We'd like a room, please?' I managed to say.

The woman fixed Iris with a steely glare. 'A *double* room?'

We both nodded at once.

With a slow movement, the woman opened the registrar and ran a bony finger down a page.

'Hmmm...' she murmured. 'You are in luck. Room 24 on the top floor. Bathroom ensuite. How long will you be staying?'

I felt Iris kick my foot. 'Until to-morrow,' I quickly replied.

'Then back to Culdrose, no doubt,' was the woman's caustic reply. 'I am Mrs Pascoe, the owner. That will be four pounds, in advance, *if* you don't mind.'

I took out a fiver from my trouser pocket and paid her.

She gave Iris the key and we followed her upstairs.

'No drinking and no noise,' said Mrs Pascoe, and left.

The bedroom had two single beds.

'The miserable bitch,' I hissed, throwing the bags on the floor. 'I bet she chose this room on purpose.'

Iris started to giggle. 'That's no problem, love,' she said. 'We can always put the mattresses together.'

In next to no time, we were on the bed. Just as my hand slid up her naked thigh, there came a sharp knocking at the door.

Both of us froze.

'Yes,' I asked. 'Who is it?'

A stern voice answered. 'It is I. Mrs Pascoe.'

I stood up, straightened my tie, and opened the door.

Mrs Pascoe stood with a face like poison ivy and an expression to match. 'You left your cap behind,' she hissed, handing it to me.

'Oh, thank you,' I replied.

'And these,' in her hand were two condoms, 'I found them on the floor.'

I felt my face redden.

Holding both condoms between finger and thumb, she dropped them into my cap. Then, with a look of disgust, tuned away. 'Young people today,' she droned on her way downstairs. 'Shocking.'

When I told Iris about the condoms, we both burst out laughing.

'Come on, Tom,' she said. 'Get changed. There's an off-licence nearby.'

A few hours later, hiding a bottle of wine under my jacket, we returned to the hotel.

Laughing like schoolchildren, we pushed the beds together.

'Just turn the sheet around and tuck it firmly in on each side,' she said.' And I'll be back in a minute.'

She disappeared into the bathroom.

I fixed the bedclothes, and with a lecherous grin, placed the condoms under a pillow. Iris slowly entered wearing a black, see-through negligee that left nothing to my imagination.

For a second I just stood and stared. My mouth fell open and I almost dropped the bottle of wine.

She fixed me with a sexy stare, and glided towards the bed. As she lay back, the flimsy material of her negligee slid tantalisingly up her legs revealing black stockings and suspenders.

'Well,' she purred. 'Don't just stand there. Pass me the bottle and get undressed.'

In a flash my clothes became an untidy heap on the floor.

We lay in the middle of the 'double' bed, our arms entwined one another. Her soft body pressed against my nakedness. At that

192

moment, the beds parted and we hit the floor with a resounding bump. It was just like landing on top of a rubber lilo.

'My back!' she cried. 'I've hurt my back.'

With all ardour subdued, I lifted myself off her.

It was obvious that Iris was in considerable pain. Her negligee was up around her waist. I reluctantly pulled it down.

Tears welled up in her eyes.

'Don't move, love,' I said, remembering my first aid. 'Just lie still for a moment.'

Black streaks of mascara began to trickle down her face. 'Lie still.' she cried,' I'm in bloody agony. Of course I'll lie still.'

'Can you move your legs?'

She tried to do so. This brought forth a tearful cry. 'Yes, but it hurts above my bum.'

After a short while, she calmed down and with my help, managed to get into bed.

That was the end of our so- called 'dirty week-end.'

The next morning, Mrs Pascoe watched as I helped Iris down the stairs.

'She has a bad back,' I said. 'Last night she...' my voice trailed off.

'Disgusting. That's all I can say,' she snapped, and grabbed the key out of my hand. 'You young people have no morals.'

'Come on, Tom, my son,' said Dutch, leaning across the table. 'What was she like?'

It was Sunday evening. Rosser was on duty and we were in the mess playing poker.

'Yeah.' Vinson added, 'we want to know everything.'

'I'll take three,' I said, taking three cards from Robby. This gave me three queens and a pair of fours.

'I'll raise the kitty, half a dollar,' then I said. 'All right. I'll tell you. But first put up or shut up.'

Each of them threw in the money.

They then added and threw away cards from their hands.

'We had this really posh room.' I said, keeping my cards close to my chest. 'With a bathroom and a great view across the harbour.'

'To hell with the harbour,' cried Paddy Brophy, laying his hand face down on the table. 'Tell us what she was *like*.'

Robby stared at me, his hooded eyes gleaming like a failed

rapist. 'Did she have nice tits?'

'Come on, Tom,' said Dutch impatiently. 'Tell us what she did to you? Did she su…'

I quickly interrupted him. Glancing at my cards, I said. 'Raise it again. Another half a crown.'

'Too rich for me,' said Robby, throwing his cards on the table.

'And me, you bugger,' added Dutch.

That left just Paddy and Vinson in the game. The other two remained in their seats, anxious expressions on their faces.

'Well. We're waiting,' cried Vinson. 'Come on, Tom, you sod. What the fuck happened?'

Like robots Paddy and Vinson added their money to the pile of coins in the centre of the table.

I looked at each one, then, in a hushed voice, said. 'She wore a black negligee.'

'Yes, yes, go on,' muttered Vinson, licking his lips.

'We lay on the bed.'

By this time the game was forgotten.

Looking deep into their eyes, I lent forward and said, 'I'll raise it a quid.'.

'Bollocks,' yelled Paddy, throwing down his cards. 'Who do you think I am? Rockerfeller.'

Tossing in a pound note, I said to Vinson, 'See you.'

Vinson glared at me, and placed his cards face upwards. He had three two's and a pair of queens.

'Tough luck, matey,' and although I didn't need to, I flashed my hand. 'Three kings and two tens,' I said, raking in the money. 'Oh, and by the way. Iris is a smashing girl. Now, mind your own business,' and walked out of the mess.

Over the next twelve months, Iris and I had weekends in Falmouth, Loe and Praa Sands. Needless to say, we never went back visit Mrs Pascoe.

At the end of August the PMO informed me I had at last earned my promotion to leading hand.

At last I could afford to increase Mum's weekly allowance.

But just as important I was now qualified to fulfil my burning ambition, to serve on a ship by myself. A week later, I put in a request to do so.

On the last Monday of the month six Royal Naval Reserve

PO's joined for their annual two weeks training. In order to qualify for their flight pay, they had to spend a few hours in the air.

Smelling strongly of rum and clad in new, single-breasted uniforms, they filed into my office.

All were over forty and had rows of campaign medals from the Second World War.

'I suppose you lot will spend the next two weeks bevied,' I said, taking down their details.

'With a bit of luck,' came a voice with a familiar Merseyside accent.

I looked up and saw a heavy-set man with red hair greying and grin as wide as the Mersey Tunnel.

'Rum, bum and backy, eh, lads?' he said, laughing.

'What part of Liverpool are you from?' I asked, stamping his joining card.

'Anfield,' he replied. 'And I don't support them in red. Are you from the 'pool?'

'Wallasey,' I replied.

'Oh,' he replied. 'One of those posh buggers, eh?' Then with a wink and a grin, he turned and left.

After he had gone, I completed cards for the other five and filed them away.

The following Saturday they were all dead.

Even now, the images of what happened haunt my dreams.

It was a typical weekend morning. Flying was in progress and the ambulances were outside. The weather was still warm and things were quiet. The chief, Bill, Dutch and myself were in the office.

'How about some tea, leading hand,' said the chief, glancing my way.

'Me,' I sighed, 'a leader of men, reduced to tea-boy.'

Just as they laughed the crash alarm sounded and the telephone rang. The chief quickly picked up the receiver.

His face visibly paled. 'Christ!' he cried, looking at us. 'The Sea Prince has crashed.'

'The Sea Prince!' I exclaimed. 'Aren't they supposed to be the safest 'planes in the navy?'

'Let's hope so,' replied Dutch, moving towards the door. 'All those reservists are onboard.'

Dutch, Dr Phillips and myself were first in Red Cross One.

195

The others, including Dr Coia, followed on in Red Cross Two.

The next few hours were the most harrowing of my life.

The tangled heap of the Sea Prince lay smouldering at the end of the runway. Its nose was completely caved in, its wings buckled and its fuselage split in two. The tail had snapped off and the engine parts and torn metal were strewn across the tarmac.

Clad in their asbestos suits, the fire fighters were spraying foam onto what was still smoking. There was nothing else left for them to do.

Christ Almighty, I thought, surely nobody could escape from such a disaster.

We leapt from the ambulance. Dutch had the first aid valise with him.

A grim-faced officer stopped him. 'You won't need that,' he said, solemnly. 'They're all dead.'

With shocked expressions, we stood and looked at one another.

'All of them?' cried Dutch. 'Good Lord....' His voice trailed away.

'Come on, you two,' said Dr Phillips. The expression in his eyes told me even he, with all his war experience, wasn't prepared for such a disaster. 'We've got work to do. Let's see what's in the far section.'

With mounting trepidation, Dutch and I managed to climb into what was left of the fuselage.

There was blood everywhere. The bodies of four reservists had been thrown from their seats. They lay in various grotesque positions, around the small compartment. Some looked unscathed. Others were heavily mutilated, almost beyond recognition.

One lay with his eyes open, an arm in the air, with his bloody intestines lying in his lap. Another slumped on the floor, arms across his face as if he were asleep.

I stood paralysed with shock.

'Come on, Tom,' said Dutch, placing his arm around my shoulder. 'We have to get them out.'

We started with what appeared to be the least mutilated body. He was lying face down. To my utter dismay I recognised the petty officer from Anfield. We carefully turned him over. The lower part of his face was a bloody pulp. One arm was a mangled mess and those eyes, devoid of life, stared at me. Biting my lip, I gently closed them with my hand.

Several naval airmen helped us to remove the bodies. One by one they were carried outside and placed on stretchers. An officer removed all identification. The white sheets covering them soon became soaked with blood.

Then came the biggest shock of all.

Two ratings passed me carrying a body. A slight breeze blew the sheet away from the face of the dead man. I immediately recognised the face of Firefly Fred.

The blood drained from my face. Here was the man who had shown me the wonders of flight. As I stared at the stretcher, the sound of his calm voice saying, 'Don't worry, old boy, everything will be all right,' echoed in my head.

Like the other unfortunate victims, he had come unscathed through a terrible war. To die like this seemed wrong and unfair. For a few seconds anger welled up inside of me. Why, God? Why? I cried inwardly, looking up to the heavens.

But I received no tangible answers.

By the time we finished laying them out, it was after eight o'clock in the evening. We had missed supper, but nobody felt like eating.

There was no ceremonial burial.

The next morning Frank Strike arrived with three black limousines.

Standing to attention, we watched in sombre silence as the coffins, each draped with a white ensign, were taken away for private burials.

Officers and men lined the route out of the station. The officers saluted while the rest removed their caps. The parade ground flag flew at half- mast.

As the vehicles reached the main gate, a guard of honour snapped to attention and presented arms. Suddenly, the familiar drone of an aeroplane filled the air. We looked up and saw the unmistakable shape of a solitary Firefly. It flew low, dipped its wings before soaring into the sky.

Firefly Fred would have like that.

13

The year seemed to fly by. Winston Churchill resigned as Prime Minister and was replaced by Anthony Eden. A state of emergency was declared in Cyprus, and Ruth Ellis was hanged in Holloway prison.

I celebrated my twentieth birthday in grand style, gulpers from everyone followed by a vicious run ashore in Helston.

Before we realised it, Christmas 1955 arrived and with it, yet another leave.

Joe, Jock Forbes and myself did the usual rounds – we even renewed our old friendship with Monica and Jessie. Phil had joined *Eagle* and Reg was still onboard HMS *Newfoundland*.

One afternoon, we were sitting in the "King's Arms" having a quiet pint and a smoke.

'I suppose you're still determined to join the Paras?' said Jock, passing a cigarette to Joe.

'You bet,' answered Joe, before taking a long gulp of his Black and Tan 'Better than slogging around the fucking parade ground like you'll be doing.'

They were due to start their National Service the following June.

On New Year's Eve we had our usual drunken party.

A week later I returned to the base. Propped up on my locker was a large coloured postcard from my old mate, Jock McBride. He told me Desperate and Lofty were with him at the Royal Naval Hospital, Bighi in Malta. Scouse Wilson had been drafted to HMS *Cumberland,* and Simbo was in HMS *Tamar,* a shore base in Hong Kong.

At the bottom of the card he added a postscript. 'P.S. Svenska sends her regards.'

With the onset of winter once more, the runways became treacherous.

One cold morning in early January the chief sent for me.

'More typing errors,' I said to myself, walking into his office.

The chief sat behind his desk, grinning like a Cheshire Cat. 'Someone up there must like you, Tom lad,' he said, picking up a white piece of paper. 'You're going on draft.'

The news hit me like a tidal wave.

'Where to, chief?' I cried. 'Where to? Is it a ship?'

The chief gave a chuckle and glanced at the paper. 'You're being sent to HMS *Decoy,* a Daring class destroyer.'

I could have kissed him. Punching the air, I yelled, 'A destroyer! A bloody destroyer! Wait till I tell my Dad.'

The chief stood up. 'You report to HMS *Drake,* that's Devonport Barracks, on the 10th February.'

Before I had time to comment, a loud cheer came from behind me. The lads had gathered outside in the corridor to await my reaction. Even the two doctors were there. They clustered around and slapped me on the back.

'Don't be fooled, Tom.' said Bill. 'It will be no joke. Those Daring's are big ships. You'll have your work cut out.'

That evening we celebrated in the NAAFI. Much to our surprise Dr Phillips, defying naval regulations, brought a bottle of champagne.

'You'll can join HMS *Drake* direct from Easter leave,' said the chief, 'and be accommodated there until *Decoy* commissions on 21st February.'

The next afternoon, Bill called me into his dispensary. .

'Sit down, Tom,' he said. 'There's a few things you'll have to learn before you join your ship. And remember, those Darings carry Sick Berth PO's, so you'll be rated up acting local petty officer.'

During the next few weeks he taught the intricacies of sick bay administration. This included everything from running a store account, to ordering medicines, staining slides and compiling a Medical Officer's Journal. 'Running a sick bay on your own is not easy. No matter how good a medic you are, if your organisation is poor, you won't last five minutes.' He went on, 'And make sure you draw the most important item in the sick bay – an electric kettle.'

With great patience, he showed me how to use a microscope, stain and read slides. 'And remember, if a blood test comes back WR (Wasserman Reaction,) positive, the man might have syphilis, so you must do it three times.'

During one session, Bill stressed the importance of something called *Pratique,'.*

'What the hell is that?' I asked.

'It's a Bill of Health. So make sure you have everyone up to

199

date with vaccinations. Especially smallpox, or they might not allow the ship in port.'

Sometimes, the others would also pass on pearls of wisdom.

'Always record the date vaccinations, x-rays and jabs are due,' said Paddy. 'And *always* liaise with the Jimmy, who, if you don't carry a medical officer, will be your boss..'

'Why do they call the first lieutenant, 'The Jimmy'?' I asked Bill.

'Well', answered Bill, scratching his head. 'It all began during the reign of James I in 1603. He changed the name of the ships from Great, Middling and Small, to First Rate, Second Rate and so on. They became known as Jimmy's I Class ships. In time the name became known as Jimmy-the-One, or simply, Jimmy.'

By the end of the month, my head was spinning. .

Two days before leaving, Bill gave me his last lecture.

'You will be on your own. At least the captain can consult with his officers. The only thing you can consult with is your medical manual. The BR 88.'

What about shore to shore telephone?' I asked.

'Not much good if you are in the middle of the ocean,' replied Bill. 'Mind you, if you are in company with a ship carrying a doctor, it can be useful. But remember one thing. '

'What's that?'

'If you make a decision, stand by it. The most important thing is to gain the confidence of the ship's company. Even if it means becoming unpopular.'

Saying goodbye was never going to be easy.

I said my final farewells to the doctors, who shook my hand and thanked me. The PMO did the same, adding wryly. 'Luckily they don't have Wrens onboard ships, eh?'

The chief did not mince words. He never shook my hand. Instead he ruffled my hair, and said, 'You'll be all right, lad. At least you'll be able to type your love letters.'

The Cornish lads also shook my hand before they went on long weekend. Like Desperate and the others, they were decent men and I would miss them – especially Bill.

During the past twenty months, Bill's unconscious sense of humour and knowledge had been a source of inspiration to me. Throughout the time we served together, he never once raised his voice in anger. In harrowing situations he always kept a cool head, quietly giving orders and calming everyone down. He was a perfect example for any young medic - especially one about to go to sea for the first time.

As the train slowly left the station, I glanced forlornly at the rooftops of Helston. It was like saying goodbye to an old friend.

The journey to Liverpool was long and tedious. After crossing the Mersey, I caught a bus from Seacombe Ferry and walked up Rappart Road.

A few familiar faces waved hello.

Mr Finnigan, an elderly, grey-haired Irishman, stood outside number 12. 'Bloody-hell, Tom,' he said. 'You look like a real jolly-jack tar with that kitbag slung over your shoulder.'

'Aye,' said big Freddy Cross, a retired bin-man. 'All you need is a parrot and an eye patch.'

Grinning at them, I replied, 'You never know, next time I might have both.'

Mum and Dad were waiting in the house. Their eyes lit up when I entered the kitchen.

I dropped my kitbag, hugged Mum and shook Dad's hand..

'You mentioned in your letter something about going into Jago's Mansions,' said Dad.

I gave him a puzzled look. 'What?' I asked. 'I never mentioned anywhere called that.'

Dad's famous dimples appeared and he laughed. ''Jago's Mansions' is a nickname for the Royal Naval Barracks at Devonport.'

'Never heard of it, Dad. Where did the name come from?'

'Well, you see it was like this, son,' said Dad. 'Many years ago, a Warrant Cook named Jago started a new way of dishing out the grub. You know, lining up with the chefs serving you.' Dad paused as we reached the front door, 'It's now called mess catering. Anyway, the navy liked this so much they used it in all the other bases. And that's why RNB is called Jago's Mansions. Savy?'

As usual, Dad was a hive of information.

Of course, Alma wanted chocolate and Mum wiped a tear from her eye.

That evening we had a celebration in "The Brighton". As if by telepathy, Joe and Jock arrived.

'That hook on your arm looks smart, Bud,' said Joe, giving it a quick rub with his hand. 'What's this I hear about you getting a ship?'

Jock arrived with a tray of drinks. He had obviously overheard Joe. After passing a gin and tonic to Mum, he gave a sarcastic laugh, and said, 'Aye, it's called HMS *Neverbudge.*'

'You two will laugh with the other side of your faces when you start your National Service,' I replied.

'Well, lad,' came Dad's laconic reply, 'at least there's no war.'

'There were over a thousand men killed in Korea,' said Joe. 'I read it in the paper yesterday.'

'Just as well we missed it, then, isn't it?' I said. 'There's only that bugger Nasser, but he won't cause us any trouble.'

'Humf,' scoffed Mum, shrugging her shoulders. 'That's what they said about Hitler in 1938. And look what happened. '

Everyone laughed as Joe ordered another round.

Dad drained his glass and sighed. 'Ah…I wish I were going with you, son. The best years of my life…'

Mum quickly interrupted him. 'Aye, and I know why, Edward Lightburn,' she said, giving him a playful dig in the ribs. 'That nurse called Maria in Bari gave you a good time, I'll bet.'

After the invasion of Sicily, Dad fell over and hurt his back and was admitted to an Italian hospital in the port of Bari. After the war, Mum found a letter addressed to Dad from a nurse called Maria. Of course, Dad denied any hanky-panky, but Mum never let him forget it.

'Did she have a daughter, Dad?' I asked jokingly. 'I might end up in Bari one day.'

Mum gave him a suspicious, sideways glance. 'Och, I wouldn't be at all surprised.'

The days seemed to drag by. Each night I pictured a sleek warship with rakish bows and guns at the ready. Tossing and turning, I could almost hear the sound of the waves and feel the deck heaving. Sleep, when it came, only made me wish tomorrow would come quickly.

As usual the farewells were long and tearful.

'Take care of yourself, son,' said Dad, shaking my hand. 'And give my best to Jago's.'

'I'll do that, Dad,' I replied with a grin.

I gave Mum and Alma a final hug and a kiss, then quickly left.

Joe accompanied me to the station. Before the train pulled away, he gave me that familiar Tommy Steele grin. 'Look after yourself, Bud,' he said, shaking my hand. 'And don't get too sea-sick.'

After what seemed a never-ending journey I arrived in Plymouth. Several sailors waited on the concourse outside North Road Station. Amongst them were two mateloes whose cap tallies told me they were from HMS *Decoy*.

One was tall, with a beard; the other small and fat with a heavy growth of stubble.

I picked up my gear and walked over to them.

'Hello, there.' I said, 'I see you're both from the *Decoy*. Are you waiting for transport?'

'That's right, me lucky lad,' replied the smaller of the two, in a strong Irish accent. 'And where might you be going?' Both wore the insignia of gunnery ratings and a row of medals from the Second World War.

'RNB,' I answered. 'I'm joining your ship. I hear she's in dry dock.'

The Irishman's pal was an able seaman, with a large belly and a ginger beard. 'Bugger me, Paddy,' he said to his friend. 'This feller's our new poultice-walloper.' Glancing at my solitary gold hook, he added. 'And a mickey-mouse killick, at that.'

The term, 'mickey-mouse,' was a colloquial expression denoting a non-commissioned officer without a good conduct badge. A badge, or stripe, as they were sometimes called, was awarded after four years man's time. You could only wear three, irrespective of how long you had served. Chief petty officers were different. They wore three brass buttons on their sleeves in place of badges.

As I had only been in the navy a little over two years I did not have any badges.

We laughed and introduced ourselves.

'I'm Shamus Alexander,' said the small Irishman. 'Paddy to you, from dear old Derry, so I am. And this big streak of Welsh rarebit, is Taff Leighton.'

'And the ship is alongside in No 4 wharf,' said Paddy, shaking hands. 'She's doesn't commission for another month. Taff and I are part of the advance party.'

'When can I see her?' I asked eagerly.

Paddy threw back his head, displaying a row of even white teeth. He gave Taff a nudge with his elbow. 'Be Jesus, he's keen, isn't he, Taff?' then added, 'Don't worry, Doc. You'll be victualled in RNB. A coach takes us to the ship every day. You can go to the wharf to-morrow, when you've finished your joining routine.'

'Where do you draw your tot?'

Taff broke into a fit of laughter. 'Bloody-hell, Paddy,' he cried. 'Not another alki Doc.'

With a puzzled look, I asked, 'What do you mean, Taff?'

Paddy answered for him. 'He means you're not another drunkard, like the other sawbones we had.'

I shook my head and frowned. 'I don't get you.'

'The other one was never sober,' replied Taff. 'The lads were afraid to go near him. Especially after tot time.'

'What happened to him?' I asked.

A lorry arrived. Taff and Paddy threw their cases in the back.

Taff removed his cap to reveal a balding head. 'Oh,' he said wiping his brow with the back of his hand. 'He was kicked off the ship. Lost his rate, too.'

I could almost hear Bill Manley's voice in my ear saying, 'Let that be a lesson to you, old man.'

The journey from the station to the Royal Naval Barracks didn't take long. Turning right at the end of St Levan's Road we passed a large, mock Tudor pub called "The Avondale".

'You'll get the best bitter in Guzz there,' said Paddy. 'Only a bob a pint, as well.'

The road became slightly winding and steep. Away to our left stretched a continual row of black, steel railings, tipped with gold-painted spikes. Lining the other side were rows of terraced houses. Almost opposite the main gate was another pub aptly named the "Royal Naval Arms".

From inside the barracks, a white ensign fluttered from a tall, masthead and a large, gold painted sign proclaimed we were now entering HMS *Drake*.

The lorry stopped outside the guardroom. Paddy looked at the duty PO. 'He's ship's company. HMS *Decoy*,' said Paddy. 'We'll take him with us to D Block. '

The time was a little after five o' clock.

'Any chance of our tot, Taff?' I asked.

He shook his head, and laughed. 'He's at it again, Paddy,' he said, glancing at his oppo.

With a look of disgust, Taff nodded his head. 'No chance. Miss-musters was at 1630.'

As we drove away I glanced up and saw a model of a galleon on top of a magnificent clock tower. Underneath the galleon was hung a flag with a Red Cross and dot, on a white background.

Paddy saw me looking at it. 'That's the Admiral's flag,' he said. 'It's always there when he is in barracks,' then added. 'I bet the bugger hasn't missed his gin and tonic.'

The lorry passed a line of wooden buildings.

'That's the regulating offices,' said Paddy. 'You'll have to report there to the Josman to-morrow. I'll show you the routine to-morrow.'

'Why is he called the 'Josman'?'

'You don't arf ask awkward questions,' said Taff. 'He's called that because he used to carry a military-style swaggerstick. Ain't that right, Paddy?'

'Aye, it is,' replied Paddy. 'And we also call him 'the Jaunty.' And don't ask me why. All right?'

They helped me carry my gear up two flights of stone stairs into a gloomy-looking barrack-room. On either side stood rows of two-tier iron bunks and lockers. Four electric lights with white shades hung from the ceiling. Three curtain-less windows allowed shafts of evening light in.

The place reeked of stale sweat and tobacco. Several sailors, some still in their number eights, others in vest and bellbottoms, sat at a long table, laughing and talking. A few lounged on their bunks smoking and reading.

As we entered the room, we were greeted with several ribald comments, ranging from, 'Had a good leave, lads?' to 'Watch your arses in the showers, here comes the sheep shagger,' and the proverbial, 'Did you get a bit?'

To which Taff gave the curt reply, 'Aye – a bit older.'

'This here is our new pill-pusher,' announced Paddy, placing his hand on my shoulder. 'So you buggers watch your step. Else he'll stick a needle up your arse.'

'As long as that's all he sticks up my jacksee,' laughed a sailor, sitting in his underpants. 'I've heard a lot about these sick bay tiffies.'

I was no longer a green horn from Victoria Barracks. All eyes followed me as I walked up to where he was sitting. Suddenly there was tension in the air.

'And just what exactly have you heard, pal?' I asked, staring down at him.

At once his dark features broke into a grin. When he stood up I found myself looking up at a six foot matelot. He threw back his head and let out a loud laugh.

'Only joking, Doc,' he said, holding out his hand. 'Only joking, and me name's Pincher Martin.'

The tension immediately disappeared.

I looked around at the unfamiliar faces. These, I said to myself, are the kind of men I'll be seeing during the next few years. These were men, similar to Dad when he was young, men who shared the dangers of the sea, sweaty mess-decks, fights ashore and the odd girl or two.

I looked around and immediately felt at home.

'Where's your mick?' asked a matelot with thick red hair and a Yorkshire accent.

I gave him a blank stare, and replied, 'What's that?'

'Your *hammock*,' he said. 'Where's your hammock?'

'I haven't got one,' I answered.

Paddy, sensing my ignorance, quickly intervened.' Jesus, Mary and Joseph, Yorky,' he said. 'They don't have hammocks in hospital. He'll have to draw one from slops.'

'Slops' was a term used for the clothing store and the store assistants who worked there were colloquially called, 'jack dusties.'

I was still confused. 'Will I have to sleep in a hammock onboard, Paddy?'

'Not unless the sick bay is full,' he replied, passing me a cigarette. 'Then you'll have to sling your mick outside in the passageway.'

'I… I've never even used one,' was my hesitant reply.

Paddy and a few others shook their heads. 'Don't worry, Doc,' he said 'We'll soon sort you out, won't we Taff?'

Taff grinned and nodded. 'I takes it, this is your first ship, then?' he said, struggling out of his blue serge jersey.

I gave a quick nod. 'Yes,' I replied, 'I've been stationed at Culdrose for the last eighteen months.'

'You'll find this lot,' said Paddy, nodding around, 'a lot different to the 'waffoos.'

'Yes, you will, ducky,' joked a matelot mincing towards the exit. 'They're different to us.'

I shook my head, grinned and stowed my gear.

The next day I did my joining routine.

The sick bay was my first port of call. Bill had told me to always make my mark with the senior medical officer. After reporting to the chief, I met Brian McCormack, an LSBA who played for the soccer team in Stonehouse.

'I suppose you heard about your townee, Scouse Wilson?' he said, over a cup of coffee.

I shook my head and frowned. 'No, Mac, I haven't.' I replied. 'You forget. I've been in the wilds of Cornwall for nearly two years.'

Mac's handsome features clouded. 'I'm sorry to tell you, he drowned in Malta.'

I nearly dropped my cup.

'You what!' I cried. 'Drowned! How the hell did that happen?'

Colin took a sip of coffee. 'Apparently, HMS *Cumberland* was tied to a buoy in Grand Harbour. Scouse got pissed and tried to swim back from the quayside.'

I sat back in my chair remembering those journeys up the line, his sense of humour and undying support for Everton.

'Bloody hell,' I sighed. 'Poor Scouse,' was all I could say.

The naval barracks were built on a hill, with roads sloping gently down towards the dockyard. Several large grey-stoned buildings lined each road. These were the main administrative and official centres. From here I could see a forest of masts, grey funnels, and cranes. In the distance, across the river Tamar, stretched the undulating hills of Cornwall.

I met Yorky and another rating, dressed like myself in fore and aft rig.

Pointing to a large, shed-like area away to our left, he said, 'That's where we draw our tot at twelve o'clock.' Yorky was on his way to the barbers and left us.

Yorky's pal introduced himself. 'I'm Pete Lamb,' he said. 'Yorky tells me you are our new doc. I'm one of the 'scribes', onboard.'

A 'scribe', was a nickname for a ship's writer.

'Pleased to meet you, Pete,' I said, shaking his hand.

Pete was taller than me, with a pale complexion, deep set brown eyes and a ready grin.

'I'll be picking up my first badge soon.' He glanced at my left arm. 'You as well, I see.'

He was part of the advance party and had been onboard for three weeks. I asked him what the sick bay was like.

'It's a fair size,' he said, as we approached the dockyard railings. 'Situated in the after deckhouse. No bathroom, though. Anyone turned in has to use the officer's heads nearby.'

'What's the captain like?'

Pete gave a throaty chuckle. 'Captain Peter Hill-Norton,' he replied, 'is a real smoothy. He is a gunnery specialist. During the war he served in the Russian and Atlantic convoys in HMS *Cumberland,* His last job was naval attache in Buenos Aires, but don't let his charm fool you. He's as tough as nails.'

'And the first lieutenant? '

'The Jimmy's a real stickler,' replied Pete. 'Lieutenant-Commander John McArdle. He's very strict, so watch your step.'

We carried on past a small Victorian church.

'That's St Nicholas's church,' said Pete.

'We've got one named the same in Liverpool,' I replied. 'It's down by the Pier Head.'

Pete laughed. 'I'm not surprised,' he said. 'Every port probably has one. St Nicholas is the patron saint of sailors.'

We arrived at a tall fence surrounding the dockyard.

From here I saw a huge aircraft carrier, with its characteristic flat top, wide funnel and island.

'Wow, I cried. 'She's a beaut. What's her name?

'That's the mighty *Eagle,*' replied Pete, laughing at my reaction. 'She'll be commissioning soon.'

I immediately thought of Phil, and strained my eyes to see if he were among the crowds on the quayside.

At twelve o'clock I joined fifty or so of the advance party for rum issue. The duty officer, Master-at-Arms and duty PO, stood around a fat, oak barrel. Around the barrel, emblazoned in brass, were the words, 'The Queen, God Bless Her.'

After producing my station card, I was handed my tot. Sippers or gulpers were against the law, so under the close scrutiny of the three officials, I downed my rum in one go.

The rum had a sedative effect and after dinner I crashed out. Shortly after one o'clock, Paddy's voice woke me up.

'Come on, Doc,' I heard him say. 'You wanted to see the ship, didn't you? We muster in ten minutes.'

I grabbed my hat and boarded a waiting coach. My heart beat like thunder as we approached the ship. Like someone in a trance, I gazed outside the window. Suddenly there she was, a formidable mass of grey steel, my home for the foreseeable future.

Shielding my eyes from the glare of the sun, I left the coach and gazed at her superstructure.

Part of the hull was mottled with patches of red lead. Scattered around her steel deck was an accumulation of wires, pipes and empty paint drums. The grating noise of riveting echoed around the wharf, while from various areas, sparks from welders flew into the air like Roman candles. There were dockyard maties everywhere; some carrying gear, others simply standing around talking.

The acrid smell of smoke and fuel-oil stung my nostrils as my eyes swept along the length of the ship.

Two sets of pugnacious-looking gun turrets, each with twin barrels, lay menacingly below an open bridge. Her long fo'c'sle swept graciously upwards, ending in knife-edged bows. On either side of the bridge was a round, bulbous structure, resembling the eyes of a giant insect. I later learned they were part of the gunnery radar system. Close by was an all-round area with lookout bays and lockers where the signalmen kept their flags.

Directly astern of these, stood a tall steel, lattice mast. From here, half hidden amongst the structure, protruded a curved section of black cowling, looking like some type of secret weapon.

Mounted either side of the superstructure, just below the bridge, were twin bofors. These were secondary armament 40mm guns.

My eyes came to rest on the after deckhouse.

Suddenly, I gave a start.

Directly above rested another twin gun turret. My God! I thought, when they go off I bet they'll rattle more than a few medicine bottles.

Something else held my attention.

A set of five enormous torpedo tubes occupied the space for'd of the after deckhouse. Clearly, my newfound home was a veritable floating armoury.

'Where's the funnel?' I said, scanning the upper deck.

Taff heard me and laughed. 'That's one of them,' he said, pointing to a curved cowling inside the lattice mast. 'And there's the other,' he added, nodding towards a stovepipe structure situated amidships.

'Strange looking thing, ain't it?' said Taff. 'Especially with those whip ariels waving in the breeze on each side.'

Taff was right. The ship did look strange. This was not the rakish destroyer of my imagination, but some futuristic-looking craft straight out of a boy's own magazine.

Glancing about as we went onboard, I said, 'It looks in a right old mess.'

'Don't let the Jimmy hear you say that,' interrupted Paddy, 'this ship is his pride and joy, so it is. The captain is away at present, so he's the gaffer.'

When we reached the top of the gangway, Paddy saluted the quarterdeck and I did the same. Out of the corner of his mouth, he muttered. 'Here's the Jimmy, now, so watch your step.'

A tall, dark-haired officer stood talking to a corpulent man in a blue, pinstriped suit. Suddenly, Blue Suit became flustered and his face turned crimson. He nervously removed a white handkerchief and mopped his brow.

A lull in the noise allowed us to hear what they were saying.

The first lieutenant's eyes narrowed as he spoke. 'The generator work better be completed soon,' I heard him say, 'or I'll report the matter to the Director of Works. Do I make myself clear?'

Blue Suit Mumbled something, turned around and scurried down the gangway.

Paddy was right. My new boss was not a man to be trifled with.

Stepping gingerly over a coil of wire, I approached him. As I did so, he was joined by a tired-looking chief petty officer, with grey hair and a weather-beaten face.

'Bloody dockyard, chief,' snapped the first lieutenant. 'Work is lagging behind. At this rate, we'll never be ready for commissioning.'

'Yes, sir,' replied the chief in a lazy West Country drawl. 'It's always the same, sir. It'll sort itself out. '

The chief saluted and walked towards the fo'c'sle.

As I approached the first lieutenant, he slowly eyed me up and down.

'Who are you?' he snapped.

'LSBA Lightburn, reporting, sir,' I said, saluting.

'Hmmm...been to sea before?

'No, sir,' I said.

'I see' he replied. He pursed his lips and added, 'You'll have your work cut out here. Keep me fully informed on how long anyone will be away from duty. Understood?'

I saluted again, and in true nautical fashion, replied, 'Aye, aye, sir.'

He then turned and walked in the same direction as the chief.

The massive frame of Yorky appeared next to me. 'What did I tell you – he's made of teak, is that one,' he said. 'Oh, and by the way, the Officer of the Day has the sick bay keys. That's him there,' Yorky pointed to a young, fair-haired sub-lieutenant

After saluting, I introduced myself. He glanced at a seaman standing close by.

'Give the LSBA the sick bay keys from the notice board, QM,' he said. Then looking at me, added, 'Return them when you go back to barracks.'

Avoiding a mass of wires and ropes, we made our way past the torpedo tubes and entered the after deckhouse.

'Have to shove off, now, Doc,' said Yorky. 'See you later.'

The sick bay was on the port side. The sliding door was open and inside two dockyard maties were kneeling down, installing a new refrigerator. One had sparse, grey hair, the other, a younger man, was dark and swarthy. Both wore dirt-stained overalls. They looked up as I entered.

'You'll need this, my handsome,' said the eldest, 'to keep your beer in when you're in the meddy.'

The air smelt stagnant and dusty.

Looking around, I grinned. 'Yes,' I said, 'I suppose you're right.'

Two metal-framed cots, attached to stanchions, rested in one corner. Opposite these, on top of a set of cupboards was a bunk with detachable wooden sides. A green curtain separated this section from the consultancy area. Here, a desk, complete with brass lamp rested against the bulkhead. Much to my surprise the side drawers were full of forms, pads of stationary and a copy of last commission's store account.

A glance at the deck-head showed a mass of pipes and electric wiring. On the bulkhead were two brass portholes firmly secured. However, I was surprised to see the brown linoleum on the deck was clean and unstained.

Next to a stainless steel wash basin was a filing cabinet, a metal surgical dressing table and a steriliser. In the for'd bulkhead was a small store, containing various medical items, including a heavy canvas first aid bag.

There was also a large, oak medical chest, complete with bottles and tins, containing various lotions and powders.

The grey-haired man slowly stood up and flexed his shoulders. 'They must have been left over from the last commission,' he said. 'You won't be able to do much in here, though,' he said. 'We're going to re-wire the place.'

'Aye,' chimed in his mate, who also stood up. 'And the paint boys are giving the place a new coat or two. Pale green and cream, I think they said.'

'Bloody-hell,' I said. 'How long will that take?'

They looked at one another.

The eldest one shrugged his shoulders. 'Depends on when the gear arrives, don't it, Harry?'

Harry grinned and nodded. 'Well,' he said, 'at least you've got a new 'fridge.' After which they packed their tools and left.

Paddy Alexander poked his head in. 'Typical dockyard maties,' he growled. 'You never know where you are with them.. Have you heard the poem about them?'

'No,' I replied. 'I didn't know there was one.'

'Well, it goes like this.'

He immediately struck a pose, and in typical Irish fashion, began:

Dockyard-maties children, sitting on the dockyard wall,
Just like their fathers, doin' fuck all.
When they get older, they'll be dockyard maties, too,
Just like their fathers, with fuck all to do!

The poem seemed to fit the occasion perfectly.

With mounting excitement, my eyes wandered around. Paddy sensed my mood.

'Well,' he said. 'You've got more room than the captain. What do you think?'

With a grin as wide as the Mersey Tunnel, I exclaimed, 'Fantastic! Bloody fantastic!'

And it really was. Gazing around, I felt so proud. This was my dream. My own sick bay at last. The thought of being medically responsible for nearly three hundred men was momentarily lost on me.

Once again, Paddy seemed to read my mind. 'In a way you've got just as much on yer shoulders as the captain,' he said, putting his cap back on.

'How do you mean?' I asked.

'To be sure now,' he said, 'you're on your own. If there is an emergency, only you can make a decision.' Paddy paused and looked around, then added, 'At least the captain has the Jimmy or the others to ask.'

'I suppose so,' I replied, 'but that's what we're trained for.'

Paddy ran his fingers through the dust on the desk. 'If you see the buffer,' said Paddy, 'he'll detail a hand to help you clean the place when you move in.'

The 'Buffer,' was the chief bosun's mate, so called because he acted as a communicator between the lower deck and the first lieutenant.

All at once, Sub-Lieutenant Forbes appeared in the doorway. His face was flushed and he was sweating.

'Come quickly, LSBA,' he yelled. 'Number One's had an accident.'

After glancing at Paddy, I grabbed the first aid bag.

We quickly made our way along the port side of the deck. At the bottom of a steel ladder lay the first lieutenant surrounded by several sailors.

'Gangway, there, let the LSBA through,' ordered the young subby.

The officer, his face contorted with pain, was clutching his left leg.

A rating tried to hand him his cap, but was ignored.

'Well!' snapped the Jimmy, 'Don't just stand there. Damn well help me up.'

Two ratings took his armpits and were about to lift him.

'Stop,' I cried. 'Don't move him. Leave him alone.'

I knelt down beside the officer. 'What happened, sir?' I asked.

'What the devil d'you mean?' he growled, his face visibly paling with shock. 'I tripped over a coil of wire. That's what bloodywell happened. It's my left foot.'

A quick glance showed acute swelling around the ankle.

'Call the barracks,' I said, glancing up at the Officer of the Day. 'Tell them what's happened and to send an ambulance and a doctor,' I added, 'and someone fetch something to cover the first lieutenant.'

A rating produced a greatcoat and did so, another placed a rolled up Burberry under his head.

My new boss was starting to sweat and had turned pale. 'Rubbish,' he gasped. 'Stop fussing. Just get me to my feet. And take my shoe off.'

'No sir,' I replied, pulling his trouser leg down. 'Your shoe is acting as a splint. Best to leave it on.'

He slumped back. After loosening his tie and undoing his jacket, he lay quiet.

A dockyard matie offered the injured officer a drink of tea from his flask. It was a kindly gesture and the man meant well.

'No,' I said, holding up my hand. 'If there are any bones broken, he may need an anaesthetic.'

My words started the injured man. 'What on earth do you mean, broken?' he moaned. Then went on, 'I'll be perfectly all right in the morning...' His voice trailed away as shock increased.

Remembering my first aid, I carefully raised his legs on a pile of old rags. It seemed to work, because after a while, some colour returned to his face.

The officer's blue eyes darkened. 'Just do as I say and get me up. I'll drive myself to my cabin in barracks.'

I remembered Bill Manley's words about imposing my authority. This, I felt, was my first test. But I had to be careful. After all, next to the captain, this officer was the most powerful on board.

'You'll do no such thing, sir,' I replied in a quiet voice. 'Just lie still until the medical officer arrives.'

'Hmmm...' he grunted, slumping back into his makeshift pillow. 'I'll speak to you later.'

The doctor arrived, and after a quick examination ordered a stretcher to be brought.

'I'm afraid you'll need an x-ray, sir,' said the doctor. 'We'll have to take you to Stonehouse.'

'The naval hospital,' roared the injured officer. 'I have a ship to get ready for sea. For God's sake man. Can't you just strap it up?'

The doctor smiled. 'Sorry, sir.'

The injured officer looked up at Sub Lieutenant Forbes.

'Inform the captain, Sub,' said the injured officer, as he was carried off the ship. 'I'll be back in no time.'

As the first lieutenant was carried ashore, Paddy tuned to me and, with a glint in his eye, said, 'Well done, Doc, that'll keep him out of our hair for a while.'

The next day I visited him in the officer's ward.

He was sitting up in bed, reading a copy of *The Times*. Over his lower left leg was a cradle, protecting a damp plaster caste.

His dark hair was neatly combed and he wore a set of yellow, silk pyjamas.

As I entered, he put down his newspaper. 'And what do you want?' he said, glaring at me.

'Oh, just to tell you that you'll be in for about a week, sir,' I replied, trying my best not to smile. 'You've torn the ligaments in your ankle.'

'Rubbish,' he grunted. 'Who told you that?'

'The ward MO,' I said. 'After all, sir, you did order me to keep you informed of *all* injuries and how long anyone would be off duty.'

A week later he returned to the ship.

The next day, while filing medical documents, the shrill sound of the bosun's pipes heralded the arrival of the captain. Shortly afterwards, the duty petty officer, a redheaded Irishman called O'Connor, came into the sick bay.

'The skipper himself wants to see you, Doc,' he said with a humorous glint in his eye. 'He's in his cabin, so chop, chop.'

My first reaction was one of panic.

Oh, my God, I thought. What have I done, now?

The captain's cabin was on the starboard side under the bridge. I hurried along the 'Burma Way,' - in small ships this was the nickname for the main passageway- up a ladder onto the wardroom flat.

With a feeling of apprehension, I knocked on the door.

'Come,' came a sharp, well-modulated voice.

I took a deep breath and went inside.

The cabin smelt strongly of mansion polish and cigar smoke.

The captain was removing an official-looking folder from a shelf. He was deeply tanned, broad shouldered with well-groomed, dark brown hair. His firm jaw and aquiline nose gave him a handsome appearance. On the left breast of his well-tailored uniform were two rows of campaign ribbons from the Second World War.

Pete was right. He certainly was a 'smoothy.'

A framed photograph of a woman and a child rested on a desk cluttered with papers. In one corner, several buff-coloured folders lay in a neat pile. On a bulkhead were shelves of official-looking books and documents. Above the desk was a framed photograph of the queen.

Two chairs rested on a plain, green carpet and hanging behind the door was the captain's overcoat and cap.

'Ah, Lightburn, isn't it?' he said, feeling his jaw.

'Yes, sir,' I replied.

'I'm afraid I've lost a filling,' he said, 'and have a very important meeting. Haven't time to go to the dentist. Can you let me have a few codeines, or something?'

Among the spare stores I remembered seeing a tin of zinc oxide and a small bottle of oil of cloves.

'May I take a look, sir,' I asked.

He opened his mouth, and pointed. 'In there,' he garbled. 'Bottom at the back.'

Sure enough, he had a small cavity in one of his molars.

'I can put a temporary filling there, sir,' I said. 'It should get you through until morning.'

The captain raised his eyebrows in surprise. 'Really?' he said. 'Then, let's get it done.'

In the sick bay I found a small glass plate in a cupboard. Using a wooden spatula, I hurriedly prepared the mixture. I also discovered a small pair of metal forceps in the medical bag.

Using the forceps, I was able to place a small amount of filling in the socket. 'You'll have a sharp, tangy taste in your mouth for a while, sir,' I warned. 'Leave it for an hour until it solidifies.'

'Hmm,' said the captain, pulling a face. 'You're right about the taste. Thank you. I hope it works.'

So do I, I thought, If it doesn't, you can blame a certain blonde, dental Wren.

While the ship was undergoing its re-fit, I was given a small office in the barracks sick bay. If any of the fifty or so advance party needed medical help, they had to report to me.

My immediate task was to order medical stores. These were listed as Scale Number 4 in my sick berth manual, for ships not carrying a medical officer.

Following the procedure laid down in regulations, I submitted Forms S549 for medical stores to be delivered by February 21st, the date of commissioning.

'I hope this includes plenty of crepe bandages for sprained ankles,' muttered the Jimmy, as he signed the form. We were in his cabin. 'I'll make sure this is sent.'

'Yes, sir,' I replied, and left.

Our squadron consisted of HM ships, *Duchess, Diamond,* and *Diana.* The squadron medical officer was carried in *Duchess,* whose home base was Portsmouth. We were due to meet *Diamond* after our work-up at Portland, before sailing to Gibraltar. Here we would sail in company with the others to Malta.

But before then there was a lot to be done.

Much to my surprise, the electricians soon finished wiring the sick bay.

'We've even given you new neon lights and fixed the air conditioning,' said the grey haired one.

'And your 'phone's working,' added his mate.

With a feeling of sheer excitement, I set about cleaning up.

Remembering Yorky's advice, I decided to go and see the buffer. I found him in a small store, sitting on a box reading the *Daily Sketch.* His name was Bill Conyon, and on his well-worn uniform were medal ribbons from both world wars.

''Ello, Doc, my 'andsome,' he said. 'And what can I do for you?'

'Any chance of some cleaning gear, chief,' I replied, 'and maybe a hand to help me in the sick bay?'

'No problem,' he gave a cough and removed his cigarette. 'Geordie,' he yelled.

A gangly junior seaman, with a shock of brown hair, appeared.

'Go with the Doc, here,' said the chief. 'Collect what he needs from the store and give him a hand.' The chief then gave me a crafty wink. 'It'll cost you a pint in the "Naval Arms" later.'

Geordie and I polished and scrubbed until the sick bay gleamed.

'You've earned yourself sippers, Geordie,' I said, wiping my hands. 'When we move onboard, you can come round.'

His young face brightened up. 'Cheers, Doc,' he said. 'But don't tell the jaunty. I'm under age and can't draw my tot until I'm eighteen.'

Anyone under the age of eighteen was designated as being 'UA.' Those who were temperate or 'T' received an extra 3d a day.

One morning an elderly seaman petty officer came into the sick bay. He introduced himself as Bill Mitchell.

'Mitch' was small, with sparse grey hair and a face like Popeye.

'Aye, aye, matey,' were his first words. 'How's the blood-suckin' business, then?'

He had humorous, blue eyes and spoke with a high-pitched, Irish accent.

'Picking up, thanks,' I replied with a grin. 'What can I do for you?'

'It's me teeth,' he answered, flashing a set of pink gums. 'I've lost me teeth.'

'How did you manage that?' I asked, trying not to laugh.

'On the piss last night,' he answered. 'Lost 'em in the Long Bar heads. Spewed me ring up, so I did.'

At which point we both burst out laughing.

A week later, after consultation with the dentist in barracks, he was fitted with a new set of false teeth.

However, this would not be the last I would hear about Mitch's false teeth.

As soon as possible I ordered all medical forms and stationery. This included an old Imperial typewriter, similar to the one at Culdrose, plus a large alphabetical index book.

I then crosschecked each man's pay book with his medical documents. This gave me a clear picture of who needed chest x-rays, injections and PULHEEMS. This last item was an abbreviation for the various parts of the body to be assessed when they had their annual medical examination. When I had finished making note of these details, my fingers were numb and my wrist aching.

Gradually, as the commissioning date loomed closer, the daily journey from barracks became monotonous. I could hardly wait to feel the sway of the deck under my feet. Like the rest of the crew, I was eager to get to sea.

14

With the commissioning date a week away, the medical stores had not arrived.

I decided to go to the hospital and see the chief pharmacist.

A feeling of nostalgia crept over me as we drove through the gates of Stonehouse. So much had happened to me since those hectic days on A1. The clock tower of Trafalgar stood out against the grey sky and the trees lining the pathways were bare. It was like coming home.

The chief pharmacist was a tall, dour Scott with white hair and large spectacles.

'Request for medical stores for *Decoy*,' he said, flicking through a small stack of forms. 'I've no received any such request. When was it sent?'

'Almost two weeks ago,' I replied.

'Well it's no here, I tell yer.'

'My first lieutenant personally sent the demand and letter to you,' I cried.

'Don't shout at me, laddie, It's no here.'

Suddenly I was filled with despair.

'We...we commission in six days,' I stuttered

'Well, you'd best be hurrying up, then,' he answered, shuffling the papers into a neat pile, 'or you'll be in trouble.'

As we drove back to the ship my heart was in my mouth.

The Jimmy was standing at the top of the gangway. He carried a telescope under one arm and was talking to the buffer.

'Make sure the fo'c'sle is properly squared off, buffer,' he barked.

The chief bosun's grumbled under his breath, saluted and walked away.

The first lieutenant turned and saw me. 'Well,' he said, raising his eyebrows. 'What do you want?'

My mouth felt dry and I badly needed a piss. 'It's about the medical stores, sir,'

'Yes, yes,' he replied angrily. 'What about them?'

'Er... the chief pharmacist in RNH hasn't received the request I gave you.'

'Nonsense,' he snapped.' I sent the ...' His voice trailed away and he stared at me. He frowned, then in an uncertain voice, added, 'them the same day you gave it to me.'

With a sigh, I replied, 'Well, sir, it hasn't reached the hospital.'

The officer gave cough. 'Yes. Well. Leave this to me. I'll...er, sort it out.'

Two days passed and still the stores had not arrived.

A telephone call to the hospital proved futile. The chief pharmacist was not available.

Thankfully, I had enough basic medicines to cope with emergencies. However, these would be insufficient to deal with the 286 officers and men.

Meanwhile, there was still much to be done.

I decided to check the first aid boxes and, at the same time, explore the vessel.

I started with the after galley. This was conveniently placed opposite the sick bay. Inside, two cooks were busy cleaning and scrubbing various utensils.

'Hello, Doc,' said one of them, 'I see you are in the same mess as us.'

Even though the sick bay was my place of duty, I would draw my tot and eat with the cooks, stewards and writers in the Supply and Secretariat mess.

'That's right,' I replied with a grin. 'They've put all the drunkards together.'

A chief petty officer cook grinned at me. His oversize girth preceded him as he shook my hand. 'I'm Joe Jackson,' he said. 'If you're on the scrounge, no victuals have come onboard yet. When they do, you can have whatever you want.'

'Thanks, chief,' I replied. 'Just checking the first aid boxes.'

It was empty.

Leading down from the after passageway was the seaman's messdecks. These housed some twenty ratings and were small and cramped with a narrow, wooden table and benches. Several ratings were busy stowing kit in their lockers.

'Watch out,' cried a tall, pale-faced seaman named Roy Cragg. 'Here comes Daktari, after some victims.'

'Relax, you miserable buggers,' I said. 'I'm just giving the place the once over.'

'It's a pity we haven't got a few Wrens onboard,' said a rating with red hair and freckles. 'You could have got your leg over.'

Up top, the passageway opened up onto a wide quarterdeck. In the middle was a set of 'squidds,' the latest type of depth charges. Hanging over the stern was a metal gash-shute, used for tipping rubbish into the sea.

Under the sharp eye of a petty officer, several ratings were scrubbing the steel deck with long handled brooms.

'Hello, there, Doc,' said the PO with a cheerful grin. 'I'm Jan Hawse. Settling in all right, then?'

'Fine thanks, PO,' I replied, shaking his hand. 'Nice to meet you. I see you lot are busy.'

'Busy,' cried one of the ratings, resting on his broom handle and nodding towards the petty officer. 'He's worse than bloody Captain Bligh.'

The PO laughed, and with a friendly growl, replied in a rich Cornish accent, 'Come on you lazy slobs, put yer backs into it or it'll be the lash for all of you.'

Up for'd housed the main artery of the ship, the operations room. Nearby, was the wardroom and senior officers' cabins.

The pay office, main galley, coxswain's office and NAAFI were situated off the Burma Way. Just for'd of this, ladders led down to various mess decks including my own.

The engine room was a world of gleaming gauges, pipes and generators.

Several ratings in overalls greeted me with a mixture of surprise and laughter.

'Watch you don't get lost, Doc,' chirped one of them. 'The last sick bay tiffy to come down here disappeared and hasn't been seen since.'

I gave them a cheerful grin, inspected the first aid box, which, like the others was empty, and left.

My reception, when I reached one of the main boiler rooms, was similar. Gazing at the huge metal monsters that powered the ship took my breath away. And the heat, even though the machines were closed down, was intense. Hell, I thought, standing on a metal plate, the temperature in here must be unbearable when everything is working.

'Come on down,' cried the chief stoker, a burly, man with a black, piratical beard. 'If you've got a few minutes to spare, you can help us do a bit of polishing.'

'No thanks, chief,' I replied with a grin.

Once more, I found the first aid box empty.

After climbing up a ladder, I arrived on the wardroom flat.

I knocked and opened the door.

Inside was the senior engineer, Commander Bishop, a tall, broad-shouldered, ex-rugby player. The other, much smaller with a pale complexion, was the 'pay-bob', Lieutenant Commander Weston. They were sitting at the table drinking tea.

'All right to check the medical drawer, sir?' I asked.

'By all means, young man,' said the Commander in a gruff voice. 'After all, this will be the emergency operating room if needs be.'

'It will indeed,' added an elderly torpedo officer, Sub-Lieutenant Handley, who came in and joined the others. 'I hope you've sharpened all your scalpels, and have plenty of medicinal brandy.'

'On the sick mess account, of course,' chimed in the pay officer.

He was referring to the chits in a small book that all victuals for the sick bay were recorded. As a result, coffee was available to the sick - especially after a hectic run ashore.

The drawer under a couch, which should have contained an array of medical stores, was empty.

Attached to the deck-head, above a long table, was a round wooden frame. This was where a ring of electric bulbs could be fitted should an operation be required.

The chairs and surrounding furniture were covered in a green, chintzy material that matched the light brown woodwork. On the bulkheads were four, gleaming brass portholes and pictures of naval battles. At the end, above the bar hung a large, coloured photograph of the Queen.

My next port of call was the coxswain's office. This was situated on the port side of the Burma Way. The coxswain's name was Jack Smith. He was a medium-sized man with a swarthy complexion and dark, brown eyes whose steady gaze could stop you in your tracks. His uniform was always immaculate, as befitting the person responsible for discipline. Around his neck was a chain to which was attached a whistle. This disappeared into his top pocket above which were two rows of medal ribbons.

'Come in, and sit down,' said the coxswain. 'I was meaning to have a word with you.'

He wanted me to circulate a daily sick book. 'Include anybody in hospital or turned in the sick bay and keep that kettle on the boil. I likes a cuppa while doing me rounds each day.'

Finally, I arrived on the bridge.

This open structure gave an excellent all round view.

Directly below on the fo'c'sle were two grey gun turrets, their deadly twin barrels trained in front. Further for'd, two rows of anchor chains attached to two capstans. On the peak of the bow, supported on either side by metal stanchions was a flag staff which would fly the white ensign when we commissioned.

The captain was sitting in his chair talking to his Number One. He turned and looked at me.

'And what brings you here, LSBA?' he asked.

I stood to attention and saluted.

'Just finding my feet, sir,' I replied. 'And checking the first aid boxes.'

The captain glanced around. 'Where is the first aid box, Number One?' he said

'On the bulkhead behind you, sir,' answered the first lieutenant, with a satisfied smile.

'Ah, yes, so it is,' said the captain. 'By the way, that filling you put in worked a treat. The dental officer in barracks was quite impressed. Well done.'

'Thank you, sir,' I said looking inside the first aid box. surprisingly, it was empty.

The captain noticed this. 'Not much in there, eh, Number One?'

'No, sir,' he replied, glancing at me. 'Not at present.'

I gave my boss a meaningful look. 'If my medical stores arrive, sir, I'll soon fix that,' saluted and left.

So far, I had only dealt with a few cuts and bruises, several hangovers and one case of venereal disease, which I referred to barracks.

With three days to go before commissioning, a crowd gathered around the main notice board outside the coxswain's office.

The ship's Daily Orders informed everyone the commissioning ceremony would start in barracks at 1000 on Saturday 21st February. We were to fall in by divisions in the barrack shed, and march to the ship. The padre would then conduct the service on the wharf.

The next morning I stood on the ship's side and watched as a variety of boxes were carried onboard. Alas, none contained my precious medical stores.

That same afternoon the diminutive figure of a chief petty officer came into the sick bay. He wore dirty overalls and a battered cap that had seen better days. His lugubrious features wrinkled into a broad grin. When he removed his cap, a mass of white hair tumbled over his forehead.

Wrapped around his hand was a dirty handkerchief.

'Just caught myself with a chisel,' he said with a grin. 'By the way,' he added,' I'm Davey Jones, the chief chippy.'

The injury did not warrant a stitch. After giving him an anti-tetanus shot, I bandaged the finger up. We then sat down and had a cup of tea.

'You know, Doc,' he said, blowing over his mug, before taking a sip. 'What you need is a sign outside the door.'

'That sounds like a good idea,' I replied, wondering why I hadn't thought of it.

'Just make a list of treatment times,' he said, 'and I'll do the rest.'

Later on I gave him what he wanted, which included the opening lines of *Dante's Inferno*. '*A*bandon Hope All Ye Who Enter Here.'

Next day, while screwing the sign onto the door, he remarked with a grin. 'That ought to put the malingerers off.'

Gradually, the noise onboard died down as the dockyard people completed their tasks. The place became less cluttered with tool -boxes, oil and dirt.

Finally, the ship was ready for commissioning.

But my stores still had not arrived.

The day before commissing, panic set in. I went to inform the first lieutenant, but he was ashore.

A frantic telephone call to the hospital did not help. The Chief Pharmacist was at a meeting and his assistants didn't know anything about my store demand.

In desperation I spoke to Don Fearnley, the sick berth chief in barracks.

'Don't worry, Tom,' he said over the telephone. 'You've done all you could. Leave it to me, I'll see what I can do.'

The next morning was bright and clear. After captain's

inspection, the Royal Naval Blue Jacket Band struck up, '*I Love To Go A Wandering*'. With arms swinging, we proudly marched to the ship.

The debris on the wharf had been cleared. Next of kin sat in rows of chairs, applauding and waving as the crew came to a halt.

We lined up in our respective divisions, facing the ship.

My chest filled with pride as I scanned her superstructure. Painted pale grey, the ship looked immaculate. Portholes gleamed, boat covers sparkled white and the freshly green-painted deck looked impeccable. From stem to stern she glistened like a greyhound waiting for the starter's bell.

The padre, clad in his purple and black robes, stood on a wooden dais in front of the captain and the officers.

The Jimmy called the ship's company to attention. His sharp voice reverberated around the wharf. Then, turning to the captain, he saluted and reported, 'Ship's company present and correct, sir.'

The captain returned the salute. 'Carry on, please. Number One,' he replied, then turned to face the crew.

'Ship's company, off caps,' cried the chief gunnery instructor. 'Stand at ease, stand easy.'

The commissioning ceremony was about to start.

Just then, I heard the sound of a car. Glancing across to my right I saw a tilly. It had stopped some distance from the ceremony. To my surprise, the bulky figure of Don Fearnley climbed out.

He saw me, grinned, and gave me a discreet thumbs up. I uttered a thankful prayer. At long last my stores had arrived.

After the padre blessed the ship, the band played *For Those In Peril On The Sea*.

To the strains of the national anthem, the commissioning pennant was run up to the mainmast. At the same time, a large, white ensign was hoisted.

The debonair figure of Captain Peter Hill-Norton then gave the order to 'Splice The Mainbrace!'

This was greeted with rousing cheers from the crew.

Young Geordie, Don and myself carried the boxes of medical stores into the sick bay.

As we did so, the first lieutenant broke away from his guests. As he walked towards us, his face broke into a supercilious grin. 'About time those damn stores arrived,' he said.

'Better late than never, sir,' I replied, giving him a cursory glance. 'Can't for the life of me think why they took so long.'

He gave me a guilty stare.

As the Jimmy turned to go, Don Fearnley coughed. 'Excuse me, sir,' he said, trying unsuccessfully to suppress a grin. 'The chief pharmacist asked me to giver you this letter, sir. He says you owe him a bottle of whiskey.'

The first lieutenant accepted the letter, and quickly walked away.

'What the hell was all that about, Don?' I asked, somewhat perplexed.

'Your boss forgot to send the demand in, didn't he?' said Don.

'How did you know that?'

Don smiled. 'I'm married to the chief pharmacist's daughter, and she told me.'

At long last, the ship was finally in commission.

'Just what exactly is a 'work-up', Buffs?' I asked.

After the commissioning ceremony, many of the ship's company adjourned to the "Royal Naval Arms".

Leaning against the bar, the Buffer was about to take a sip of his beer. 'It's a pain in the fucking arse,' he replied, then added. 'Cheers, Doc, I likes a man who pays his debts.'

The air was thick with tobacco smoke and the seasoned smell of alcohol. On the walls hung several photographs of warships past and present. Behind the bar two hefty barmaids attended the needs of a few dozen thirsty sailors.

From the jukebox, the strident voice of Elvis Presley, singing *Blue Suede Shoes,* competed with raucous laughter and noisy conversation.

'That's OK, Buffs,' I replied. 'But is the work up as bad as that?'

The dapper figure of the coxswain stood next to the Buffer. His weather-beaten face broke into a frown.

'No,' he said. 'It's *worse* than a pain in the arse. Ain't it, Bill?'

'Why is that, then?' I asked, giving them a curious look.

'Well, it's like this,' muttered the Buffer, taking another pint glass in his hand. 'All parts of the ship are tested. The guns, speed trials, damage control, the lot.'

'Portland's in Weymouth, isn't it, Buffs?' I asked.

The Buffer nodded in agreement. 'In the mean time,' he said.

'We've got four weeks to prepare ourselves, and that includes your medical teams.'

'Looks like I'll have my work cut out, then,' I replied.

My first aid parties were made up of members of the Supply and Secretariat branches.

Shortly afterwards, Pete, who was sitting with some of the cooks and stewards, beckoned me over to their table.

'I suppose you'll want us to start dashing around with those bloody Neil Robertson stretchers soon, eh?' he asked. 'Harry, here,' he said, nodding towards Leading Steward Stokes, 'and me, when we was on the *Barfleur,* nearly dropped the butcher over the side. Remember that, Harry?'

Harry Stokes was the Jimmy's steward. He had brown, curly hair, and he was built like a rugby scrumhalf. 'Do I ever,' he replied. 'After tot time, it were. This silly bastard,' he motioned with his glass towards Pete, 'was half pissed. He hadn't strapped the butcher in properly see. We was lowering him down from the fo'c'sle and he almost slipped out onto the deck.'

My first night onboard proved to be memorable.

At precisely ten-thirty, the shrill blast of the bosun's pipe ordered 'Pipe down.'

After sleeping in the barracks, the sights, sounds and smells were very different. The light above my bunk reflected against the two empty cots opposite. The cabinet loomed like a hooded figure in the dark. Above, the tangled mess of wires and pipes snaked across the deck-head, disappearing into the shadows.

I switched off the light and instantly fell asleep.

Thinking morning had arrived, I felt someone's hand shaking my shoulder.

'Wake up, Doc,' came a voice. 'There's been an accident'

Groping upwards, I flicked the switch. The sudden slash of light hurt my eyes. I blinked, and sat up.

The leathery face of Jan Hawes stared at me. Droplets of rain dribbled from the peak of his cap onto his oilskin.

'You'd best come, quick,' he said. 'One of the stewards has injured himself.'

In an instant I was awake. After slipping on my clothes and grabbing the first aid valise, I quickly followed him.

The sick bay clock told me it was a little after two.

At the bottom of a ladder leading to my mess lay the crumpled figure of Harry Stokes, the first lieutenant's leading steward. He was unconscious and lay quite still. One leg was leg tucked under him. He was bareheaded and his uniform was soaking wet.

'Someone get a blanket and cover him up,' I ordered, 'and be quick about it

Kneeling down I checked his pulse. It was full and bounding. Feeling gently around his head I discovered a large swelling. Using my torch I discovered one of his pupils fully dilated.

Suddenly, all those special watches in A1 bore fruit.

From behind came an official-sounding voice.

I glanced up and saw Sub-Lieutenant Handley. He was Officer of the Day. He looked tired and rivulets of rain ran down his oilskin.

'Let's get this man moved right away,' he ordered.

'No,' I cried, looking up. 'He is not to be moved under any circumstances. Phone barracks. Tell them to send an ambulance immediately.'

By this time Harry was covered with a blanket. After turning him on his back, I gently placed his head to one side.

'I'd like a word with you,' said the sub-lieutenant. 'Right now.'

'Keep an eye on him,' I told Paddy Alexander, who was close by.

Out of earshot of the others, he glared at me and said, 'I insist you call out the medical officer of the guard.'

In port, warships carrying a doctor took it in turns to be medical guard. This also included shore bases. Tonight, HMS *Eagle,* was guard ship.

'Sir,' I began. 'This man may have a fractured skull. He badly needs a surgeon. I don't think we've got time to wait for the guard MO. If he dies while we wait, sir, you will be responsible.'

My last statement seemed to shake the young officer. He visibly paled. 'I see,' he replied. 'I only hope you know what you're doing.'

Even if the doctor from *Eagle* came, I told myself, he couldn't do much except send the injured man to hospital. Nevertheless, I was sticking my neck out. If I were wrong, it would certainly end up in a noose!

The ambulance arrived. I recognised the bedraggled figure of Pete Cronin.

'Have you called the medical officer of the guard, Tom?' he asked, kneeling down with me.

'No, Pete,' I replied. 'Look at his pupils.'

Pete did as I asked.

'Christ, Tom,' he whispered. 'I think you are right. But you know the drill. He has to be seen by a doctor before you send him to hospital.'

'Bugger the drill, Pete,' I said. 'I'm taking him straight in to Stonehouse.'

The journey did not take long.

As luck would have it, Surgeon Lieutenant Fulford, my old boss from A1, was in the receiving room. He immediately recognised me.

'Ah, young Lightburn, I see,' he said, with a tired smile. 'Seems you've had a busy night. Got his F. Med 10?'

My God, I thought. Now I am for it. The F. Med 10 was an admittance form signed by a doctor.

'Er...no, sir,' came my hesitant reply. 'He hasn't been seen yet. I brought him straight in.'

I then told him what I thought the injury might be.

'Indeed,' replied the doctor, pursing his lips. 'We'd better take a look at your man, then.'

As we left the room, the duty chief gave me a stern look. 'You could be in serious trouble, you know,' he said. 'I'll have to report this.'

Nodding my head, I replied, 'Yes, chief, I know.'

After examining Harry, the doctor turned to me and in a quiet voce, said, 'By jove, I think you're right. Let's get him to x-ray.'

The night duty staff took over amd I returned to the ship.

Shortly after nine the next day the sick bay telephone rang.

I immediately recognised the voice of the first lieutenant. He did not sound at all pleased.

'The PMO in barracks wants to see you right away,' he said. 'I suppose it's about the business last night with my leading steward. How is he?'

'Don't know yet, sir,' I replied. 'I'll keep you informed.'

'Make sure you do,' he replied, and put the 'phone down.

The grey-haired figure of the surgeon commander glanced up as I entered his office.

'You know why I have sent for you, don't you?' he said, arching his eyebrows.

'Yes, sir,' I replied.

'It seems you have broken my standing orders, and gone against all procedures for admitting patients to hospital.'

My mouth felt dry. 'Yes, sir,' I replied.

The PMO sat back in his chair, drummed his fingers on his desk and peered at me. 'The charges I could make against you are serious. You realise that?'

A deep-seated feeling of nausea gripped my stomach. This is it, I said to myself. Goodbye naval career - hello disgrace.

Licking my lips, I replied, 'Yes, sir. I do.'

The PMO lent forward. 'I will have to report you to Captain Hill-Norton. You understand?'

'Yes, sir,' I replied hoarsely.

With one hand the PMO stroked his chin. 'Right, you may go.'

As I turned to leave, he added, 'However, young man, your patient was operated on and is doing well.' The serious expression on his face suddenly disappeared. 'When I was young, I made a few rash decisions. Lucky for you, yours was the right one. Now, away with you.'

During the next two weeks everyone worked frantically preparing for the work up.

Everybody worked like beavers. Everything, from the fo'c'sle to the gash-shoot, was scrubbed and painted. Gun turrets and barrels were washed till they gleamed. High above, two brave matelots gave the lattice mast a fresh coat of black paint. Down below in boiler and engine rooms, metal plating, gauges and dials shone like silver. The galleys became havens of sterility and every mess-deck was rendered spotless.

Meanwhile, I became somewhat unpopular with Digger Barnes, the Chief Gunnery Instructor.

'You can't take twenty men away for bloody chest x-rays,' he exploded.

The Buffer and myself were in his office.

Digger was a tall, straight-backed man with black, well-greased hair parted in the middle. 'The Buffer and meself,' he said, 'need these hands. We're moving mid-stream at 0900 tomorrow to take on ammunition. The Jimmy will do his nut, when he hears about this.'

'Sorry, chief,' I replied. 'But they have to be done in the hospital. The x-ray machine in barracks is defective.'

'Well, you can't have my lads,' he retorted, throwing the list I had given him on his desk. 'And that's final.'

'What about yours, Buffs?' I asked.

The Buffer removed his cap, and ran his fingers through his hair.. 'Well...' he said with a sigh of resignation. 'All right. It's five of me working party, but I suppose it has to be done.'

Just then the tall figure of the first lieutenant appeared in the doorway.

''Morning, Chief,' he said.. 'We tie up to a buoy at 0930. I expect we'll be back alongside about noon. We'll need every available hand.'

Bloddy-hell, I thought, Now, I'm for it.

'Morning, sir,' replied Diggcr. After shooting a withering glance at me, he continued, 'The LSBA, here, wants to take twenty hands for chest x-rays to-morrow at 0830.'

The officer's dark brown narrowed. 'Can't your damn x-rays wait?' he snapped. 'Ammunitioning ship is more important than your x-rays.'

'Sorry, sir,' I replied hesitantly. 'It's the only time the radiographer can fit us in this week, The PMO insists they have to be done before the ship sails for Portland.'

'The PMO *insists*, does he?' boomed the Jimmy. 'We'll soon see about that.'

Later that morning the sick bay telephone rang.

I immediately recognised my boss's voice. 'The PMO assures me those men will be back by 0930 tomorrow,' he growled. 'In time to help ammunition ship. Make sure they are. Understood?'

Before I had time to answer, he hung up.

At eight o'clock next morning, the x-ray party and myself boarded a coach. A red flag was hoisted to the mainmast signifying explosives were about to be taken onboard.

'Don't be adrift,' said the Chief GI. 'Or you'll all be in the rattle.'

Unfortunately, on the return journey the coach broke down outside the hospital. After a frantic telephone call to barracks a lorry was sent for us. By the time we returned to the wharf it was eleven o'clock. The ship wasn't due back till twelve. Everyone seemed more upset at not getting their rum than missing the ship. Remembering the Chief GI's words, I realised I could soon be in trouble – again.

Cold and shivering, we stood on the side of Flagstaff Steps and watched as the ship came alongside.

The tall figure of the Chief GI stood at the top of the gangway. The expression on his rain-soaked face told me I was in for the biggest bollocking of my life.

Under his oilskin, the creases in his trousers were knife-edged and despite the rain, his black boots and gaiters shone like glass.

My explanation for being adrift fell on deaf ears.

'Sorry, you say. The coach broke down, you say,' snarled the chief. 'By Christ, you will be. See me at 1700 in my office.' Then he strode away.

With a worried sigh, I returned to the sick bay and flopped down in a chair. The next time men under punishment mustered, this would include me.

However, my fears were soon dispelled.

The Chief GI sat in his office, jacket undone, smoking a cigarette. Ammunitioning had gone smoothly and he smelt heavily of rum.

'In future,' he said, breathing alcohol fumes all over me, 'for fuck's sake, give me at least a week's warning if you want anyone for jabs or whatever. That way we'll get along fine. OK?'

'Fair enough, chief,' I replied.

The chief stubbed out his cigarette, stretched his arms up, and yawned. 'Oh, and by the way,' he said. 'This'll cost you a pint in the "Naval Arms".'

The word soon got around that this was my first ship, and I was a bit 'green.' This attracted the usual crop of malingerers and hypochondriacs. Not surprisingly, these arrived whenever work had to be done.

One morning, in the middle of storing ship, an overweight seaman named Harry Woods reported sick.

'It's my back, Doc,' he cried. 'Every time I moves, it kills me.'

'Sorry to hear that, Slinger,' I replied, glancing through his bulky medical documents. 'Would you like a quick shot of rum, Slinger?'

Slinger's eyes lit up.'Cheers, Doc,' he replied, licking his lips.

233

I went on. 'It might help the pain. There's a small bottle at the bottom of that store.' I pointed to a door in the bulkhead. 'Get it for me.'

With a wide grin, he quickly bent down and opened the door, and looked inside.

'Can't find anything here,' he said.

He stood up. In an instant he realised what he had done.

The grin faded from his face.

'Quite right, Slinger,' I replied, tapping his back. 'And there's nothing there also.'

Then there was the case of Normal Clegg.

One morning, a tall, pale, junior seaman came into the sick bay.

He had a shock of dark wavy hair and stood, head bowed, nervously running the rim of his cap through his fingers.

'What's the problem, Cleggy?' I asked.

'It's me, er...' He paused, looked up and added, 'balls, Doc. Me balls.'

He told me they ached all the time, and had done so for the past two months.

After examining him, I could find nothing wrong. Nevertheless, I gave him some weak painkillers and told him to report to me the next morning before passing water.

Further tests proved negative.

The following day he returned complaining of the same problem. 'They're killing, Doc,' he moaned, clutching his middle.

In desperation I referred him to the medical officer in barracks.

The doctor sent him back with a note addressed to me, which, to my amazement, read, 'This man has been masturbating too much. I have advised him against overdoing this. Perhaps you could also have a word with him.'

'But I don't do it!' cried poor Norman. 'It's me girl friend, Wendy. She's always doing it to me. In the pictures, in her house, on Plymouth Hoe, everywhere. She can't keep her hands off me.'

'Well,' I said, trying my best not to laugh, 'you'd better tell her to pack it in. When you've been at sea for a long time, it's OK to use 'Miss Fist, the five-fingered widow,' now and then. But overdo it and you'll develop the dreaded black spot.'

'The black spot,' he said with a look of alarm. 'What's that?'

'You develop a spot on the palm of your hand,' I replied,

trying to keep a serious face. 'It's a sign of what we medics call 'Wanker's Doom'!'

'Bloody hell,' he replied, staring at his hand. 'Wait till I tell Wendy.'

During the next fortnight I was kept busy giving injections against everything from typhoid to tetanus, not to mention numerous smallpox vaccinations.

I reminded the Jimmy he was due for his smallpox vaccination. We were in his cabin. 'Not at the moment. LSBA,' he said. 'I'm too busy. Are there many who need injections?'

'Quite a lot, sir,' I replied. 'I'll have them done before we reach Gib. It'll be important in order to obtain *Pratique.* "

The captain was overdue for his smallpox vaccination. Shortly after two o'clock he sent for me.

'This won't prevent me from attending a meeting tomorrow, will it?'

After sterilising the special needle and cleaning the captain's arm with cetavalon, I broke the ends of a small filament containing the vaccine.

'No, sir,' I replied, blowing the colourless material onto his upper arm.

Without puncturing the skin, I applied the point of the needle in a series of rapid movements onto his arm, which left a small red area on his arm.

'Your arm might itch slightly and you might feel a bit shivery. I'll leave some aspirins in case that happens.'

He thanked me and rolled down his sleeve. For the first time, I noticed the ship's crest above his desk.

'Excuse me, sir,' I said with an air of curiosity. 'What's that picture on the ship's crest?'

The captain put on his jacket, straightened his tie and cleared his throat

'Oh that hood with a lead attached?' he said, brushing a sleeve with his hand. 'It's called a 'Lure'. Apparently it was a medieval method of attracting hawks. Someone swung it in the air, the hawk mistook it for a bird, and the hawk was caught. It acted as a decoy. Hence the name of the ship. Satisfied?'

'Thank you sir,' I replied, looking at the crest. 'And...er, the motto underneath?'

The captain's finely chiselled features broke into a grin.

'You are an inquisitive blighter, aren't you?' he said, sitting down. 'It's Latin, and means 'Beware What I Hide.' Now, if I can get some work done?'

'Yes, sir. Thank you, sir,' I replied and left.

The Supply and Secretariat mess was situated up for'd, on the port side. Twelve cooks, four stewards and two writers lived in cramped conditions not far removed from the days of Nelson. Each man slept in a hammock. Metal lockers, including my own, were arranged around the bulkhead.

Every day, after rum issue, the duty cook arrived carrying two large aluminium trays full of food. In every junior ratings mess, this, too, was a daily ritual. Each day someone was detailed off to collect the meals from the galley.

Today it was the turn of a corpulent cook from Newcastle, Big Geordie Harris. Before joining up, the big man was an all-in wrestler. He was as strong as an ox, and nobody argued with him.

While filling the first aid box in the galley, I asked him why he joined the navy.

'Well, Doc, it was like this' he said, pounding a huge lump of dough. 'It was either spending me life beating heads and twisting necks, or doing this.' He then lifted up the dough, plopped it on a table and attacked it with his fists. 'Besides,' he added, tearing the mass apart and sprinkling it with flour. 'My probation officer thought it might be good therapy.'

'Grubs up,' he yelled, clattering the tray on the table. 'Babies heads and Manchester tart.'

Babies heads were small beef pies and the chefs delighted in marking smiling faces on the pastry.

Of course, there were the usual complaints about the food.

'You bloody chefs ought to be shot,' cried Jerry Johnson, stooping down to place a portion of food on his plate. Jerry was a writer. He was built like a racing snake, with dark, wavy hair. 'This is the third time we've had babies heads this week. Can't you buggers cook anything else?'

'Away with you,' replied Big Geordie, flopping a pie onto his plate. 'As they say in the Russian navy, *toughskie shitskie*. If yer don't like it, slap in to see the padre.'

These were the men who would make up my first aid parties.

The thought of squeezing Big Geordie into a Neil Robertson stretcher almost made me choke. As for Jerry Johnson, I don't think there was a stretcher small enough to fit his skinny frame.

However, these questions would shortly be answered.

The next morning, those who were off duty mustered on the quarterdeck.

'Don't you lot ruin my lovely green deck,' cried Mitch. 'My lucky lads have only not long painted it.'

'Pay no attention, Doc,' chirped Paddy Alexander. 'If he loses those teeth of his again, you can put one of those tourniquets things around his neck, and give us all some peace.'

Dark clouds threatened rain, and everyone wore foul-weather jackets or oilskins.

Spread out before them was an assortment of bandages, slings, splints and tourniquets. There was also the infamous Neil Robertson stretcher. At each end, a rope was fixed into a metal eye. These ropes were used to control the movement of the stretcher when it was lowered or raised.

I stood facing them, and said, 'when action stations are sounded, you report to your first aid post.'

I looked around and spotted Pete Lamb. 'Pete will be in charge of the for'd party in the seaman's mess-deck.' Pete grinned and gave a mock bow.

'Our esteemed scribe, Jerry Johnson, is Doctor Kildaire in the canteen flat and Big Geordie is medico in charge of the after party. As well as the others, he will have Harry to help him.'

Harry Bridges, a small, stout man from Portsmouth, was the canteen manager. He was the only civilian on board and was in charge of the NAAFI.

'Not again,' grumbled Harry. 'I was a firstaider on board the *Surprise,* and I can't stand the sight of blood.'

'My job,' I went on, 'is to circulate and go wherever needed.'

Nodding towards the pale-faced Paddy Murphy, I added. 'Paddy will be my runner and man the sick bay 'phone when I'm away. Any questions?'

Nobody answered.

I lectured them about shock, control of bleeding and the dangers of moving casualties.

'More wounded men and women die from shock and clumsy handling than their injuries. If possible, always treat them on the spot and send for me or the MO.'

We then practised putting on slings, splints and bandages.

'These will be all right for polishing our shoes for divisions,' said Pete, applying a large shell dressing around Big Geordie's head.

Geordie gave out a loud yell and grabbed the dressing. 'Hey, you're supposed to be bandaging my head, not my mouth.'

'How about this, Doc?' cried Danny Wilde, a small, chubby cook. Folding a sling in half, he made a triangular-shaped handkerchief, and tied it around the lower part of his face. 'Stick'em up,' he said, pointing two fingers. 'Your money or your tot.'

'Put them away,' said another cook, called Podger Smith. 'He was with Slack Alice last night, and I know where those fingers have been.'

Pete, who had received some first aid training in his last ship, splinted up the lower leg of Scouse Kilbane, a ginger-headed steward from Liverpool. Scouse immediately bent his 'injured' leg under him, then using a long thigh splint as a crutch, cried out. 'Shiver me timbers. Has anyone seen Black Dog?'

'No', replied, Bungy, kicking his crutch from under him. 'But I hear someone on board has the black spot.'

The next few days were devoted to practical work. This included moving men about in a Neil Robertson stretcher.

'Who will volunteer to be the 'casualty'?' I asked, looking at them.

'Paddy Murphy will, won't you matey?' said Big Geordie. 'He's the smallest and nobody will miss him if we drops him over the side.'

A startled look came over Paddy's face. 'Piss off,' he cried, 'Just because you're fourteen stone and built like a brick shit-house, don't mean you can boss me about.'

'Oh, no,' replied Big Geordie, raising both hands towards Paddy's neck.

'All right. all right,' cried Paddy, hastily backing away. 'You win.'

Shiner Wright wrapped a first field dressing around Paddy's head while Bungy and Podger strapped the bamboo casing around him.

'He looks just like one of them Jippo Mummies,' commented Scouse Kilbane.

'I've met a few of them in Alexandria,' joked Jerry Johnson, 'only they had bigger tits than Paddy.'

To add a touch of realism, Danny Wilde disappeared into the after galley and returned holding a bottle of tomato ketchup. He then smeared a large blob of it onto the bandage.

'There now,' he said standing back. 'You looks in a real bad way, Patrick my son.'

'Make sure those straps are secure,' I said, when Paddy was firmly ensconced in the stretcher. 'And don't forget to test them.'

'Steady on you lot,' croaked Paddy, gazing up at his tormentors. 'I feels like a sardine.'

'And smell like one as well,' added Slinger Woods, giving the straps an extra tug..

Our enthusiastic party carried Paddy onto the port B gun deck under the bridge. This attracted several comments from ratings busy painting and cleaning.

'Throw the bugger overboard,' was one such comment.

'Leave him there to suffocate,' came another.

'See if he floats, Doc,' cried Jan Hawes.

With panic in his eyes, Paddy rapidly turned his head from side to side. 'You bastards better be careful,' he whimpered. 'I'm an only child.'

Slowly the party lifted the stretcher up and rested it on the guardrail of B gun deck. Big Geordie held onto the head rope. Pete went below on the fo'c'sle to grasp the end rope. Slowly, they lowered the cumbersome stretcher over the side.

Just then, a gust of cold wind whipped up and blew the stretcher from side to side. The heavens opened and it poured down.

'Help!' cried Paddy. 'Don't drop me, for fuck's sake.'

Suddenly there came a sharp, snapping sound. I looked down and, to my horror, a few strands of the rope had parted.

Fear engulfed me like a cold chill.

The stretcher was a good eight feet from the deck and continued to sway dangerously. Below on the fo'c'sle the strong wind and rain hampered Pete's efforts to secure the rope.

In a flash, everyone bent over and tried to grab hold of the stretcher. The rain made the bamboo and canvas slippery and hard to grasp.

The sickening sound as the rope continued to snap echoed above the wind and rain.

In desperation, I yelled to a couple of sailors, sheltering against the rain. 'Lend a hand here.'

They immediately hurried over.

'Careful,' I cried. 'Don't pull on the rope, it's snapping.'

Just then Big Geordie bent over the side. 'Hold on my legs,' he yelled.

Straight away we clutched hold of his thighs and legs.

With surprising agility, Big Geordie levered himself over the side.

Just as the rope parted he grabbed the rim of the stretcher with his hand. 'Keep still, Paddy,' he shouted. 'I've got you, matie.'

The rain was ignored as everyone clasped hold of Big Geordie's legs.

Hanging onto the stretcher, he cried. 'Haul away, lads. And be quick about it.'

As we pulled them inboard, relief flowed through me like a tidal wave.

We quickly undid the straps of the stretcher.

Wide-eyed and pale, Paddy slowly staggered to his feet. 'Y...you m...mad bastards,' he stuttered. 'I c...could have been killed.'

The tall, fair-headed figure of Commander Bishop walked past.

'By jove,' he cried, peering at Paddy's 'blood' stained head bandage. 'You chaps certainly believe in realism.'

Later on I carefully checked all the ropes on the other Neil Robertson stretchers. With the work up looming up, I had a feeling they would be needed again.

15

Two hours before we were due to sail, the rain-soaked figure of Able Seaman 'Tansey' Lee, the ship's Postie, came into the sick bay.

Using a small aluminium teapot, I had just brewed up.

'Somebody loves you, Doc,' he said, handing me half a dozen official brown envelopes and two private letters. 'I wish I got as much mail as that.'

'What do you mean, Postie?' I said. 'You are married, aren't you? Surely you get stacks of letters?'

A worried frown appeared on Tansey's brow. He glanced at the deck.

Suddenly I realised he was trying to tell me something. A ship's medic not only has to deal with injury and sickness, but also personal problems. So far, this had not occurred, but the worried expression on Postie's face told me something was wrong.

'Haven't had any mail for some time now,' he replied. 'Edna has gone to stay with her mothers in Huddersfield.'

The sound of the wind and rain splattering against the glass of the portholes only added to Postie's mood of depression.

'I see,' I said, 'sit down and have a cuppa.'

I poured out two mugs of tea.

'Have you tried 'phoning?'

'Aye. But her mother tells me she's always out.'

'How long have you been married?'

'Five years, next month,' he replied, then added dolefully. 'Spent most of them at sea.'

'Can you get any leave? A weekend, or something?'

He gave me a wry smile. 'There's no leave now. We sail straight away for Gib after the work-up.'

'I'd speak to your Divisional Officer if I were you, Tansey,' I said, standing up. 'But you can see me anytime.'

After he left I felt somewhat frustrated. I had not really helped him. However, Tansey had at least confided in me.

Amongst the official mail was a letter from home, one from Jock McBride and a bundle of *Liverpool Football Echoes*.

Mum was keeping well, not that she would say otherwise. She

met Joe's mother who told her that Joe was now in the Parachute Regiment. Mad sod, I thought, laughing to myself. One of these day he's going to get himself killed.

Tony was still in Pentonville and I made a mental note to drop him a line After all, I told myself, blood is thicker than water, and grudges cannot be held forever.

The *Echo* reported Liverpool's depressing fortunes in the second division. These would eventually be passed around to the lads onboard from Merseyside, including the Evertonians.

Jock McBride was now a leading hand. He told me Desperate had been passed over for his hook because he got drunk and fell into Grand Harbour. He concluded by adding, 'a certain blonde nursing sister sends her regards and asks when are you coming to Malta?'

'D'y hear there,' came the strident sound of the ship's tannoy. 'Close all screen doors and scuttles. Special sea-dutymen to your stations. Hands fall in for leaving harbour.'

The time was ten a.m. on Wednesday, 14th March 1956.

The greatest adventure in my life was about to start.

Outside the sick bay I could hear Mitch barking orders to his men. 'Let go the stern ropes,' I heard him cry. The rest of his commands were lost in the howling wind.

The vibrations of the deck sent shivers running through me. Gradually the ship slowly pulled away from the wharf. I took a deep breath and clenched my fists. At last we were on our way.

As we passed under the gaze of the Commander-in-Chief, those fell in on the upper-deck were ordered to 'face the port.'

Despite the inclement weather, crowds had gathered on the Hoe, reminding me of a summer day a few years ago.

As I peered out the porthole, the woodlands of Drake's Island slowly faded from view as we cruised through the breakwater. Then came the slow, rolling motion as the ship hit the open sea. Gradually, a feeling of nausea gripped me and my stomach began to churn. Remembering Nelson was always seasick was small consolation as I reached across for a tube of pink tablets.

Feeling like death, I staggered outside. After taking several deep breaths, I began to feel better.

The bridge and superstructure swayed like a bobbin in a bath. The gale whipped at the radar aerials and halyards, bending them like bowstrings. Under the steel deck, the steady throb of the engines sent a quiver running through me. Clutching the guardrail, I let the icy spray splatter against my face.

Shock waves ran through the ship as it rose sharply before thundering back into the sea. Explosions of watery spray cascaded over the fo'c'sle soaking everything in sight. My God, I thought – is this what I volunteered for?

Under a threatening sky, Plymouth slowly faded from view. In the distance the dark green waters of the English Channel with its fleet of white horses stretched as far as my eyes could see.

This, I told myself, was the same route taken by sailors from the beginning of time. It was the same sea on which my father, and countless others, had gone to war. This was the world of Drake, Nelson, Fisher and Cunningham, and I was part of it.

The sound of the bosun's pipe brought me to my senses.

'Special sea-duty-men fall out. Duty watch fall in. '

In the mess, one or two sat with their heads in their arms. Others lay motionless in hammocks, swaying with the motion of the ship.

'Take these tablets and go on the upper deck,' I said to those whose colour matched their white shirts. 'Take some deep breaths and eat a piece of dry bread or hard tack. That way, you'll have something to spew up.'

The sight and smell of Scouse Kilbane munching merrily on a greasy bacon sandwich left over from breakfast did not help matters. 'Roll on tot time,' he laughed, 'looks like there'll be plenty left over, eh?'

Instantly, several men made a dash for the upper deck.

My first night at sea was a miserable hell. The ship seemed to have a life of its own. Sleep became impossible. Every time the ship reared up my body levitated. Gripping the sides of my bunk, I was flung upwards before flopping back into the mattress.

With my stomach churning like a whisk, I decided to get up. Unfortunately I hadn't secured everything properly.

Bottles crashed, trays of instruments flew around like poltergeists and I grasped hold of anything stationary. Locked drawers flew open and pillows took off like guided missiles. The tea pot, half full, arched in the air, spraying its contents over the place.

At times, my feet seemed to leave the deck as the ship pitched and tossed like a rubber duck in a bath.

Roll on death, I moaned, and let's have a long stand easy.

A little after midnight, Nobby Clark, a corpulent able seaman came in. His nose was as red as a beetroot and his ruddy face glistened with rain. His foul-weather clothing dripped like a tap, sending rivulets of water onto the deck.

Around his finger was a dirty, blood-soaked handkerchief.

'Cut it on me knife, Doc,' he said, waving his hand in the air. He looked around. 'I sees you've 'ad a bit of trouble, eh?'

'Yeah,' I replied, cleaning his finger. 'I'm afraid this will need stitching, Nobby. Is it always as rough as this?'

'Rough?' he replied. 'This is nowt Wait till it really blows a bastard. Then you'll know about it.'

I gave Nobby a shot of medicinal brandy and lay him on my bunk, with his hand on the side rest. Remembering the advice in Dad's war story, I waited for the up-roll of the ship before inserting each of the four stitches. When I finished, Nobby grinned, and said. 'Didn't feel a thing, Doc, got any more of that brandy?'

Very gradually, the weather improved and cases of *mal de mer* disappeared.

The sick list consisted mainly of coughs and colds and the occasional cut head or finger.

One morning as I entered the Burma Way, a sharp cry of pain came from the paint store. Pushing a metal door open, I went inside.

Surrounded by shelves of tins, a broad-shouldered matelot with dark, untidy hair, sat on the deck. Kneeling by his side was a sailor holding a dirty cloth to his mate's head.

'Perfect timing, Doc,' cried the sailor holding the cloth. 'Seldom, here, has had a slight accident with a tin of paint'

Removing the cloth, I examined the injury. 'It's not serious,' I said. 'Come to the bay and I'll clean it up.'

'Will it hurt?' asked Seldom, holding his head.

'That's all right,' remarked his pal with a smirk. 'Seldom won't feel a thing. Will you, mate? Where there's no sense, there's no feeling.'

'Seldom,' I said, giving the injured man a curious look. 'Why do they call you that?'

Before the 'casualty' had time to reply, his mate, answered, 'Because he *seldom* does any work. That's why.'

Just then, a spotty, pale-faced sailor poked his head around the door.

Seldom greeted him with a smile.

'Watcha, Tanky,' he said, holding a grey handkerchief to his head. 'Any chance of a quick tot before Daktari, here, bandages me up?'

Tanky had the most important job in the ship. He was responsible for looking after the rum. Every day at 1130, under the eagle-eye of the coxswain, he issued the precious liquid to each mess.

The sight of Seldom's injury made Tanky's blue eyes sparkle with humour.

'Don't tell me you fell over in your sleep, Seldom?' he grinned. 'You couldn't have hurt yourself working.'

Later that same day the ship underwent sea trials.

This involved the captain manoeuvring the ship about at high speed. Luckily, the sea was relatively calm. This, however, did not save chaos reigning throughout the ship.

'The ship will turn to port,' came the pipe.

Suddenly, the ship heeled over. The bulkheads heeled over at an acute angle. Standing with my feet apart, I clung onto the cot rail. A gushing noise came from within the pipes under the sink and the door of the main medical cabinet crashed open. For a moment, I thought we might capsize. But with agonising slowness, the ship gradually became upright.

However, worse was to come.

The next day, daily orders stated there would be a practice shoot at 1400.

'Close all screen doors and scuttles. X gun will fire in five minutes,' was piped.

Earlier the 'Jack Dusty', a tall, stores petty officer, named Harry Morrison, issued everyone with plastic earplugs.

'You'll need these, Doc,' he warned. 'Especially when those guns open fire.'

Waiting anxiously, I heard the whining noise of the hoist bringing up shells from the magazine.

The noise, when the guns fired was earsplitting.

The re-coil as the shells left the guns was like an earthquake. Dust, asbestos and bits of grime fell like confetti from the deck-head and I was sent crashing against the sick bay door.

I squashed my hands over each ear and closed both eyes.

By the time several salvos had been fired, I was a nervous wreck.

The voice on the tannoy saying, 'Firing is now complete,' was like a message from heaven.

I slowly slumped onto the deck. My head was spinning and I felt numb. What on earth, I wondered, will happen when all the guns fired at once!

One day I would find out.

Shortly after nine o'clock the next morning, the sick bay telephone rang.

I was busy putting a crepe bandage on a sailor who had sprained his ankle.

'First lieutenant, here,' he said. 'Come and see me at once.'

Wondering what was up, I made my way to his cabin. On his desk lay a clutter of folders, papers and signal logs. Secured to the bulkhead was a heavy-framed photograph of an attractive-looking woman, sitting with a child on her knee.

'Ah, Lightburn,' he said, tapping a signal in his hand. 'The day after we arrive in Portland there is to be a disaster relief exercise.'

'Yes, sir,' I replied. 'The Buffer warned me something like that would happen.'

'Good,' he said, with a sly grin. 'This is the plan. You and your first aid party will land at 0900. You will take with you enough medical supplies and equipment to assist an imaginary local authority following an earthquake. Clear so far?'

'Yes, sir,' I answered. 'How will we transport it all?'

'A lorry will be on the jetty to take you to the affected area. There, you will be responsible for setting up a suitable medical post. Umpires from *Osprey* will adjudicate and pass you slips of paper telling you where casualties are. You and your team will be closely monitored and a report made to me. Understood?'

I blinked nervously. 'Yes, sir. I'll get on to it straight away.'

I immediately checked the details concerning landing parties in my BR88. I mustered the medical team in the sick bay and explained what was to happen.

'What will the rig be, Doc?' asked Scouse Kilbane.

'Foul-weather gear. The forecast is heavy rain,' I replied. 'Each of you will carry a first aid bag, a pencil, and notebook. Write all names and injuries in it. Report here at 0700 and bring your respirators in case there's gas leaks or something. Any questions?'

With expressions of resigned misery, they glanced at one another.

'What about our tot?' asked Big Geordie.

'Yeah,' chimed in the tall, fair-haired figure of Spud Tate. 'We're not going to miss that are we, Doc?'

Shaking my head and grinning, I said. 'Don't worry, you drunken rabble, you'll get it when we return to the ship.'

The night before we were due to arrive at Portland, I had my first serious casualty. Around two in the morning Jock Weir, the black-bearded chief stoker came into the sick bay. His battered cap partially covered his head and he looked tired.

'You'd better come to the boiler-room,' he said. 'Knocker White's had an accident.'

As I gingerly climbed down into the engine-room, the warm smell of diesel oil and the steady throb of the engines hit me full in the face.

Knocker was sitting up against a bulkhead, holding his left arm. His face was like chalk and he was soaked in sweat. A stoker was kneeling down holding a cup to the injured man's lips. A quick glance told me he was going into shock. .

'What happened?' I asked, carefully touching the man's arm.

He immediately winced with pain. 'Slipped on the plating,' he muttered.

'Lie down flat, Stokes,' I said, and added, 'somebody put something under his feet.'

After gently cutting away the sleeve of his overalls, the limpness of his hand and swelling told me his forearm was fractured.

'Keep him still, and don't move him,' I said, glancing up at the white-overalled figure of Commander Bishop. 'I'll be back in a minute, sir.'

When I returned, I knelt beside him. 'I'm afraid you've broken your arm, Stokes,' I said. 'I'm going to give you a shot of morphia to help kill the pain. Then we'll get you to the sick bay.'

Making note of the time, I injected the drug into his shoulder muscle. 'Someone get him a cup of tea. And put plenty of sugar in it.'

'Cheers, Doc,' he muttered. Then with a wry grin, added. 'At least it's not me drinking arm.'

247

Very carefully I put a sling around his shoulder to support his arm and managed to help him to the sick bay.

'It's just as well we reach Portland tomorrow, Knocker,' I said, helping him into bed. 'You'll have to be x-rayed and put in plaster.'

I put his arm in a splint, and telephoned the bridge

'What on earth do *you* want?' came the impatient voice of the first lieutenant.

After explaining what had happened, I suggested a signal be sent to the sick bay at Portland, informing them of the man's injury and requesting a motor launch.

'Are you sure it's broken?' he said.

'I'm positive, sir,' I replied.

We arrived at Portland harbour at six the next morning. At last the wind had dropped and the sea was relatively calm.

Wrapped up in his overcoat and overalls, Knocker was helped into the waiting launch by a few sailors. I held his medical documents in an envelope. We were joined by the tall figure of Tansey Lee, the ship's postie, carrying a bulky canvas sack.

'We'll pick you both up from the jetty at 1600,' said the bearded figure of Sub-Lieutenant Goodwin, the Officer of the Watch. 'So don't be adrift.'

Using a series of whistle signals, the coxswain ordered the launch away. The ambulance was waiting and Tansey left to collect the mail.

The sick quarters at HMS *Osprey* was situated high on the crest of a hill, overlooking Portland Bay.

Much to my surprise, the stocky frame of Wardmaster Lieutenant 'Bogey' Knight stood in the entrance.

''Morning, sir,' I said, saluting.

His dark eyes stared at me. 'Thought I'd seen the back of you, Lightburn,' he replied, returning my salute. 'What trouble are you bringing me this time?'

I glanced at Knocker. 'Just a fractured radius, sir,' I replied. 'And maybe you could let me have some penicillin and condoms.'

'Condoms,' he snorted. 'You've come here for work-up. Not to go gallivanting ashore.'

'We're off into the Med. after our work-up, sir,' I replied. 'And RNH only sent me a few boxes,'

Bogey gave a cough.' Hmm…I see,' he growled, eyeing me with suspicion.

While I collected my medical stores, Knocker was x-rayed and his arm put in plaster.

A few hours later, he had recovered. Dicky Barton, a pal from Stonehouse, was decent enough to give us both sippers.

'Watch out for Wardmaster Sub-Lieutenant Hardy during your exercise,' he said. 'He's one of the umpires, a tall, weedy bugger, with a pockmarked face. He's a real bastard. Watches everything you do with binoculars.'

A tilly took Knocker and me to the jetty. Waiting there was a sailor from the base. In his hand he carried a large, canvas sack.

'The chief found this outside the mail office,' he said. 'It's full of mail for your ship.' He handed the bag to me.

I frowned and glanced at Knocker. 'Where's the postie?' I asked alarmed.

'Search me,' replied the sailor, shrugging his shoulders. 'Nobody seems to have seen him.'

The sound of the coxswain's whistle heralded the arrival of the launch.

'We've got the mail,' I shouted down to Pincher Martin, the coxswain of the launch. 'But there's no sign of Postie.'

'Can't wait,' replied Pincher. 'The skipper's about to sail.'

After a final glance around, I helped Knocker on board.

Surely, I told myself, he hasn't gone on the trot. Suddenly, I was wracked with guilt. What if, by not reporting Postie's problems, I had inadvertently caused him to go AWOL

A short while later I was talking to Postie's DO. 'You should have told me about Able Seaman Lee's domestic problems, Lightburn,' said Lieutenant Taylor. We were in his cabin in the after deckhouse. He was slightly built, but his schoolboy complexion was offset by dark, penetrating blue eyes. 'You do realise, I'll have to report this to Number One?'

'Yes, sir,' I replied, racked with guilt. 'Sorry, sir.'

I returned to the sick bay and waited. Shortly after the ship sailed, I was summoned to see my boss.

He sat back in his chair while I repeated the conversation I had with Postie.

'You should have spoken to his DO before this happened,' he said, stroking his chin. 'I'll send a signal and maybe the police in Huddesfield will pick him up.'

'What will happen to him, sir?' I asked, feeling somewhat

relieved. 'He seemed very worried and...'

'You should have thought of that before,' he snapped angrily.

I felt physically sick. Poor Postie, I thought, he will probably be sent to detention and dismissed the service. A sense of failure crept through me. If only I had intervened and spoken to Lieutenant Taylor sooner...

That afternoon, Big Geordie and I assembled everything from DDT powder to Primus stoves.

'What the hell will we want these for?' asked Big Geordie, holding up a feeding cup.

'If you ever get injured, and can't move,' I replied, folding a blanket, 'you'll find out. And don't forget that tin of chloride of lime. We may have to disinfect the water supply.'

Next morning, in the pouring rain, the medical team put everything into a lorry waiting on the jetty. This included four Neil Robertson and six army collapsible stretchers.

My valise was well stocked with drugs, ranging from morphine to metal vials full of assorted tablets.

'Bloody hell, Doc,' gasped Pete. 'We've got enough stuff here to cure the fleet.'

'That's the general idea, Scribes,' I replied, passing a box of dressings up to Spud Tate. 'Those bloody umpires won't catch us out...I hope.'

The exercise involved the whole ship's company, all of whom transported their equipment shore.

And still it rained.

The 'disaster area' was a disused stone quarry. A team of rain-soaked officers and chief petty officers waited for us. All carried plastic-covered clipboards and wore foul weather clothing.

We began the task of unloading our gear.

Straight away I recognised Wardmaster Sub-Lieutenant Hardy.

'Name?' he snapped, taking a pencil and lifting up the plastic cover of his clipboard.

I told him.

'Right,' he replied, rain dribbling down off his cap. 'Select an area and set up an emergency medical post. What will be your main priorities?'

'Safety of the staff and patients, sir,' I replied. 'Near a road and water supply, concealed from contaminated areas.'

He pursed his lips. 'Hmm . . . yes,' he murmured. He then

looked at the equipment the team had unloaded. 'Why so many Neil Robertson stretchers and splints?'

'Better to be safe than sorry, sir,' I replied.

He made a note on his board. 'Right. Carry on,' he said, and squelched away.

Dicky Barton was right. He really was a bastard.

By now, everything and everybody was completely soaked. I felt like telling this beady-eyed prick of an officer to stuff his splints where the sun doesn't shine.

The scene resembled a battlefield, circa 1914.

Two 'bombed' buildings stood at the foot of a large hill. Soggy red flags, indicating some sort of emergency, hung limply on poles at various places. Holes, half-filled with brackish water and jagged stumps of trees, dotted the landscape.

And still the rain came down, making movement underfoot treacherous.

'Every bugger's going to go down with 'flu, after this,' groaned Shiner Wright, unloading a stretcher off the lorry.

'Trench foot, more like it,' quipped Spud Tate, wiping rain from his eyes.

The building I chose for our emergency medical station consisted of four walls and half a roof. Nearby was a muddy streak of water which, I presume, had once been a stream. All around, orders were being barked, as ratings plodded about up to their ankles in mud.

The bedraggled figures of Paddy Alexander and Seldom appeared. They carried a roll of canvas. 'The Buffer thought you'd need an awning over you,' said Seldom. 'He also said it would cost you another pint.'

'Cheers, lads,' I replied with a grin. 'If we don't all go down with pneumonia, he's more than welcome.'

Paddy and Seldom busied themselves covering the roof, while the medical teams were kept busy dealing with a series of mock injuries.

Sub-Lieutenant Hardy hovered over Paddy. 'That is not the way to apply a sling,' he cried. 'You'll strangle the patient like that.'

'I'll fuckin' strangle you if you're not careful,' muttered Paddy, under his breath.

'What was that you said?' snorted the officer.

251

'I said, I'd be more careful, sir,' replied Paddy, glaring at him.

The rain was slowly turning the area into a swamp.

The sub-lieutenant stomped away and stationed himself near the edge of a steep hill. Using his binoculars he surveyed the scene. Two other umpires stood some way behind him.

'Bastard,' I said, putting a first field dressing on the head of a sailor. 'He doesn't miss a trick.'

Suddenly, there came a dull rumble followed by a loud shriek.

I looked up in time to see Hardy disappear down the hillside.

'Help!!!' he cried, tumbling into a heap of mud.

'Quick,' someone shouted. 'The hill has subsided.'

Everyone dropped whatever they were doing and rushed towards the morass of black mud that was once a hill. One or two fell over trying to grab hold of the injured officer.

In a flash, the disaster exercise became the real thing. 'Come on, lads,' I cried, gabbing my valise. 'Someone bring a stretcher.'

When we reached the scene, Hardy was up to his shoulders in black, sandy mud. A crowd of sailors looked down, trying to reach him with their hands. He had lost his cap and his greying hair and face was splattered with mud. Frantically waving his arms, he cried out, 'It's my leg. It's my leg. For Chrissake, get me out, I'm sinking.'

Seldom threw him a rope. 'Grab hold, sir,' he yelled. 'And we'll heave you out in no time.'

'Should have left the bugger to sink,' growled Paddy, as he and others hauled away.

Finally, looking like a rhinoceros emerging from a mud bath, the sailors pulled him up onto the grass verge

Sub-Lieutenant Hardy was completely covered in slimy soil and his face was contorted with pain. Reaching with his hand, he clutched his lower leg.

'It's broken, I tell you,' he cried.

He was right. After gently rolling up his trouser leg, I could see the slight protrusion of a bone under the skin. 'I'm going to give you a shot of morphia, sir,' I said, 'then we'll get you out of here.'

'Send for the MO,' he cried, weakly.

'I already have done,' I replied, giving him the injection.

After immobilising his legs, we gently lifted him into the Neil Robertson stretcher. A surgeon lieutenant arrived and I told him what had happened.

'Good work,' he said. 'Let's get him into the ambulance.'

As we did so, I turned to Paddy, and said in a loud voice, 'Good job we brought plenty of Neil Robertson stretchers, wasn't it?' The head of Sub-Lieutenant Hardy poked up from under the blankets, and after moaning incoherently, slumped back

The exercise was cancelled.

When we arrived at the wharf, the ship, shrouded in palls of rain, was a welcome sight. 'I hope Tanky's got the rum ready,' sighed Big Geordie, unloading a box of soggy bandages. 'If ever I've needed me tot, it's now.'

The Buffer was right. Work-ups certainly were a fucking pain the arse!

16

The day after leaving Portland, we were joined by one of our sister ships, HMS *Diamond,* (Commanding Officer, M. G. Howarth, DSC. RN). She took station on our port beam, and together we ploughed through the sea, pitching and rolling in perfect unison.

She looked identical to *Decoy.* The lines of her superstructure stood out against the grey sky, halyards shivering in the wind as signals flashed between the two ships. *Diamond's* sharp bows dipped and rose as they cut through the dark green sea - it was like watching a replica of our selves.

After taking passage through the English Channel into the Bay of Biscay, the weather deteriorated. The ship corkscrewed through the waves like a demented sea-monster. Each violent movement sent me bouncing against the sides of my bunk. Everything rattled like milk bottles in the wind. Rain and sea spray splattered against the closed scuttles. Sleep became impossible and once more, I thought we might keel over.

The next morning, my first customer was Paddy Alexander. 'In case you're wondering what's happening, Doc,' he said. 'We're in the middle of a force six gale, so we are.'

Paddy's black oilskin glistened with rain. He carried his cap in his hand. His hair was a tousled mess and a trickle of blood ran down the side of his face.

'Bashed me nut on the hatchway, so I did,' he said, wiping his face with the back of his hand. 'You wouldn't be havin' a drop in the bottle, now? I'm fuckin' freezing.'

'It's in the fridge,' I replied, putting a plaster over his cut. 'Have a swig, but leave some for me.'

I had got into the habit of bottling my tot and drinking it later on. It helped me to sleep at night. However, the bad weather during the past few days had put a few lads in my mess off their tot, so rather than see the precious liquid go to waste, I bottled it. When word got around, business suddenly picked up.

'How long will this bloody storm last, Paddy?'

Paddy took a swig and replaced the bottle. 'Thanks, Doc,' he sighed, running his tongue across his upper lip. 'That's just what the doctor ordered. It should be a bit calmer tomorrow when we arrive in Gib.'

Before leaving, he said, 'Cheers. When this plaster comes off, I'll be back.'

After Paddy left, a stocky able seaman with a face the colour of death came in. 'Come in, Craggy,' I said, pushing a chair in his direction. 'What's the problem?'

Ray Cragg was a national serviceman and had a history of gastric problems.

'It's my guts again,' he muttered. 'I just can't keep anything down.'

His stomach was tender to touch and he had a raised temperature. 'I'm turning you in here, Craggy,' I said. 'When we arrive in Gib tomorrow we meet up with the *Duchess.*' (Commanding Officer, H. G. Austin. DSO. RN.) I'll take you to see the squadron MO.'

He was the first rating I had admitted into the sick bay.

I placed him on a light diet, stopped his tot and dosed him up with magnesium triscillicate.

For once I fell in for entering harbour. This was my first visit to a foreign land and I did not want to miss anything. We were still dressed in blues, as tropical rig could not be worn until the end of May.

Jutting into the clear blue Mediterranean sky, the enormity of the Rock took my breath away. It hovered over the port like a guardian angel, casting a protective shadow over the entrance to *Mare Nostrum.*

The sea was calm and a warm, aromatic breeze fanned my face. A mass of red terracotta roofs swept upwards from the base of the harbour. These formed the backdrop to several warships secured to buoys or alongside wharves. A forest of masts and funnels reflected in the blue waters, and huge cranes towered in the air like giant predators. This then, was my first exciting glimpse of Gibraltar, gateway to all ports east of Suez.

'Do you hear there?' came the Jimmy's voice over the tannoy. 'The American aircraft carrier you see anchored away to port is the USS *Constitution.* She is carrying the film star, Grace Kelly to Monaco for her wedding to Prince Ranier.'

All eyes focussed on the aircraft carrier. From her yardarm fluttered a large Stars and Stripes. On her flight deck stood several silver sabre jets gleaming in the morning sun.

'I wonder which officer is giving her one?' muttered Jerry Johnson from the corner of his mouth.

'All of them, I expect,' whispered Scouse Kilbane, 'the lucky bastards.'

We tied up at a wharf aft of HMS *Duchess*. Berthed on the opposite side of the harbour were two light cruisers, HMS *Glasgow* and *Sheffield*. There were also several smaller ships from other countries including France and America.

Waiting on the quayside was Harry Stokes, the Jimmy's leading steward. Standing next to him was the Postie flanked by two burly naval patrolmen. He looked pale and drawn, no doubt wondering what fate awaited him onboard.

'I'm off to visit the squadron MO,' I said to Cragg, who, by this time, was feeling a lot better. 'I'll ask him to come and see you. He can also check on Knocker White's arm. '

'Cheers, Doc,' replied Cragg. 'Maybe he'll re-instate my tot.'

After saluting *Duchess's* quarterdeck I went into the after deck house and knocked on the sick bay door.

'Wait,'echoed a stern voice.

I knocked again.

The door slid open. Facing me was a stout, red-faced, three-badge petty officer.

'Are you deaf?' he spat. 'I said wait,' and closed the door.

He's probably been at sea too long, I thought. Nevertheless, it was no way to address a fellow medic.

The door finally opened. I shot a piercing glance at Red Face.

'Thank you,' I said. 'Do you normally treat medical staff like that?'

'Petty Officer Burgess was obeying my orders.' Standing behind the PO was a tall, thin-faced surgeon lieutenant. He had fair hair and spoke with a pronounced Merseyside accent. 'We were just finishing the clinic.'

'Clinic,' I said to myself. He must think he's still in Fazakerly General.

On top of a nearby dressing trolley lay a few kidney dishes containing used gauze swabs and instruments. The dark linoleum on the deck was stained and the brass scuttles needed a good polish.

'Well, sir,' I said, looking at the PO. 'He might have said so.

We are in the same branch, after all.'

'And I am much senior to you,' replied Red Face. 'So bear that in mind.'

'You don't say,' I answered sarcastically.

The doctor gave a cough and sat down at his desk. 'I am Surgeon Lieutenant Jones,' he said.' And you are...?

I introduced myself to the doctor and told him about Cragg.

'Why can't he come over himself?' interrupted the PO. 'The MO is very busy.'

I ignored him.

The doctor stood up and reached for his cap. 'Very well, leading hand,' he said. 'Let's take a look. You stay here, PO,' he added, looking at Red Face. 'I won't be long.'

With a final glare at the PO, I followed the doctor outside.

As the MO entered my sick bay, Cragg dropped his western on the deck.

'Morning, lad,' said the doctor. 'What seems to be the trouble?'

'It's me guts, sir, I've always had a lot of bother with me guts.'

'Hmm...' he said, reading Cragg's medical history. 'So you have.' He then turned back the bedclothes and examined Cragg's abdomen.

'Well,' he said, 'you seem to have made a good recovery. Keep him on the mag trisillicate,' he said, writing on Cragg's medical documents, 'and no rum or greasy food. He can live in his mess and be put on light duties.'

'Yes, sir,' I replied.

'I'll see him again when we reach Malta.' Before leaving, he turned to me, and in a quiet, but firm voice, said, 'Try not to be so rude to Petty Officer Burgess. He is a senior PO, and *you* are very junior.'

While he was here I sent for Knocker White.

'When you arrived in Malta,' said the doctor, writing a medical report on an F Med 6, 'have him seen by the orthopaedic specialist.'

After he had left, Cragg rolled his eyes up and pulled a face.

'You two haven't exactly hit it off, have you?' he said, grinning.

'Wait till you see his PO,' I replied, filling the kettle.

Two letters from home arrived. Mum had seen the specialist

and was all right. In her letter, she wrote, 'Your Dad says when you go to Malta, go to a place called the Gut and visit the Texas Bar. He says they sell the best 'vino collapso' on the island.'

Joe was being sent to Cyprus with the 3rd Parachute Brigade, Jock Forbes was still in Aldershot and Phil and Reg were at sea.

When I read that Tony was due for parole soon, my heart missed a beat.

Midway through the morning, Jan Hawes came into the sick bay. 'What will happen to Postie?' I asked. Jan said he had a slight headache, which was just an excuse to scrounge a cup of tea.

His redbrick features broke into a frown. 'Oh he'll probably get a warrant, or get slung off the ship.'

'What's a warrant, Jan?' I asked, pouring him a mug of tea.

'The junior ratings fall in on the upper-deck. The Postie faces them. Then, the 'swain will stand behind him and take his cap off. The Jimmy will read out the charges from a warrant followed by the punishment. Bit like the old days when you got the lash in front of the ship's company.'

Early next morning the ship slipped her moorings and we entered the Mediterranean. The sky was a cloudless, cobalt blue, and the sea like a millpond.

Once again I fell in for leaving harbour. The dry, dusty sirocco, fresh from the sands of North Africa, caressed my face. Across the straits, the coastline of Spain shimmered in a heat haze. *Decoy,* as the senior ship, was in the van. Together we constituted a squadron known as Group B Darings. With glowing pride, I watched as the three warships, line abreast, glided gracefully through the sparkling waters.

'Hands, fall out,' piped the quartermaster from the bridge. 'Duty watch, close up.'

'Next stop,' said Paddy Murphy, rubbing his hands together, 'Malta, George Cross.'

His remark reminded me of another of Dad's stories.

'So you'll be going to Malta, eh?' he said. 'Battered to pieces during the war they were - day and night. The poor buggers had to take to the catacombs.'

He went to tell me that the catacombs were rock-cut tunnels used in ancient times as tombs.

'Only safe place for them.' His voice took on a more sombre

note. 'Malta had more bombs dropped on it than London or Liverpool. In 1941 it was the most bombed place on earth, especially Valletta and the dockyards. I know, because some of the lads and meself went ashore and helped to carry the corpses from the ruins. Women and kids.' He paused. 'The old king awarded the island the George Cross, and by Christ, they earned it.'

Later that morning, the dwarf-like figure of Mitch came into the sick bay.

His leathery face looked as if it had collapsed. His toothless grin told its own story. 'It's me teeth, Doc,' he gabbled. 'Lost them last night in Gib.'

'You'll have to wait till Malta, Mitch,' I said, grinning. 'They've got a good dental department at Bighi. Maybe they'll give you a new set of gums.'

Each evening I would go on the bridge and fill in the number of sick in the ship's log. Usually the captain, sitting in his high chair would be conning the ship. The first lieutenant was invariably next to him, together with the officer of the watch. Occasionally the captain gave an order to the wheelhouse, altering the ship's course.

The open bridge gave a perfect view of our surroundings. Directly ahead, the bows, cutting through the dark water, sent waves of phosphorescence swishing along each side of the ship. The moon, half hidden by wisps of grey clouds, cast a pale glow on a calm sea.

Perhaps it was my imagination, but the sky seemed darker than at home. The myriad of stars, sparkling like diamonds, appeared larger and more distinct than those above Merseyside.

I imagined myself in one of Drake's galleons, setting out to circumnavigate the world. Or, better still, on the swaying deck in one of Hornblower's wooden walls, waiting to engage the enemy.

'Ahem.'

Turning around I saw the first lieutenant. His face showed up clearly in the dim, red lighting.

'I'll be sending a signal to Malta requesting *Pratique,*' he said quietly. 'I take it everyone's had their jabs and everything?'

'Yes, sir,' I replied. 'There's still a few medicals outstanding, but we didn't have time to do them in Gib. As a matter of fact, sir,' I went on. 'You still haven't had your smallpox vaccination.'

'I see,' he replied curtly. 'Remind me when we arrive in Malta.'

During the next few days the ship's company practised a variety of evolutions including 'abandon ship,' and 'man overboard.'

Whenever 'away sea-boats crew,' was piped, I would grab my life jacket, medical valise and quickly scramble aboard one of the cutters. I clung onto the wooden seating for dear life as the cutter was lowered and the falls released. With a spine-shattering flop the vessel would hit the rolling sea. The crew would then begin pulling away to 'rescue,' an imaginary drowning man. By the time I returned, I was soaked through and my face caked with salt.

The day before we were due to arrive in Malta, the door opened and in came Cragg. His face was ashen and he held both arms tightly across his abdomen.

'It's me guts again, Doc,' he said, obviously in pain. 'I've been sick and every time I go to the heads, it's like treacle.'

He was clearly going into shock. When I examined his abdomen, he flinched, and cried out. He then vomited into a dish. My heart missed a beat. The contents were like ground coffee grains. His pulse was slow and weak. At first I thought he might have food poisoning. But the colour of his vomit made me suspicious.

'Don't worry, Craggy,' I said, trying to comfort him. 'You're going to be all right.'

Placing an enamel basin on the deck near him, I drew the curtains, and took down my BR 888. What I read made my heart miss a beat. According to the manual, Cragg probably had a perforated gastric ulcer. If he didn't receive proper treatment, he could develop peritonitis and die.

I grabbed the telephone and asked to speak to the first lieutenant. 'Please come quickly to the sick bay, sir,' I said. 'I think we have an, emergency.'

Meanwhile Cragg lay still and quiet. His pulse was still weak and his blood pressure low.

The Jimmy arrived and listened intently as, out of earshot of Cragg, I told him the problem.

'Right,' he said, reaching for the telephone. 'Bridge, Number One here. Let me speak to the captain.' After quietly explaining the crisis to the captain, he turned and said, 'The transmitting room will contact *Duchess* on the ship-to-ship telephone. The call will be transferred here and you can speak to the medical officer.'

In a surprisingly short time, the sick bay telephone rang.

'Surgeon Lieutenant Jones here,' crackled the voice of the doctor. 'What's the problem?'

I told him.

'Give him an injection of morphia,' said the doctor, 'I'll come over. Keep him warm and give him nothing by mouth.'

The first lieutenant listened to the conversation.

'I'll inform the captain. We'll stop the ship and send a launch for the MO.'

'What's going on?' sighed Cragg, after the Jimmy had gone.

'I'm sending for the MO, Craggy,' I said, trying not to alarm him. 'Just as a precautionary measure, mate. You'll be OK. Don't worry.'

Quite abruptly, the engines became quiet and the ship slowed down. The captain's clipped voice came over the tannoy. 'The ship has stopped to embark the squadron doctor. There is no cause for alarm. We will get under way as soon as possible. That is all.'

The ship stopped and began to roll like a log.

'Away motor boats crew,' echoed the pipe.

The doctor, accompanied by PO Burgess, soon arrived.

After examining the contents in the basin, he murmured, 'Hmm...I see what you mean.'

'His blood pressure is dangerously low,' whispered the doctor to his PO. 'It's a good job we brought the glucose and saline drip.'

The first lieutenant came in.

'How soon can we get under way, Doc?' he asked the MO.

The MO took the officer to one side, and in a subdued voice, said, 'We need to get to Malta quickly. Could you ask the captain to send a signal to Bighi requesting a launch meet us on arrival?'

'It's that serious, then, Doc?'

'Yes. He's lost a lot of blood. I'm going to give him a glucose and saline transfusion.' He turned to PO Burgess. 'You can return to the ship, PO. We'll be able to manage here.'

Burgess's rubicund features broke into a frown. 'Are you sure, sir?' he said, shooting a withering glance at me. 'Lightburn here, isn't very experienced.'

'I know what to do, sir,' I answered confidently.

With that the PO sniffed the air contemptuously and left.

The doctor scrubbed up while I prepared everything.

I took out a metal canister and bottles of clear solution from the bag. The doctor put on a mask and rubber gloves. He carefully removed the sterile rubber tubing from the canister. I handed him a piece of cotton wool soaked in spirit. After wiping the top he attached the tubing to the bottle and allowed some of the solution to run through.

'This might hurt a bit,' he said to Cragg, cleaning his arm, 'but try and keep still. It won't take long.'

The cannula was expertly inserted into a vein in Craggy's arm, and tapped down.

'You'll be chatting up the nurses in Bighi in no time, Craggy,' I said, holding his head and giving him a few sips of water. 'Try and get one for me.'

The MO stood up, peeled off his gloves, and wiped his brow with a piece of gauze.

'Keep it steady at thirty drops a minute,' he said, sitting down. 'And thanks for your help.'

I filled the kettle.

'That was a damn good job, sir, if you don't mind me saying so. Did you do your training in Liverpool?'

His pale blue eyes lit up in a smile. 'My accent raised a few eyebrows in the wardroom,' he said, taking a sip of tea. 'But it doesn't bother me,' and added. 'Yes. I interned at Sefton General.'

By this time we were at full speed. The ship rattled and vibrated as we cut through the ocean. During the night, the MO and I did a four on, four off watch.

The MO changed the saline and glucose drip, and by the early morning Cragg had regained his colour. The MO then sat down and wrote up his findings on the F Med 10 while I removed the bottle.

The southern shores of Malta hove into view. The sky was cloudless and the sea, covered in a steamy heat haze, shone like molten silver.

The time was just after six a.m.

'Stand by to receive a launch, port side,' sounded the pipe.

'We'll have to put you in a Neil Robertson stretcher, Cragg,' said the MO. 'Do you feel up to it?'

'I think so, sir,' replied Cragg. 'The old gut isn't playing up so much now.'

'We'll be entering Grand Harbour shortly,' said the MO. 'The launch will be waiting when we arrive in Kalkara Creek. How are you feeling?'

'Not too bad, thanks, sir,' replied Cragg, levering himself up on his elbows.

The first lieutenant came in. 'Twenty minutes,' he said.

'Can I have a few of my first aid party, sir,' I said. 'They know the drill.'

'Very well,' he replied, reaching for the telephone. 'Pipe, all available members of the first aid party to the sick bay.'

Sccouse Kilbane, Big Geordie, Jerry Johnson and Paddy Murphy appeared.

Big Geordie immediately took charge. 'Right, lads,' he said, rubbing his hands together. 'Come on Scouse, let's get a stretcher. One of you bring a blanket.'

From the porthole, I watched excitedly, as the ship passed through the breakwater into Grand Harbour. I could only see out of the port side of the ship.

'That's Ricasoli Fort,' said Pincher, standing next to me. 'It's one of the biggest forts in the Meddy. If you look you can see the guns of the battery. And that's Rinella Creek,' he added, pointing to a large inlet, busy with small craft.

'Bloody hell,' I cried. 'What's that up there?'

On the left, overlooking Grand Harbour, stood what looked like three classical Roman Villas. Built of yellow sandstone, the masonry shone like gold in the morning sun. The biggest of the three was in the middle. Several stout, Doric columns supported a wide, triangular pediment and from its apex fluttered a white ensign.

'That, my handsome,' replied, Pincher, 'is where we're heading – Bighi hospital.'

The warm air hit us like a furnace as we carried Cragg onto the upper deck. Scouse and Jerry scrambled down the gangway into the launch. Big Geordie, Jerry and two other matelots carefully lowered the stretcher to them. Meanwhile, the coxswain of the launch kept his craft steady by holding a hooked pole to the gangway.

Several of the crew gave Cragg a friendly wave and shouted comments about 'loafing,' and 'swinging the lead.'

With two blasts of the coxswain's whistle, the duty stoker started the engines.

'How are you feeling, Craggy?' I asked loosening the straps of the stretcher. 'We'll be there shortly, matey.'

The launch cut through the crystal clear water, sending a mini-bow wave rippling along the hull.

'Over there,' said Pincher, pointing to his left, 'is Fort St Angelo.'

Jutting out into the harbour was an enormous fortress. Its crenellated walls swept majestically downwards onto a bed of rocks. On top of the battlements stood a square tower with a white ensign flying from a flagpole – a witness to the impregnability of this once -heroic island.

'And that's Fort St Elmo,' remarked Big Geordie, pointing away to our right. 'Further along you can just see the ramparts of St Lazarus Bastion. That's where they planned the invasion of Sicily and Italy.'

Further along a mass of irregular, flat-topped buildings rose upwards. Some had a facade of archways and balconies. Others appeared to balance precariously above one another. Many had brightly painted galleries and shuttered windows. They appeared to spring haphazardly in a jumbled heap from the harbour road. Numerous church spires and domes dominated the skyline. All were built, so Pincher told me, of local yellow limestone, gleaming like glazed ochre in the morning sunlight.

'The biggest of the church domes you can see up there belongs to the Carmelite Church,' said Pincher. 'It's nearly as big as St Peter's in Rome.'

Craft, simliar to those in Venice, cruised around the harbour. Each vessel was propelled through the water by a man standing at the back, manipulating a single oar.

'What are those?' I asked, shielding my eyes against the sun. Most of them had been to Malta before and were familiar with the island.

'They're the dghajas, (pronounced 'diceos'),' replied Big Geordie. 'Dom Mintoff, the Prime Minister, believes in free enterprise. They'll take you ashore or back onboard. But always remember to haggle or else the tight buggers will rob you. Each is named after a Catholic saint. Those eyes painted on the side are called 'the eyes of Osiris.' They are supposed to protect the boat from harm.'

'Load of rubbish,' cried Scouse Kilbane. 'One of them bloodywell sunk on me a few years ago when I was here in the *Vigo*. Had to be rescued by a fuckin' motor launch.'

Secured between buoys were the battle-class destroyers, *Barfleur, Agincourt* and *Armada.* I remembered seeing them in Plymouth. White canvas awning covered each fo'c'sle. Motor launches from every ship rolled alongside, attached to a boom.

One of the heroes of the Battle of the River Plate, HMS *Cumberland,* was also tied to a buoy, reminding me of Scouse Wilson's tragic drowning.

Two aircraft carriers were also secured in the middle of the harbour. Pincher saw me staring at them.

'Them's the *Eagle* and *Albion,*' he said. '*Albion's* on her way back from the Far East. Lucky buggers will be home soon.'

The launch came alongside a small jetty. The walls of the hospital loomed high and I could see a balcony separating two columns of windows which I later discovered were wards.

Looking up I saw the square tower. At its base was an entrance, protected by two columns supporting a roof.

'How are you feeling, Craggy, old son?' I asked, tightening the straps of stretcher.

'A bit rough, Doc,' he replied, licking his lips. 'and thirsty.'

'Hang on,' I replied. 'We'll soon have you tucked in, surrounded by a bevy of beautiful nurses.'

The lift took us up to the receiving room We placed Cragg on a table and removed the stretcher. Geordie and the others waited outside and had a smoke.

After a brief examination by a doctor, we were told to take Cragg to M1 ward. Two SBA's wheeled Cragg across a stone courtyard. In front was the middle building I saw coming into the harbour. The rounded columns and pediment looked even more impressive than they did from the harbour.

'That's the sisters' quarters,' said an SBA. 'Forbidden territory, to the likes of you and me.

Away to our right two rows of half columns separated a balcony. Behind these, large windows opened into wards. Two stone bridges lead onto the lower balcony. Nearby, signs read x-ray department and orthopaedic out-patients.

The first person I saw when we entered the ward was the burly figure of Desperate. He wore a white gown, and in one hand he carried a bedpan, covered with a piece of jaconet. Despite being heavily tanned, he still looked as if he needed a shave. When he saw me, his face lit up like a belisha beacon.

'Tom, you bugger!' he exclaimed. 'How's life on the ocean waves?'

The smell from the bedpan when he came close made me wince.

I shook his hand. 'Hello, Des, still in the shit, I see.'

He laughed and turned away. 'Be back in a minute,' he said and disappeared towards the heads.

By this time Cragg was safely ensconced in bed.

The wards were spacious, with stone floors. Large shuttered windows led onto a balcony. From a high ceiling came the whirr of electric fans. At the head of every bed was a roll of neatly-rolled mosquito netting. Several patients, clad in pyjamas, sat around a highly-polished table, drinking cups of tea.

'I'll be in to see you to-morrow, Craggy,' I said. 'My old pal, Desperate, the fella you saw me talking to, will look after you. Don't worry.'

Suddenly, from behind, came a familiar female voice.

'Hello, *Leading* Sick Berth Attendant Lightburn.'

When I turned around, my heart missed a beat

Standing before me was Sister Johannsen.

I had almost forgotten how beautiful she was. Her blue eyes were exaggerated by a smooth, golden tan. She threw her head back and laughed. 'Goodness me,' she cried. 'The cat has got your tongue. Yes?'

'Er...yes,' I managed to say. 'I think it has.'

Desperate arrived and stood a few yards away. He gave a discreet cough. 'Excuse me, Sister,' he said, quickly glancing at me. 'It's time for rounds. The MO will be here in a minute.'

'Thank you, Morgan,' she replied, without looking at him. 'I'll be with you in a minute.' She smiled at me and added, 'Will you be coming here again?'

My mouth had dried up. 'Yes,' I replied. 'Tomorrow morning.'

'Good, I'm on duty then,' and in a whisper, added, 'must go now. See you tomorrow, Thomas. And don't look so worried.'

Worried! For a moment I was in a state of shock. Bloody-hell, I thought, after all this time, she actually remembered my name. I hardly heard Desperate telling me Lofty Small was on nights and Jock McBride worked on the orthopaedic ward.

'I'll tell them you have arrived,' he went on. 'We can have a few wets in the canteen. OK?'

'Oh, er… right, Des,' I replied. 'Definitely. I'll be back in the morning to see Craggy. I'll have to push off now, mate. The launch is waiting.'

We shook hands. As I left the ward, Sister Johannsen gave me a smile and a small wave. I was so excited, I almost forgot to make an appointment for Knocker to see the orthopaedic specialist.

As we entered Dockyard Creek, I saw the three Darings hove to alongside the wharf. On each one the duty watches were busy rigging up canvas awnings over the fo'c'sle.

Tied up on the opposite side were two dark grey destroyers flying the stars-and-stripes.

'Bloody Yanks in town, I see,' remarked Big Geordie. 'The tarts will be out in force tonight, I expect'

'Fuckin' great,' chortled Scouse. 'It's been ages since I had a jump.'

'Dirty bugger,' said Paddy Murphy in disgust. 'And you a married man, too.'

That evening Pete and I went ashore. We shared a diceo with Taff Leighton and Paddy Alexander. Crossing Grand Harbour was an exhilarating experience. Warships, ranging from destroyers to aircraft carriers, lay at anchor. White canvas awnings covered each fo'c'sle and quarterdeck. All were painted pale grey and lay in the water like predators at rest.

Quite unexpectedly, the penetrating sound of the bosun's pipe pierced the evening air announcing colours. 'Attention on the upper deck. Face aft and salute,' echoed around the harbour. White ensigns were reverently lowered ending the nightly ceremony of 'Colours.' This was immediately followed by the 'carry on.'

As if by magic, a mass of lights lit up the harbour like a Christmas Grotto.

Down lighting was switched on casting eerie shadows which played along the side of each ship. The towering walls of Forts St Angelo and Ricasoli became illuminated, adding a touch of medieval mysticism to the scene; and further along, the golden masonry of Bighi hospital shone like an Emperor's Palace, reminding me of Sister Johannsen.

My eyes swept around the harbour. Suddenly, I felt humble and proud. This was the Royal Navy I had imagined - silent, quietly alert and ready for any eventuality.

'You can see the Three Cities from here,' said Taff Leighton, pointing across the harbour. 'Fort St Angelo is part of Vittoriosa, and where we are berthed in Frenchman's Creek is Seneglea. Across the way, there, is Cospicua.'

'Why do they call them 'cities,'?' I asked. 'They don't look very big.'

'Er...it goes back yonks,' replied Taff, searching for an answer. 'Something to do with the Knights of St George.'

Pete began to laugh. 'That's where the Maltese get the saying, 'Once a knight is quite all right. But three times a night's too much.'

The boatman was not amused.

'How much, Jose. Two bob?' said Paddy when we were half way across Grand Harbour.

I looked up at the burly figure of the oarsman silhouetted against the evening sky. His dark, leathery face wrinkled into a smile. 'One shilling, not enough,' he said, shrugging his shoulders. 'You give me two. Yes? Not for me, but for my diceo.'

Custom House steps was crowded with sailors. Some were haggling with oarsmen over fares, others stood around laughing and joking. We walked through a dark archway into a narrow, winding road. Taff and Paddy said a quick goodbye and dived into the nearest bar.

In front of us were rows of old buildings, with paint flaking off shutters and doors. 'They're the doss houses,' said Pete. 'If you are too pissed, and miss the last liberty-boat, you can always crash in one of them. But if you do, make sure you keep your money-belt next to you.'

I grinned, and let my eyes slowly wander upwards towards the lights of Valetta.

'Come on, Pete,' I said impatiently. 'Show me where The Gut is.'

17

We crossed a narrow road and walked down a side street.

'We're going to take the lift up to Barraka Gardens,' said Pete. 'It's the quickest way to the town.'

Several sailors from other ships had the same idea.

We left the lift and hurried past a large garden overlooking Grand Harbour.

After crossing a cobbled square we passed the ruins of what must have been a fine-looking building. 'That used to be the Opera House,' said Pete, 'till the Jerries bombed it.'

The leathery features of the elderly reflected the hybrid history of the island dating back to the Phoenicians. Groups of men in shirtsleeves sat in doorways smoking, while fat women, carrying baskets of washing stood and gossiped.

They paid no attention as we passed - after all, Malta had been a garrison island for over a century.

We arrived at a wide, well-lit, crowded road. Groups of young people sat outside cafes sipping drinks, listening to juke box music.

'This is Kingsway, Valetta's main street,' said Pete. 'Gets quite busy at night.'

Several pairs of pretty, dark-haired girls in coloured dresses paraded arm in arm. As they passed us, each giggled but kept their eyes averted. Small cliques of elderly women in black followed closely behind.

'Don't even think of it,' said Pete, giving me a sideways glance. 'You'll need a marriage licence to trap one of those. Until then, they're well chaperoned, usually by their grannies.'

'Pity,' I sighed, drooling at another raven-haired beauty. 'What about those in The Gut?'

'You'll soon find out,' he said dryly.

Making our way through a side street, we came to a narrow alleyway jam packed with servicemen. There were red, white and blue berets of the French, the crumpled pork-pie hats of the Yanks, soldiers in khaki and a splattering of the Brylcream boys. But the bulk of the bustling crowd wore round caps of the Royal Navy.

'Well,' said Pete, gazing around. 'Here it is, dear old Straight Street.'

'Strait Street,' I replied, shooting him a glance. 'I thought you said we were going to The Gut.'

'This is The Gut,' he replied, rubbing his hands together. 'But its official name is Strait Street.'

A fog of tobacco hovered like a smokescreen in the air. Peels of raucous laughter and the occasional scream mingled with music from jukeboxes. On either side, gallery balconies with open shutters jutted out from high walls. Carpets were draped over iron balcony rails and washing lines, festooned with clothing, hung limply in the warm, night air. Stout women in white aprons sat on chairs, soberly gazing down at a scene they had witnessed hundreds of times.

'You seem to know your way around, Pete.'

'I ought to,' he replied with a grin. 'I was stationed at Manoel Island in Sliema for two years.'

The Gut sloped downwards, disappearing into a mass of dimly-lit bars. Each bar looked the same: whitewashed walls with dingy lighting. Lounging near doorways, heavily made-up women in tight fitting dresses beckoned passers by.

'Big eats, clean sheets, Jack,' cooed one.

'Piss off,' replied Pete. 'I'm fed up, not hard up.'

The girl put her tongue out. 'Cheapskate English,' she cried, and gave him the bent elbow

A couple of American sailors, arms around each other, staggered to a halt and began slobbering all over her, before going inside.

We passed "The Egyptian Queen", "The Blue Peter", "Harry's Bar" and others. Finally, we arrived at the "Texas Bar".

Behind a small counter stood a fat bartender cleaning glasses. He wore a pink shirt and his fleshy face looked as if it hadn't been shaved for a year. Standing near was a peroxide blonde, wearing a black dress and a false smile.

'Come in, Jack,' she said. 'Drinks very cheap in here. I give you special price.'

'I bet that's not all she'll give you,' said Pete from the side of his mouth.

The place was full. A few of the lads from our ship sat at a table. Seldom, Scouse Kilbane and Big Geordie were amongst them.

'Hope you've got plenty of penicillin, Doc,' cried Seldom. He leant across the table and gave Scouse a playful push. 'This randy bugger's already had his end away with Sweaty Betty, here.'

'Ah, shit in it, you,' replied Scouse, shoving his empty glass in front of Seldom, 'and get them in.'

Pete ordered a bottle of Marsala wine.

'Bloody-hell, Pete,' I said, taking a mouthful. 'This tastes wicked. My old man must have cast-iron guts. Let's leave this and go to the Jippo Queen and see the dancing girls.'

The "Egyptian Queen" was bigger than the other bars. The sound of Spanish music and castanets hit us as we entered. In the centre, dancing the Flamenco, was a girl with jet-black hair wearing a swirling green dress. Stamping to the music, she threw her head back, rattled her castanets, and glared seductively at the faces below. Everyone clapped and cheered each time she twirled, straining their eyes hoping to catch a glimpse of white thighs and black underwear. The scene was brash, bawdy and licentious.

'This is more like it, Pete,' I said, staring at the girl.

'Get 'em off,' cried a sailor, trying to reach up at her.

'Put yer laughing gear around this,' yelled a marine, grabbing his crutch.

Others yelled, and shouted more obscenities. The girl smiled and ignored them.

I ordered two beers and watched her. 'Bloody-hell, Pete, are all the parties like her?'

'No way,' replied Pete. 'She's just here to bring in custom.'

The music stopped and with a swish of her skirt, the girl left the table and vanished through a door.

This brought forth a cacophony of boos and catcalls.

'Come on, Doc,' said Pete, downing his drink. 'Let's see what "Harry's Bar" has to offer, then we can go and have steak, egg and chips at"Ben Marl's".'

'Where's that?' I asked

'It the best big eats in The Gut,' he replied, wiping his brow with a handkerchief.

"Harry's Bar" was quite full.

Tommy Steele's melodic rendering of '*I Never Felt More Like Singing the Blues*' filled the air. I smiled to myself, thinking of Joe, wondering how he was.

Harry Morrison, our red-haired Jack Dusty, and the wrinkled face of Paddy O'Hanlon, the Chief Engineer, grinned as we came in.

'Brought many French letters ashore, Doc?' said Harry. 'I'll let

271

you have a tin of tea tomorrow for a couple.'

Luckily I had a few with me. 'I hope you buggers remember to use them,' I said, slipping him and the chief a small, a few. 'Or else it'll be the needle.'

Paddy laughed and bought Pete and me a drink.

Suddenly, a voice from behind growled, 'Well. Well. Well. If it isn't the cheeky sprog from the *Decoy?'*

I turned around and saw the bloated features of Petty Officer Burgess. His jacket was open, displaying a partially unbuttoned shirt and an overhanging paunch. His rubicund features appeared bloated and his cap was pushed back on his head. Next to him stood a Chief ERA from *Duchess.* Both looked bleary-eyed and worse for wear.

'What are you drinking?' he slurred, poking my chest, 'lemonade.' As he spoke, a shower of spittle hit me in the face.

'Go back onboard and sleep it off,' I replied, wiping my face and turning away.

He grabbed my arm and flicked the tie out of my jacket. 'Don't turn your back on a senior rate,' he said.

At that moment Paddy O'Hanlon intervened. 'Pack it in,' he said to Burgess. 'The Doc didn't mean anything.'

Burgess turned to Paddy, and slurred, 'Bugger off, I'll sort this little sod out.'

He then pushed me again with hand, knocking me against Paddy.

That was it. I swung a punch which landed on the side of his head.

He staggered back, clutching his face. 'You bastard,' he cried. 'Hit a senior rating, eh? I'll have your hook off you for this.'

Several members of both *Decoy* and *Duchess* moved menacingly towards us.

'Need any help, Doc?' said one of our crew.

'You lot keep out of this,' ordered Paddy O'Hanlon. 'We'll sort it out.'

But I was in no mood for compromise and tried to hit Burgess again. Pete quickly grabbed my arm. 'Don't be an idiot.' he yelled. 'You'll get a warrant like Postie and lose your rate.'

'Go on, you two,' said Paddy, 'Bugger off, before there's a bloody riot.'

'The chief's right, Doc,' said Pete. 'Let's piss off.'

By this time, Burgess was sitting at a table, nursing his head. Pete grabbed my arm and usheered me towards the door.

'You haven't heard the last of this,' yelled Burgess, as we left. 'You'll hear from the squadron MO, mark my words.'

The warm air cleared my head. We lit a cigarette and made our way up the crowded street.

'Real tiger when you get going, aren't you?' said Pete.

'Well,' I replied, taking a deep drag, 'the sod asked for it. Do you think he'll report me?'

'I wouldn't put it past him,' replied Pete. 'But Paddy and Harry saw everything. They'll back you up.'

'What about you, Pete?'

'Me,' he laughed. 'I'll make out the warrant!'

Shortly after eight the next morning Mitch came into the sick bay. I was sitting at my desk. He wore a faded set of number eights and a battered cap. His rubbery face looked more pale and haggard than usual.

'Bugger me,' I said.' You look like death warmed up. I see you got my message about your dental appointment in Bighi at 1100.'

His blood-shot eyes blinked and he gave me a weak, gummy grin. 'I don't know about the bloody dentist,' he mumbled, 'but I've a hell of a hangover. You wouldn't have one in the bottle, would you?'

When he spoke, his face seemed to collapse into a dozen fleshy folds. Suppressing the urge to laugh, I suddenly remembered Bill Manley's magic remedy.

I stood up. 'Sit down, Mitch,' I said, 'I've got just the thing for you.'

Using a mortar and pestle, I quickly mixed the ingredients into a fine powder. Mitch's blood-shot eyes followed my every move. 'You aint going to poison me, are you, Doc?' he muttered.

'Relax, Mitch,' I said, emptying the powder into a glass. 'Now, when I add water, I want you to drink it all down in one. OK?'

The water immediately produced clouds of effervescence which erupted into the air like a volcano. 'Quick,' I shouted, 'knock it back.'

'Talk about Doctor Jekyl and Mr Hyde,' he said, and hurriedly did as I asked. He smacked his lips and burped. 'By gum, that was bloody dynamite. What the'ell was it?''

273

Touching my nose with my forefinger, I replied, 'A secret potion, discovered in China and known only to a few sick bay tiffies.'

By the time we were in the launch on our way to Bighi, Mitch was back to his normal, chirpy self. He looked unusually smart in his number one uniform and for the first time, I noticed he wore several rows of medal ribbons.

'Bugger me, Mitch,' I said. 'I bet this isn't the first time you've been to Malta, is it?'

Mitch's eyes lit up. He gave a short laugh. 'No, son,' he said. 'The first time was on the old *Ledbury* in 1942. I was an AB and us and the *Penn* came into Grand Harbour secured to a Yankee cargo ship called the *Ohio.*'

'Why was that, Mitch?' I asked.

'Y'see, there was this convoy,' said Mitch. 'We'd left the Clyde with fourteen merchant ships. They had to get through as the islanders had no ammunition or any aviation fuel, and little or no food.' His voice suddenly took on a sombre note. 'By the time we reached Malta, there were just five ships still afloat. We lost the carriers *Eagle* and *Foresight,* the cruisers *Manchester* and *Cairo* and quite a few destroyers. The *Ohio* was a fast merchant ship, and carried aviation fuel, food and ammo. Even so, she was bombed to buggerey and her back was broken. So, in order to stop her sinking, the two destroyers kept the *Ohio* afloat by attaching themselves to each side of her.'

He paused again. 'They called the *Ohio* the ship that saved Malta, and so it was. The Malteese all came out and cheered us in, there was even a band playing 'Rule Britannia.' It were some sight, I can tell yer. Operation Pedestal, they called it.' His face brightened up and he laughed. 'We paid for nothing ashore that night. I even got free jump down The Gut.'

We arrived alongside Bighi jetty and went into the receiving room. 'Don't wait for me,' said Mitch. 'I've been here before. I'll make me own way back to the ship.'

I entered the ward and eagerly looked around, but there was no sign of Sister Johannsen. Instead, the first person I saw was a tall, nursing sister carrying a tray. She smiled and asked what I wanted.

At that moment Mick Quinn, a thick set LSBA I knew from Stonehouse, came over. When he told the sister who I was, she smiled again and left..

'Where's Sister Johannsen, Mick?'

'Keep you're eyes off her, mate,' he said. 'I would have thought after Stonehouse...' his voice trailed away.

'What do you mean, Mick?'

Mick gave me a quizzical look. 'The buzz got around that you were giving her one.'

'No such luck,' I replied with a short laugh, then added, 'By the way, is Desperate on duty?'

'No,' replied Mick. 'He's on this afternoon.'

I wrote the ship's telephone number on a slip of paper, and handed it to him. 'Give Des this number and ask him to ring me if he can,'

Cragg's pale face lit up when he saw me.

'The lads sent you some copies of Tit Bits,' I said, placing a roll of papers on his locker. 'Pincher and the rest send their best. Oh, and Seldom says you still owe him half a dollar from last pay day.'

Cragg gave a forced laugh. It was obvious he was missing his mates.

'So,' I said flatly. 'What's happening? How are you feeling?'

'They're giving me something called a barium meal test tomorrow,' he said with a sigh. 'You wouldn't have a tot on you, by any chance?'

'Sorry, mate,' I replied. 'I could do with one myself. Pity Sister Johannsen isn't on duty. I was looking forward to seeing her.'

'Bloody hell!' exploded Cragg. 'I almost forgot.' From under his pillow he took a small, white envelope. His voice dropped to a whisper, 'She asked me to give you this.'

Cragg went on, 'Told me not to tell anyone.' He lent forward in bed, and added, 'Are you and her, er...?'

I shook my head. 'No way,' I replied, putting the envelope in my pocket. 'We just know each other from Plymouth. That's all.'

'Aye,' muttered Cragg, giving me a disbelieving look. 'And I'm Queen of the May.'

With a promise of another visit, we shook hands and said cheerio.

We never met again. A week later he was invalided home.

Once outside the ward, I tore open the letter. The bright sunshine hurt my eyes, making me blink as I read it. Written on pink notepaper, her neat handwriting jumped out at me. She apologised for not being on duty, and went on, 'Telephone me this evening at 1700 at the number enclosed. Say you are Lieutenant James. Anita'

I read the letter three times, noticing that she had signed her Christian name.

No, I told myself, I was not dreaming. She actually wants me to telephone her. Suddenly, the sun seemed brighter, the sky bluer and the water a shade clearer.

When I returned to the ship, Jim Smith, the coxswain gave me daggers. 'The Jimmy wants to see you, so chop, chop.'

After saluting the quarterdeck, I gave him a puzzled look. 'What the hell have I done now, 'swain?'

The coxswain pursed his lips. 'Something about a fight ashore.'

Well I'll be buggered, I said to myself. That bastard Burgess has reported me after all.

The first lieutenant's desk was awash with papers and in front of him lay an official-looking manual.

'Ah, Lightburn,' he said, sitting back in his chair. 'Do you know why I've sent for you?'

'I think so, sir,' I replied.

He lent forward and said, 'Surgeon Lieutenant Jones has informed me you assaulted his PO last night,' he said. 'Is this true?'

'Yes, sir,' I replied, licking my lips. 'I did.'

Tapping the manual, he stared at me. 'I've been checking in QR and AI's (Queen's Regulations and Admiralty Instructions.) and what you did is very serious. Do you understand?'

I nervously shuffled my feet, and replied, yet again, 'Yes, sir.'

He cleared his throat, 'Tell me what happened.'

I did so.

'So, you were provoked?'

'Yes, sir. He hit me first.'

'Do you have any witnesses?'

'Yes, sir. Leading Writer Lamb, Petty Officer Morrison and Chief O'Hanlon.'

He raised his eyebrows. 'I see,' he replied. 'But you do realise hitting a senior rating is a grave offence, don't you?'

'I do, sir, but…'

The first lieutenant interrupted me. 'No buts about it,' he said. 'You could lose your hook and be dismissed the ship.'

This last statement made me grimace. A trickle of perspiration ran down my back.

With a sigh, he glanced at me. 'You do know that in a month's time you're eligible for promotion to Acting PO, don't you?'

Good God, I said to myself. I had completely forgotten about that. 'Yes, sir,' I lied.

'Well,' he said with an air of dismay. 'I'll see what I can do. But, it may be out of my hands. Do I make myself clear?'

'Yes, sir, I replied hoarsely. 'I do. Thank you. '

'I'd save your thanks, if I were you,' he replied.

When I reached the sick bay my legs felt weak and my shirt was soaked with sweat.

That evening I asked for an outside line, and telephoned Sister Johannsen from the privacy of the sick bay. After a few seconds a female voice answered, asking me what I wanted. Using my finest wardroom accent, I replied. 'Er…I am Lieutenant James. I'd like to speak to Sister Johannsen, if I may?'

After a short she came to the telephone. 'Hello, is that you, Thomas?'

'No. It's Cary Grant,' I joked.

Her laugh sounded like a waterfall. 'And I must say,' she answered. 'Now, listen carefully. Are you off duty on Saturday?'

I gave a start and nearly dropped the telephone. 'Yes,' I replied. 'I have leave till 0800 on Sunday.'

'Good!' she exclaimed. 'Can you meet me outside the Phoenicia Hotel in Valetta tomorrow, at, say… 1400?'

For a moment I could hardly believe my ears. She was actually asking *me,* a lowly sick bay tiffy, for a date.

'Are you still there, Thomas?'

'Yes, yes,' I answered. 'I am. Yes, 1400, the Phoenicia Hotel.'

'Lovely,' she replied. 'Bring some civilian clothes. Must dash someone waiting to use the 'phone. And call me Anita. All right? Bye for now.'

Call me Anita, she had said. With a click of the telephone she was gone, leaving me slightly dumbfounded, but shaking with excitement.

And civvies, what, I wondered would I need them for? A dance – a night club maybe? Whatever she had in mind sounded expensive and it was blank week. I would have to ask Pete for a sub.

Pete was in the mess reading a book, others sat around in their

277

shorts, writing letters, smoking and talking.

'Hi, Pete,' I said. 'Can I have a word with you, private like?'

'What's the problem?' he asked, once we were on the upper-deck.

'Two things,' I replied, passing him a cigarette and lighting it. 'Any chance of borrowing a fiver till pay day, and where in Valetta is the Hotel Phoenicia?'

He raised his eyebrows and gave me a curious look. 'A fiver's no trouble,' he said. 'But what's with the Hotel Phoenicia? That's officers' territory.'

'I'll tell you later, Pete,' I replied, avoiding the question. 'But don't say anything. All right?'

He nodded, put his hand in his pocket and gave me the money.

'Now,' he said. 'To get to the Hotel Phoenicia, go to Kingsway, the way we went last night. Turn left and go through the City Gate. You'll come to a bus depot with a huge fountain in the middle. The hotel is way to your right with a bloody great sign. You can't miss it. '

The next morning seemed to drag by. I spent most of the time compiling details for the medical officer's journal. These included all cases of venereal disease. So far, there had been none of the latter, but judging by what I had seen ashore, these would be forthcoming.

Before 'stand easy' at ten o'clock, I went to the mess. There was nobody there so I quickly changed into my number ones. I then packed a shirt, tie and dark blue jacket in a holdall.

Making my way to the sick bay I was spotted by the Chief GI. 'What's this, then?' he said. 'Going on a short week-end, eh?'

'No, chief,' I laughed. 'Just a few things for Craggy.'

'Up Spirits,' was piped, followed at 1200 by 'secure,' and details of shore leave.

I decided to give myself an hour to get to Valetta. At 1300, just as I was about to lock up the sick bay, the door opened and Yorky came in. He was pressing a dirty handkerchief onto his head. A trickle of blood oozed between his fingers.

'Bumped me 'ead on the 'atchway,' he said with a mournful expression. He immediately glanced at my hold-all. 'Were you going ashore?'

Cursing him under my breath, I replied. 'I was,' I said, with a sigh. 'Sit down and let's see what you've done.'

He had a nasty laceration on his forehead.

By the time I had inserted four stitches it was almost two o'clock.

Christ Almighty, I thought. Anita will think I've stood her up.

After telling Yorky to see me again in the morning, I managed to scrounge a lift in the ship's launch to Custom House steps.

Following Pete's instructions, I soon found the hotel.

Outside the entrance stood a shiny, black, Rolls Royce. Close by was chauffeur in a smart, green uniform. He was smoking and taking to a tall commissioner, dressed immaculately in scarlet livery.

I looked anxiously in all directions, but there was no sign of Anita.

I was suddenly anxious.

With a sigh, I discreetly moved behind a stone pillar, cursed Yorky and lit a cigarette. My watch read ten minutes to three. I was almost an hour late.

Just then the sound of a motor car engine startled me. I turned and saw a green, two-seater MG. Behind the wheel sat a woman with dark sunglasses. Tied around her head was a red and white spotted headscarf. For a moment, I did not recognise her.

'Hello, Thomas,' said Anita, taking off her sunglasses. 'Sorry I'm late. Had to pick up the car.'

I felt as if a heavy weight had been removed from my shoulders

'Er. . that's all right, 'I replied. 'I was held up myself.'

'Put your bag in the boot, and climb in'

I did as she asked and when I sat down the fragrance of her perfume made my head spin.

When the car moved off, the warmth of the air ripped past like a jetstream. With the wind flapping around her headscarf, we sped through Floriana and into the countryside.

'Where are we going?' I shouted.

She shot me a glance. 'To a beautiful beach in St Paul's Bay.'

'Isn't that where St Paul landed and turned a rock into water or something?'

Throwing her head back, she flashed a set of white teeth and laughed. 'Yes, that's right. It won't take us long. And it's the local wine we'll be drinking. Not water.'

The roads were narrow and winding She drove with reckless

abandon, taking the numerous hairpin bends like Stirling Moss.

'Do you always drive this fast?' I asked, tightening my grip on the side of the car.

'Why, Thomas?' she said mockingly. 'Are you scared?'

'No,' I lied. 'Just curious.'

'Everyone in Malta drives fast,' she shouted. 'Even the bus drivers go fast. I don't think they have to take a test and the police don't seem to worry.'

Much of the rolling countryside was dusty and arid. This was emphasised by scores of dry-stone walls separating fields and farmhouses. Olive groves grew in clusters while scrawny cattle scavenged for fodder. Citrus, carob and pine trees littered the slopes, intermingled with grapevines.

After passing through a large town called Mosta, with its beautiful cathedral dome, we reached high ground where the scene changed dramatically.

Away to our right, shimmering under a mind-boggling blue sky, stretched the waters of the Mediterranean. Waves gently lapped around rocky creeks and inlets. Sandy beaches flashed before my eyes and in the distance a thin line of black smoke curled high on the horizon.

Anita glanced across and saw me.

'You like the sea, don't you, Thomas?'

'Yes,' I replied. 'I once read that the sea is like a woman. Unpredictable, mischievous and sometimes untrustworthy.'

'Thomas,' she laughed. 'Untrustworthy? How dare you?'

Quite abruptly, we arrived on a spur overlooking a wide expanse of golden beach. The white sand sloped into the clear green water, which abruptly changed into dark blue where the sea deepened.

She stopped the car.

'My God,' I gasped. 'What a view.'

'There,' she said, squeezing my thigh with her hand. 'I told you it was beautiful. Now, Thomas, I suggest you change into your civilian clothes, and wear a tie.' She looked pleadingly at me, 'Do you mind. It will look better.'

I quickly leapt out of the car and did as she asked.

'You look very smart, Thomas,' she said glancing at me. 'I recognise that jacket from Plymouth.'

'Yes,' I replied, climbing into the car. 'It's the one I wore when we went to the pictures.'

'Ah, yes,' she said, humming a few bars of *'Singin' in the Rain,'*. 'I remember it well.'

We drove along a winding coastal road and arrived at an attractive building with a red terracotta roof. A sign on the yellow masonry read, appropriately, "Hotel Valentine".

'Here we are, Thomas,' said Anita, removing her sunglasses, and staring around. 'Lovely, isn't it?'

'It's pretty deserted,' I replied. 'Where is everybody?'

'There is a fishing village nearby,' replied Anita, opening the car door. 'The people keep to themselves.'

With a mischievous glint in her eyes she came close to me. 'I hope you don't mind, Thomas,' she said, placing her arms around my neck. 'I've booked us in for the night. Is that all right?'

For a moment I was dumbfounded. Then, the significance of what she had said suddenly hit me.

Hells bells, I thought. She wants me to sleep with her. Did I mind? I could have punched the air with joy.

Instead, I cleared my throat, and mumbled. 'Er... yes. That's all right.'

'Good,' she said. 'That's settled. And don't worry about the money. Everything is taken care of.'

Waiting in the lobby of the hotel was a stout, middle-aged woman. She had greyish hair tied in a bun and wore a plain, black dress. Her deeply tanned face wrinkled into a smile. 'Good afternoon, sister,' she said. 'How nice to see you again.'

'Hello, Mrs Aquilla,' replied Anita. 'How are you? How is Mr Aquilla?'

The lady shrugged her shoulders despairingly, and spread her hands. 'Asleep as usual. Come,' she added, giving me a benign smile. 'Your room is ready.'

We followed her up a flight of stairs and stopped outside a door. Mrs Aquilla handed a key to Anita. 'Supper, as usual, at six,' she said, and went downstairs.

The first thing I noticed was a large double bed covered with a pale blue quilt. Above the headboard was a crucifix, which, for some unknown reason, made me feel uneasy. On either side of the bed stood a table and a bedside lamp. There was no telephone. A few coloured pictures of Valetta hung on walls decorated in pale yellow. In one corner was a well-polished wardrobe and dressing table. Two French windows opened onto a small balcony and nearby, a half open door led into a bathroom. Hanging from the centre of the ceiling was a solitary light and multicoloured lampshade.

Anita walked to the open windows. 'It's so lovely here,' she said, taking a deep breath.

I dropped the luggage and stood behind her.

'You've been here before, haven't you?' I said, putting my hands on her shoulders.

She turned, and pulled me against her. 'Now, Thomas,' she said, coyly. 'Yes I have. I've been here a few times with one of the sisters from the hospital. We come here to get away from everything.'

She reached up and we kissed. Her lips were soft and wet. My heart began to pound and when she pressed her hips against me, she knew I was ready.

'Oh, Thomas,' she gasped, 'be a gentleman, and make love to me.'

I quickly shrugged off my jacket as her fingers fumbled with my shirt buttons. I unzipped her dress, letting it fall in a crumpled heap at her feet. In next to no time we were lying on the bed naked.

There was no time for preliminaries.

Our lovemaking was long and passionate. Her body felt like velvet and afterwards, bathed in perspiration, we clung together, breathless but relaxed.

'That was wonderful,' she whispered, and snuggled into me.

A warm breeze filtered through the windows and fanned our naked bodies. In one easy movement, she rose from the bed and stood naked in the moonlight. Her hair hung down her back like a horse's mane. She was, without a doubt, the most beautiful woman I had ever seen.

She returned and sat on the edge of the bed. For a few seconds neither of us spoke. Later, with our arms around each other, we fell into a sound sleep.

When we woke up it was dark. I watched as she stretched her arms up. Except for white areas around her breasts and midriff, her body was the colour of burnished oak. Silhouetted against the evening sky, she reminded me of those Greek statues I once saw in the Liverpool Museum.

We went onto the balcony. The moon hung in the sky like a

pale lozenge, sending a warm glow onto the calm waters of a crescent-shaped bay. The sea lapped around the edge of a wide ribbon of sand and away to our left, lights from the fishing village heralded the oncoming night.

'Anita,' I said, staring straight ahead. 'There's something I want to ask you.'

'Yes, Thomas' she replied, brushing a few strands of hair from her face. 'What do you want you know?'

I turned her towards me. 'Why me?' I said. 'After all. You could have anyone you wanted, doctors, officers, any number of men.'

'That is just the point, Thomas,' she replied. 'All they wanted was to get me in bed. You were always the perfect gentleman. Even in Plymouth when you got into trouble, you never mentioned my name to anyone,' she added, 'and besides, you really are quite good-looking.'

I felt my face going red.

'Now,' she said holding me close. 'Let's take a shower. I don't know about you, but I'm absolutely famished.'

Anita changed into a simple blue dress and sandals. There was only a young couple with two small children in the dining room. They nodded and smiled as we entered.

We ate rabbit stew.

'This is the traditional dish of Malta,' said Mrs Aquilla, placing the food in front of us. 'So I hope you enjoy it.'

It was delicious, especially accompanied by a bottle of local red wine.

Later, our bare feet sank into the soft sand as we leisurely strolled along the deserted beach. The darkness had brought out a million stars, making us feel like the only people on earth.

She whispered in my ear. 'This really is perfect. Isn't it Thomas?'

I didn't reply.

Instead, when we kissed, the momentum of our embrace carried us back into the sand

The next morning we left the hotel shortly after six. Dawn had broken and the air felt fresh and cool. Once more Anita tore along the narrow roads at breakneck speed. Before we reached Valetta, we stopped and I changed into my uniform. It was just after seven o'clock when we arrived outside the Phoenicia Hotel. It was Sunday and the air was filled with the sound of church bells ringing.

'I'm on lates this week,' she said, 'and nights over the weekend.'

'And we're sailing next Monday, to carry out exercises near here, of all places.'

She reached over and kissed me, 'I'll telephone you before you sail and we'll arrange something. Think of me, won't you?'

'I've never stopped thinking of you, Anita,' I said. 'And I don't think I ever will.'

When I arrived back on board I was greeted with more than a few catcalls.

'Dirty stop out,' cried Pincher, who was about to go on watch.

'Hope you catch the boat up,' chimed someone else.

'Has she got a mate, Doc?' asked Slinger Wood, the duty quartermaster. 'I don't care how old she is.'

'Bollocks,' I replied. 'I've just been visiting an old oppo and his wife I knew in Guzz.'

'A likely bloody story,' growled the Buffer, grinning at me. 'Anyways, you've got a few customers waiting outside the sick bay. Oh, and your boss on the *Duchess* wants to see you at 0900 tomorrow. OK?'

I gave a start.

The events of the past twenty-four hours had made me forget about my run-in with Burgess.

With thoughts of warrants, dismisal and disgrace, I hardly noticed Scouse Kilbane and Slinger Woods waiting outside the sick bay.

'Mornin', Doc,' grunted Scouse.

Slinger did not speak. Instead he nervously shuffled his feet and stared at the deck.

'What's the problem?' I asked, sliding open the door.

'We'd like to see you, private like,' replied Slinger

I immediately sensed what was wrong. 'OK,' I said. 'You first, Slinger.'

He gave me a quick apprehensive glance and followed inside. I slid the door shut. After the glare of the morning sunlight, the sick bay seemed dark. I blinked and sat down.

'What up, then, Slinger?' I asked. 'Or do you want me to guess?'

Slinger's chubby face reddened. He hesitated before speaking. And when he did, he spoke in a half whisper. 'I...er, think I've caught the boat up,' he said, nervously licking his lips.

'You mean you've caught a dose?'

My forthright question started him. He gave a quick start and coughed. 'Yes, I think so.'

His symptoms were classical. A slight, yellow discharge and a burning sensation when urinating.

I made out a VD Case card (FMed 16), re-assured him that his penis wasn't about to fall off and took a sample of blood from his arm.

'What's that for, Doc?' he asked.

'Just routine,' I replied. 'Come and see me first thing in the morning before you have a piss,' I said. 'I'll have to examine your urine and do a slide. Then we'll go and see the MO.

By this time, the colour had returned to his face. 'Cheers, Doc,' he said, then added, 'All this is confidential, aint it?'

'Of course,' I replied. 'Don't worry. Tell Scouse to come in on your way out.'

Scouse entered wearing a sickly grin.

'Guess what?' he said, scratching his crutch. 'I think I've caught something.'

An examination of Scouse's medical documents told me this was the third time he had caught a dose

'Again,' I replied. 'You ought to keep it in your bellbottoms, matey, or one day your balls will explode and drop off.'

Scouse laughed. 'Just think,' he replied. 'If that happened, I'd be able to join the Luton Girl's Choir.'

He knew the procedure but before he left, he said, 'What about me rum?? You won't stop it will you?'

'Sorry, Towns,' I replied. 'You know the routine by now. No tot, just a jab up the bot.'

Next morning I did a two glass test of their urine. In each case the first sample showed threads of pus, indicating infection. I then heated a thin wire loop until it glowed.

'Christ Almighty,' cried Slinger, visibly paling. 'You're not going to put that thing down the eye of my welt, are you?'

'Calm down,' I told him, touching the end of the loop on the back of my hand. 'This is just to take a sample for a slide. Then, the MO will look at under the microscope and we'll see exactly what

285

the problem is. So don't worry,'

I did not have to explain anything to Scouse. He had seen it all before.

'Don't forget to ask me if I'm allergic to penicillin,' he said, with an air of an expert. 'Some stoker on my last ship came out in purple rash after the Doc gave him a jab of that. The rash stayed longer than his dose.'

Shortly before nine o'clock the three of us went onboard *Duchess*.

The MO was sitting at the desk. PO Burgess was absent.

I told him about the two cases outside in the passageway.

'They can wait,' he said. 'Sit down. I'm sure you know why I've sent for you.'

'Yes, sir, I do.'

'The offence, if officially reported, is a serious one,' he said.

He handed me a cigarette, took one himself and lit both of them.

'PO Burgess has his faults. I know he drinks too much. But he has good reason. He lost his wife and ten year old son during the Blitz,' the MO paused, 'and he sometimes goes a bit haywire.'

'I didn't know that, sir,' I replied. 'What do you want me to do?'

'If you were to apologise,' said the MO, scratching his chin, 'I might be able to persuade him to drop the charges.'

Perhaps the MO was right. Looking back the affair did seem like a storm in a teacup. I quickly made up my mind and agreed.

'Good,' he said. 'PO Burgess will be back in a minute. I'll see your two cases, then I'll leave you to it. All right?'

'Yes, sir,' I replied.

The MO examined both slides under the microscope, then saw them separately, and prescribed penicillin and potassium citrate.

Shortly after the MO left, PO Burgess came in. He gave me a sour look. 'What's this? More trouble I expect.'

For a moment I was not sure what to say. After what the MO had told me about him, I felt slightly ashamed. I bit my lip and studied the deck.

After taking a deep breath, I said,'About last week, PO, I'm really sorry. I was wrong to hit you, and I want to apologise.'

Burgess gave a cough. 'You do, eh?' he said in a quiet voice. 'Are you sure it's not just to save your own skin?'

I shot him a quick glance. 'That as well,' I replied. 'But I am sorry. Believe me.'

He took a deep breath and looked at me. 'All right,' he answered, lowering his voice. 'We all make mistakes. Christ knows, I've made a few in my time. Fair enough. Let's shake hands?'

'I hope your face is all right,' I said, taking his hand.

He laughed, and touched the side of his face. 'I'm OK,' he said,' and by the way, my name's Bob. What's your moniker?'

With a sigh of relief, I told him.

'Right-ho, Tom, me lad,' he said with a grin. 'That's a pint you owe me when we next meet ashore. OK?'

The week dragged by. On Saturday Pete and a few others enjoyed a vicious run ashore in Floriana. Sunday saw me nursing a thick head and dolling out more of Bill's hangover cures.

Daily Orders told us we would sail in company with *Barfleur* and *Armada*. Noticing we would be anchoring in St Paul's Bay immediately reminded me of Anita.

The next morning, sick parade consisted of a rating with a sore throat and another with a cold in the head. Daily Orders stated hands would fall in for leaving harbour at 1200.

Just after ten o'clock came a pipe ordering me to report to the brow for a telephone call. My heart missed a beat. It's her, I thought, and rushed to the top of the gangway.

'Hello?' I said, grabbing the ship's telephone. 'Is that…'

Before I had time to finish, a male voice cut me off.

'Hello, Tom, Desperate, here, how are you?'

Trying hard to disguise my disappointment, I answered, 'Fine, Des. This is a pleasant surprise. How are you and the lads?'

There was a slight pause. I heard Des give a cough.

'I take it you haven't heard, then?' he said.

'Heard what?' I answered.

'Sister Johannsen was killed in an RTA yesterday. It's all round the hospital.'

'What!' I gasped, unable to believe my ears.

'Her car went off the road on the way back from St Paul's Bay. They were DOA on arrival in Bighi.'

I felt the blood drain from my face. 'Are you sure it was her? She was supposed…' my voice trailed off.

'Yes,' replied Desperate. 'I thought I'd better tell you. I knew you were good friends in Guzz.'

The reality of his words slowly hit me. My mind was in turmoil and for a few seconds I could not speak.

Desperate's voice brought me to my senses. 'Are you still there, Tom?' he said.

'Yes, yes,' I replied, leaning against the bulkhead with one hand. 'I'm still here. You mentioned 'they.' Was she with someone else?'

'Aye,' replied Desperate. 'Some officer called James, Lieutenant James.'

'Jesus Christ!' I gasped.

Suddenly shock was tinged with jealous anger. She had lied. She had not been on duty after all. Instead, she was with him, sharing the same bed we had used the previous Saturday.

The thought made my stomach churn.

I don't remember saying goodbye to Desperate.

'Are you all right, Doc?' The voice of the QM slowly filtered through to me. 'You look as if you've seen a ghost'

I did not reply. By the time I reached the sick bay my eyes were blurred with hot tears.

18

At midday the ship eased past Grand Harbour, slipped through the breakwater, headed up the coast and anchored in St Paul's Bay. The beach appeared narrower and the fishing village almost non-existent. The only thing that hadn't changed was the red terracotta roof of the Hotel Valentine.

Thankfully the next seven days were hectic. Working in tandem with the other ships, we practised every evolution in the book. Sailing line abreast, the five ships cut through the sea, sending bow waves soaring in the air like whale spouts.

Standing on the ship's waist, I let the wind tear at my uniform. Wiping spray from my face, I watched as each ship manoeuvred together with perfect precision. As our vessel changed direction and heeled over, the angle was so steep I could almost touch the water. Gradually, the slope of the deck changed, the masts and superstructure moved against the blue sky and the ship became upright.

We were issued with anti-flash gear and life belts. The AF clothing consisted of a white, Balaclava-like hood and long gloves made of absorbent material that itched like hell.

Action stations sounded day and night. The ship's company practised damage control exercises, while my first aid parties dashed around, dealing with mock casualties. With the help of the Chief 'Chippy' and an electrician, we rigged up the emergency lighting in the wardroom table and turned the place into a makeshift operating room.

'Fine thing,' joked the Chippy. 'We've got an operating table, hardly any surgical instruments, and no bloody anaesthetic.'

'Don't worry, chief,' replied Pony Moore, the young electrician. 'If you have to have yer leg cut off, the Doc could use one of our saws.'

Sometimes, we acted as guard-ship while *Eagle's* aircraft practised night flying. This meant myself and the seaboat's crew sitting in a whaler swung outboard in readiness for any emergency.

I looked across at the dark shape of the carrier and wondered if Phil was on duty. I gave a short laugh. Perhaps he might be thinking the same about me.

We watched, as each jet zoomed off the flight deck, leaving behind a trail of orange sparks.

'It's when they land, you've got to watch out,' came the experienced voice of Paddy Alexander. 'That's when the buggers crash.'

As each aeroplane landed, the pilot immediately cut the jet's engines. Like an invisible hand, the hook on the undercarriage caught the arrester wire, bringing the aircraft to a shuddering halt.

'They must be bloody mad,' said one of the whaler's crew. 'I don't know how they manage to see the ship, let alone land on the deck.'

Just then a jet landed and there was an ear-splitting explosion. We gasped in horror, as a plume of bright, orange flame leapt into the air. Straight away the ship increased speed towards the carrier, but there was nothing we could do. We watched in silence as the fire crew sprayed foam over the wreckage, before clearing it away.

'Poor bastards,' sighed Paddy. 'They never stood a chance.'

The night before we were due back in Malta, Pete came into the sick bay on a pretext of having a headache. It was after supper, and I was lying on my bed, hands behind my head, staring at the deck-head.

'What's wrong, Doc?' he said, sitting down. 'The 'buzz' is you got some bad news before we sailed. You've hardly been to the mess. Now, I'm no medic, but something's not right.'

Reaching for my cigarettes, I lit one then threw the packet at him. 'Yeah,' I muttered. 'You're right, Pete. I did get a bit of bad news.'

I told him about Anita, and what had happened to her. It was a relief to talk to someone, and I felt as if a weight had been lifted from me.

'Blimey!' he exclaimed. 'No wonder you were upset. I don't blame you, mate. How do you feel now?'

'I'll be all right,' I replied, 'but, keep it to yourself, will you, Pete? It's sort of private, like.'

'Don't worry,' he said, leaning across and stubbing his cigarette out in an ash tray, 'Mum's the word. Now how about a cup of your famous tea, eh?'

The *Eagle* led the way into Grand Harbour, while the other ships followed behind. This time I did not fall in. Instead I busied myself cleaning the sick bay. By the time I had finished, the ship was alongside the wharf at Corradino Creek.

'Mail is ready for collection,' was piped. Shortly afterwards, Postie came into the sick bay with a bundle of official envelopes and newspapers from home. My heart nearly stopped when I read Tony had been released on parole. However, I breathed a sigh of relief when she told me he had decided to stay in London.

'I think he has got himself mixed up with some cronies he met inside,' wrote Mum.

The headlines in the *Daily Mirror* reported Cypriots still clamouring for independence from Turkey. News that Archbishop Makarios, head of the Greek Church, was openly encouraging armed resistance against the British troops gave me a start. Trust Joe, I thought, to be in the thick of trouble.

I went to the mess and handed Scouse the papers. 'More bleedin' work for us,' he said, reading the front page of the *Liverpool Echo*.

'What do you mean?' asked Seldom. 'More work?'

'The buzz is,' replied Scouse, glancing at the headlines, 'we'll have to go and patrol the coast of Cyprus to prevent guns and stuff being smuggled from Greece to these EOKA terrorists.'

'He's right,' chimed in Pincher. 'Our ships have been patrolling there for quite some time. I've got a mate on the *Undine*. She's sailing for Famagusta tomorrow.'

'Where the fuck's Fama... whatsitsname?' came the muffled tones of Slinger Wood from inside his hammock.

'It's a port in Cyprus, you nitwit,' replied Seldom. 'Didn't they teach you anything at school?'

That evening Pete, Big Geordie and Spud Tate managed to coax me ashore.

'It'll do you good, Doc,' said Pete privately. 'Nothing like a few wets to dull the old brain.'

We did a swift run down The Gut, calling at Ben Marl's restaurant for steak, egg and chips.

Afterwards, we piled into a taxi, did the rounds of bars in Floriana. Pete, Spud and Big Geordie were well away, arms around one another. Even though I had matched them drink for drink, I felt relatively sober. We decided to go back onboard and caught a taxi to Custom House Steps.

The wharf was crowded with sailors, some clinging onto one

another, others singing while one or two vomited the night's beer into the bay.

The mighty *Eagle,* lit up like a magic lantern, lay in the middle of the harbour. Other warships lay close by, anchored between two buoys. The diceos were working overtime, ferrying men to their ships. Even so, the crowds increased and one or two fights broke out.

Big Geordie and I sat on the stone floor with our backs against a wall. Pete and Spud shared a bollard and smoked a cigarette.

'Jesus,' slurred Spud. 'We're going to be all night waiting for a diceo. The next liberty boat isn't till two o'clock. That's nearly an hour.'

'How about crashing in one of the doss-houses?' said Pete.

Before any of us had time to reply, a loud roar came from near the quayside.

'The silly bastard's going to swim for it,' cried someone.

Suddenly, the memory of Scouse Wilson flashed through my mind.

Scrambling to my feet, I pushed my way through the mob. A tall, broad-shouldered sailor was stripped off to the waist. His pale, muscular body caught the light from a nearby lamp. To my surprise I saw it was my old pal from Wallasey, Phil Leatham.

'Give me some fuckin' room, you lot,' he yelled, moving to the edge of the wharf. 'I'm fed up waiting for the soddin' liberty boats.'

With arms outstretched, he prepared to dive into the water. Just as he was about to do so, I grabbed him around the waist, shouting, 'Phil! ' I cried. 'It's me. Tom. For fuck's sake don't jump'

He stopped and looked at me.

'Bloody hell, Tom, lad,' he exploded. 'How are you, mate? Come on board tomorrow. I'm going for a swim.'

The crowd broke into a series of loutish cheers. He bent his knees slightly and placed his arms behind him. I clung onto him, yelling, 'Don't do it. The current is too strong. A mate of mine drowned last year trying to swim back to the *Cumberland.* . Someone help me.'

Phil's strong hands tried to push me away. 'I'll be all right, Tom,' he said. 'Leave me alone.'

At that moment Big Geordie, Pete and a few others dragged him to the ground.

'Bastards,' he cried, struggling. 'I'll fill the lot of you in.'

We managed to hold him down while I talked some sense into him. 'It's true Phil,' I said, holding one of his arms. 'Scouse Wilson drowned in this harbour last year. Use your loaf, man. The current's too strong.'

He finally realised the stupidity of his actions and relaxed.

By this time a liberty boat from our ship arrived.

'Come on, you silly bugger,' I said, helping him up. 'I'll ask the coxswain to give you a lift to *Eagle*. We pass it on our way back to French Creek, and he can hardly miss it.'

Pincher Martin was the coxswain. He agreed, and after Phil had dressed, we took him and a few of his shipmates to the carrier.

On the way I told him Joe and Jock were in the Army and Reg was still in HMS *Newfoundland*..

He threw back his head and gave a horsey laugh. 'That Joey Woods must be crazy,' he said. 'I'm sure he thinks he's got wings.'

I grinned and said, 'At least he doesn't imagine he has water-wings, like some silly sod I know.'

Pincher Martin's comment about 'more sea-time,' was correct. A week later, the captain cleared lower deck and addressed the ship's company.

Standing on a platform on the fo'c'sle, his bronzed features broke into a sly grin. 'I hope you can hear me at the back,' he said, then added, 'as most of you know, there is trouble in Cyprus.' He went on to tell us about the Greeks wanting their independence from the Turks. He also emphasised the fact that terrorists were being sent arms and ammunition from the Greek mainland. He concluded by stressing, 'Even though Archbishop Makarios has been deported to the Seychelles, he is still supporting these bloodthirsty bandits, and our job is to intercept any craft which might be carrying arms to them. We sail for an eight-week patrol in two days.'

'Holy Mary, Mother of God,' grumbled Paddy Alexander. 'I bet the bugger volunteered us. Eight bloody weeks, I ask you...'

At 4p.m. on May 5th, the ship left Grand Harbour for Cyprus.

As usual, the sky was a deep, peacock blue, and the sea glittered like glass.

Summer had 'officially' arrived, and white tropical uniforms became the rig of the day.

After an uneventful four days, we arrived off the south coast of

293

Cyprus. We dropped anchor outside Limossol harbour. This sleepy port, with its medieval castle, lies on the edge of a coastline studded with cedar trees, grape vines and lines of yellow orange groves. In the distance rose the Troodos Mountains, dark and brooding against the pale morning sky.

Early each day a foggy heat haze shrouded the glassy sea. The offshore breeze cooled our bodies as we watched schools of silvery-grey dolphins bound playfully around the ship.

Ocassionally a boarding party would be sent across to investigate a suspicious-looking fishing vessel. However, no arms or ammunition were ever found. After several such encounters the boarding crews became familiar with the Cypriot fishermen. They even got to know some of there the names.

'I'll be buggered,' cried Taff Leighton, climbing back on board after yet another fruitless search. 'Old Spiros gave us a shot of Keo brandy. Not bad stuff either.'

But after a few weeks even this became a tedious chore.

This humdrum existence was broken by the usual games of tombola, kite-making competitions, and mess decks movies. These plus damage control, gunnery and a host of other evolutions helped to break the monotony.

The highlight of each week occurred when we anchored off Kyrenia to collect mail.

On one such visit, I lied to the Jimmy by saying I expected a parcel of medical stores. He therefore allowed me to accompany Postie ashore to collect the mail.

'If he takes French leave this time,' quipped Dusty Miller, a young ordinary seaman, 'he'll probably get his bollocks blown off by a bomb.'

Spud Tate, who was a leading seaman and Chats Harris were issued with 303 rifles and a round of ammunition.

'Fat lot of use this will be if we're ambushed,' said Chats, securing his webbing belt. 'One poxy round. That'll keep the buggers at bay, I must say.'

'Wrap it in,' replied Spud. 'Who the hell d'you think you are? Audie Murphy?'

The ship's launch dropped us off at the end of a wooden jetty.

'We'll be back in half an hour,' shouted the coxswain.

Waiting ashore was a young second lieutenant and four squadies armed with sten-guns.

294

When we clambered ashore, the officer gave us a weak smile and saluted. 'Better chop, chop,' he said. 'We've had a spot of bother here of late.'

No sooner had he spoken, than a car stopped at the end of the jetty. The door opened and a shiny object arced in the air towards us. What happened next seemed to take ages but was over in a few seconds.

'Take cover!' cried one of the soldiers.

To my surprise, the officer dived off the jetty followed by the four soldiers.

Not being used to this sort of thing, we stood rooted to the spot. Meanwhile, the object bounced a few yards away, rolled, then stopped. Suddenly, the penny dropped. 'Run like fuck.' shouted Tansey. 'It's a bloody bomb!'

The two sailors dropped their rifles, and together we set a new Olympic record for the hundred yards dash. Waving my arms at a couple of passers by, I yelled. 'A bomb! A bomb!'

They seemed unperturbed, looked at each other, and carried on walking. We continued running, and ducked behind a wall at the end of the jetty. With baited breath, we waited, but nothing happened.

After a while, I poked my head around the wall. Close by, I saw the young officer and the soldiers swimming for the end of the jetty. Spud, Chats and myself helped to pull the bedraggled figures out of the water.

'Clear the area,' gasped the officer. 'Everyone, keep you heads down.'

Once again, we waited, but nothing happened.

Suddenly, there was an almighty explosion. The ground shook and everyone instinctively ducked. When we plucked up enough courage to look up, the end of the jetty had disappeared. All that remained was a pall of black smoke and bits of wood scattered about like pieces of flotsam.

We slowly stood up. My legs were shaking and the others were as white as ghosts.

'Christ on a crutch,' exploded Spud Tate, staring at one of the soldiers. 'Does this sort of thing happen often?'

'Yeah,' replied the soldier. 'Last week we lost three of our lads in an ambush not far from the mail office.'

'The mail office,' cried Postie. 'Bugger this. I'm resigning.'

295

'What was that Dusty Miller said about getting your bollocks blown off, Tansey?' I said, on the way back to the ship. 'It's a damn sight safer at sea.'

A few day later I received a shock of a different kind.

Into the sick bay came the gangly figure of Junior Seaman Norman Clegg. His face looked paler than usual. Straight away I thought he had been 'bashing his bishop,' again.

But I was wrong. In fact he had severe tonsillitis, and a raging temperature

After admitting him to the sick bay, I started him on a course of penicillin, gargles and light diet.

His temperature remained high. I checked his condition regularly but fell asleep around four in the morning.

'Call the Hands,' at six-thirty woke me up.

Straight away I went to see how Cleggy was.

At that moment my heart leapt into my mouth. A feeling of abject horror ran through me.

Cleggy was lying rigidly still. His eyes stared in front of him and his mouth was partially open. Oh, my God, I thought, he's dead. I've killed him! I felt my bladder weaken and cried out, 'Cleggy. Are you all right?' Using both hands, I shook him furiously by his shoulders.

Cleggy instantly looked at me. 'What's the hell are you doing?' he croaked. 'What's all the shouting about? You frightened the life out of me.'

I nearly pissed myself with relief. Feeling as if a ton weight had been lifted from me, I replied. 'Frightened the life out of *you*?' I gasped. 'You were lying with your eyes open . . .' I didn't finish.

Cleggy sat up and rubbed his eyes. The soreness of his throat prevented him from laughing. Instead, he grinned. 'I forgot to tell you,' he said. 'I have lazy eyelids. They don't fully close at night. Frightened the life out of me Mum, I can tell you.'

'I don't know about your old girl,' I replied, 'but it scared the shit out of me.'

Much to the delight of the crew, it was announced we were to visit Aqaba, a military base in Jordan.

'Be Jesus,' said Paddy Alexander. 'We'll have to go to Port Said and down the Suez Canal. It'll be so hot you'll be able to fry eggs on the deck.'

'At least we'll be able to get a few Jippo AFOs,' said Scouse Kilbane.

'What the hell are those, Scouse?' I asked.

Scouse and Paddy were busy painting the quarterdeck.

Scouse rolled his eyes up in mock disgust. 'Don't you medics know anything?' he said. 'Them's the best porno books you can get in the Middle East.'

'You don't say,' I replied, raising my eyebrows. 'I'd have thought you would have had enough of sex by now.'

'Ah, dear old Port said,' said Paddy, sniffing the air. 'To be sure, you can smell the place well before you see it. Lock up your jewellery. If any of those jippos come on board they'll not leave empty handed.'

As we approached Port Said, the clear blue waters of the Mediterranean suddenly changed to murky green. The smell, drifting from land, made me catch my breath.

'This place certainly chucks up,' cried Shiner Wright.

'Just like your feet at night,' replied Bungy Williams.

'Bloody hell, Doc,' gasped Pete, holding his nose between finger and thumb. 'It's a good job you and the chippy chlorinated the water tanks yesterday. I wouldn't fancy drinking anything we take on here.'

The harbour, surrounded by warehouses and official-looking buildings, was crammed with shipping, many of which were oil tankers.

The air was like an oven and the miasma of a thousand toilets brought tears to my eyes.

'Bloody hell, mon,' cried Big Geordie. 'Now I knows why they call this place the arse-hole of the Meddy.'

We anchored and were immediately surrounded by a fleet of small boats, selling everything from bubble-pipes to toy camels.

One of these jostled alongside the port side of the after deck house. An unshaven, leathery-faced boatman, dressed in a long, off-white, dishdasha waved a grubby bundle in the air.

'Best dirty books, jack,' he yelled, 'dirty postcards of my sister – all very cheap.'

A knock came at the door. I turned around and saw the first lieutenant. Behind him stood a fat, greasy Egyptian in a white uniform. He wore sandals, and under a large, bulbous nose hung a black, walrus moustache. Hanging from the side of a red fez, strands of black hair dangled down the side of his unshaven face. Beads of perspiration dribbled from his swarthy forehead and his eyes looked bloodshot. In one hand he carried a fly swatter which he casually flicked around his head.

'This is Captain Mohammed Ackmem,' said the Jimmy. 'He is a port official, and wants to see your medical records before he will issue the ship with *Pratique.'*

For a moment I was taken aback. I knew from news bulletins that relations between Britain and Egypt were strained, but this was quite unexpected.

The 'Greasy One' smiled weakly at me. 'Good morning,' he said in perfect English. 'Can I see your medical records?' When he opened his mouth a strong smell of garlic issued forth, making me wince.

I handed my medical record book to him.

Placing his fly swatter under his arm, he opened the book.

'Sod's Law,' immediately intervened.

'Ah,' he said, his eyes lighting up. 'I see you have here a name that is due a smallpox vaccination. Why is this?'

I shot a worrying glance at the first lieutenant, then at the official 'That can't be true, sir,' I said. 'Everyone was vaccinated in Malta.'

'Then who is this, Lieutenant Commander McArdle?' he replied, dabbing his forefinger at the open page. 'It say here, 'due smallpox, 1st May. It is now nearly June.' With a smug expression he showed me my own notation.

I could hardly believe my eyes. Of all the names in the book, he had to pick that of my boss.

'I am the officer in question,' said the first lieutenant rather meekly. 'An oversight on my part. I am sure this can easily be remedied. The LSBA can vaccinate me now, can't you Lightburn?'

'Er. . yes, of course, sir,' I hastily replied.

The official dropped my book on the desk. 'This is not good enough,' he said. 'It takes a few days to see if the vaccine has worked. How will I know this if I allow you to sail down the canal? Your ship is officially not medically fit. You realise, I have the power to prevent you from continuing your journey?'

'But surely....' stuttered the first lieutenant.

The official held up his hand. 'Would you allow me to have a private word with your medical man, here?'

The Jimmy's face was scarlet. He coughed nervously. 'Of course,' he replied.

After he and the Coxswain had left the sick bay, the official quickly turned to me, rubbing his hands.

'Please,' he said, 'you have penicillin, yes? And needles, and a syringe. Yes? And some condoms?'

'Of course,' I replied, turning my head away to avoid his breath.

'Excellent,' he replied. 'Give me them, and all will be well with your officer. And hurry.'

I did as he asked. In a flash I placed a large vial of procaine penicillin, needles, a syringe and some condoms in a large envelope and handed it to him.

'Good, good,' he said and stuffed the envelope inside his jacket. 'Ask them to come in.'

The first lieutenant looked as if he were about to explode. 'I must protest...' he began.

The official held up his hand. 'Please, please,' he said, with a toothy grin. 'All is well. Your medical man here has promised me he will vaccinate you, and have you looked at again as soon as possible.'

Colour returned to the first lieutenant's face. He raised his eyebrows and, somewhat relieved, replied, 'Good. Will you now kindly sign the *Pratique* document, and we can get under weigh.'

He did so, bowed slightly, and left.

Paddy Alexander certainly knew what he was talking about.

The journey down the canal was slow, tedious and scorching hot. The temperature was 120 degrees Fahrenheit and there were several cases of acute sunburn. Lime juice and salt tablets were provided in each mess, and everyone warned to take extra fluids.

On our way up the Gulf of Aqaba we sighted a warship. I was on the upper deck having a smoke. 'What ship's that, sir?' I asked Sub Lieutenant Forbes. Training his binoculars on the vessel, he replied. 'She an Egyptian frigate. The jippo's have banned Israel from using the canal. They are also blocking the Gulf to prevent Israeli shipping passing through. Could be a dodgy situation.'

Aqaba came as a welcome relief, with entertainment provided by the army.

The day after we arrived, Pete and the others were in the NAAFI enjoying a few beers. All of a sudden, the piratical figure of the Chief Stoker burst in.

'Quick, Doc,' he cried, perspiration streaming down his face. 'There's been an accident. The Chief Cook has just fallen off his camel.'

Naturally, this was greeted with uncontrolled mirth.

'Slaughter the camel,' cried Danny Wilde. 'It'll probably taste better than the toad-in-the-hole we had last night.'

When I arrived, the crumpled figure of Jacko Jackson was sitting on the beach. His pale face was contorted in pain, and he cradled his left arm across his body.

'That fuckin' camel was pissed, I tell you,' moaned the chief. 'Someone ought to shoot the soddin' thing.'

'What happened?' I asked, gently examining his arm.

'It threw me off its back!' he replied, accepting a cigarette and a light.

An ambulance arrived and took us to the sick quarters.

'Fractured, I'm afraid, old son,' said the doctor holding up an x-ray of Jacko's arm. 'Have to put you under for a few minutes, and set it.'

An hour later, fully recovered, and feeling relieved his ordeal was over, we sat in the canteen enjoying a cup of tea. 'No more bloody camels for me. No siree. That last bugger gave me the hump!'

Jacko was not the only 'casualty.'

The day after we sailed, the wrinkled face of PO Mitchell appeared around the sick bay door.

He smacked his lips together, and gave me a gummy grin. 'Lost them again, Doc,' he muttered. 'Somewhere in the desert, I think.'

It was a rush to get him seen by the army dentist, but we made it in time.

Later the next day we left Aqaba. On either side of the narrow gulf, mountain ranges swept gracefully into the sea. When darkness suddenly fell, the glow from the evening sun changed their colour from light brown to burnished gold.

However, I did not envy the unfortunate soldiers who had to endure the searing heat, the flies, and, of course, the occasional grumpy camel.

19

The sight of Malta brought the memories of Anita flooding back. But as we sailed into Grand Harbour, I told myself she had gone forever, and I had to try and move on.

The harbour seemed unusually full of warships. The cruisers *Birmingham* and *Jamaica* lay at anchor along with the aircaftcarrier *Albion*. There was also a large contingent of French and British destroyers.

However, it was an American cruiser which caught my eye. The ship was painted a lighter shade of grey than ours, with high, sloping bows on which were mounted twin 6inch guns.

'That's the USS *Salem,*' said Postie. 'Bags of ice-cream onboard her.'

'Aye,' added Pincher Martin, securing a rope around a bollard. 'The gals down The Gut will be out in force tonight.'

Much to Mitch's delight, his dentures from Aqaba arrived in the mail.

'Be Jezus,' said Mitch, fitting them in his mouth. Straight away his prune-like features became firmer. 'Just in time too. I've been invited to meet Earl Mountbatten.'

'Give over,' I replied. 'You, meeting Mountbatten, how come?'

'It's a film they've just made called "The Battle of the River Plate",' said Mitch excitedly. 'It were made around Malta. Anyone who was at the battle has been invited to the première.'

'Bloody hell, Mitch,' I replied, giving him a doubtful look. 'What with that Operation Pedestal and now this, you seemed to have been everywhere in the war.'

'And so I was, matey,' he said with glowing pride. 'I was an Ordinary Seaman onboard the *Exeter*. Old 'Dinger Bell' was the captain, God bless him. We had over fifty men killed during the battle. We were so badly hit, we had to go down to the Falkland Islands for repairs.'

'And when and where is this film going to be shown?' I asked.

'At the cinema at Corradino, next Saturday,' he replied. 'That there American cruiser was used as the Jerry pocket battle-ship *Graf Spee*. All the bigwigs will be there. You can come with me as a guest, if you like?'

'Don't be daft, Mitch,' I told him. 'How can I come? I was only five when the battle was fought.'

Mitch gave me a wide, toothy grin. 'You won't have to fall in with us old buggers. Just come along and see the film. Anyway, everyone will be too pissed to notice.'

The next day, the tall figure of the first lieutenant entered the sick bay. He came straight to the point. 'You are due to be rated up Acting Local PO. I'm glad to say that spot of bother you had ashore has been cleared up. Put in your request, and you can see the captain to-morrow. Understood?'

For a moment I was speechless. Me, a petty officer? I had only been a leading hand for a year. Now, at the ripe old age of twenty, and after only three and a half years service, I was to become a senior non-commissioned officer in Her Majesty's Navy!

I swallowed before answering. 'Er... yes, sir, thank you, sir,' I replied, hardly believing my ears.

The next day I was sent to the barracks at St Angelo where I was issued with a new set of insignia.

My doeskin uniform, with its shiny brass buttons, made me feel like Admiral Nelson. The gold crown and anchor on my cap shone like the crown jewels. I straightened my jacket. If only Mum and Dad could see me now, I thought, they'd be as proud as punch.

A knock came at the sick bay door and John Smith, the coxswain came in.

'Congratulations, PO,' he said grinning. 'But remember, you are only acting *local* petty officer. You'll have to revert to leading hand at the end of the commission.'

'Yes,' I replied, still admiring myself. 'Pity. Isn't it? But till then, it means more money, *and* neat rum every day. '

Of course, there were ribald comments from some of my former messmates. When they saw me, everyone jumped up and saluted.

'Attention, everybody.' cried Big Geordie. 'Here comes *Petty Officer* Lightburn. Petty meaning small; officer, meaning pig - a small pig. Come round for gulpers, Doc.'

'The first two rounds are on you, tonight, PO,' said Pete with a grin. 'After all, with your pay rise, you'll be able to buy us all doubles.'

And I did. That night we celebrated in grand style.

The next morning, however, was spent dispensing Bill Manley's special hangover cure to each of them, including an extra strong dose for myself.

My new mess was a world apart from the previous one.

For a start, it was bigger, with more hammock space and larger metal lockers. We even had a mess-man to collect food and wash up after every meal. Everywhere I looked there were veterans who had been through the Second World War. Many, like Mitch, were approaching the end of their twenty-two years service.

My first visit to the mess was greeted with a series of friendly comments.

'Bugger me,' cried Jan Hawes. 'A genuine mickey-mouse PO. You'd best come and have a tot out of me bottle, Doc.'

My first badge was due in November. Glancing at my crossed anchors, my left arm felt slightly naked.

'We'll be all right for frenchies, lads,' cried Harry Morrison, 'And penicillin .'

'Not to mention those hangover cures, we've heard so much about,' laughed Daisy May, a burly stoker PO. 'Welcome, Doc. But watch your step if you bend down.'

My first tot of neat rum made me gasp for breath. Gradually, the fiery, brown liquid infiltrated my system, making my eyes water and setting my guts alight.

A few days later, Mitch came into the sick bay. He smacked his lips together and grinned.

'Now that you're one of us, so to speak,' he said, with a glint in his bleary, blue eyes. 'It would fittin' if you came to that film I told you about. Wouldn't it?'

'Mitch,' I said, glancing at my left arm. 'I'd feel a bit out of place. Compared with you lot, I'm as green as grass.'

He stroked his chin. 'Don't worry now,' he replied. 'I'll look after you. And besides, during the battle, I copped a piece of shrapnel in me leg, and the sick bay tiffies did a grand job fixing me up. So, it's my way of saying thanks to you lot. Anyway, I'll need someone to keep me sober.'

On Saturday evening, dressed in tropical whites, Mitch and I made our way to the Corrodina Canteen. The row of medals jangling across his chest made me feel self-conscious. Every rating, senior or otherwise looked old enough to be my father.

'Here, Doc,' said Mitch, handing me a metal hip flask. 'You'd best have a shot of this afore we go in. Steady your nerves, like.'

The glow on his ruddy complexion told me he had imbibed more than a few already. However, he was right. I was in need of some Dutch courage and took a deep swig. It was neat rum and almost blew my head off.

The hall was crowded. Clouds of tobacco smoke drifted upwards and the air was alive with laughter and conversation. Mitch was in his element, meeting old shipmates from the war years.

He introduced me to a corpulent Chief Cook, called Bob Shilling. 'This is my medical adviser,' said Mitch, handing his hip flask around. 'He's our Doc. Looks after me, so he does.'

He gave me a sly wink.

I quickly caught on. 'Yes,' I replied, tapping my pocket. 'I have the tablets in case you have another turn.'

He placed an affectionate arm around the CPO. 'Bob and me were on the old *Exeter*, weren't we, me old mucker?'

'Aye,' replied Bob, accepting Mitch's flask. 'And a grand job you did when the steering got hit. Ran up and down the length of the ship like a whippet he did…'

Mitch quickly interrupted him. 'Pack it in, mate. It were a long time ago.'

By the time we emptied Mitch's hip flask, I was seeing double. Mitch clung to me, and stammered. 'You'd best stick with me, Doc, me old son. I'd best be keeping an eye on you.'

This made me laugh. It was me who was supposed to be looking after him.

The strident voice of a Chief GI echoed round the hall. 'All personnel involved in the Battle of the River Plate, fall in. Chiefs on the right, then PO's and other ratings.'

Mitch grabbed my arm. 'Follow me,' he murmured.

He led me into a line of petty officers and a few ratings. One or two gave me more than a curious glance as I fell in next to the diminutive Mitch. On my left stood a tall, grey-haired Stoker PO. He looked down, and gave me a drunken grin.

'If I faints, Doc,' he said, 'you can give me the kiss of life.'

I grinned back, and under my breath, muttered, 'You can bugger off. I'd rather be shot than poisoned.'

Once more the voice of the Chief rang around the hall. 'Attention!' he barked, as Earl Mountbatten and his retinue entered.

I glanced to my left and immediately caught a glimpse of the great man. Dressed immaculately in his tropical uniform, he cut a dashing figure. He was medium height and deeply tanned. On his chest were half a dozen rows of medals. Behind him came several high-ranking officers.

'Stand at ease, stand easy,' ordered the Chief GI.

As I staggered Mitch took hold of my arm and said, 'If he sees you've no badges, tell him you got into trouble and lost them.'

My knees felt weak and I needed to urinate. As the party of officers made their way along the line, I heard the deep, plumming voice of the great Earl. On one occasion he laughed. When he sees me, I thought, he really will have something to laugh about.

I stood like a statue as Mountbatten and his party stopped at Mitch.

Mountbatten smiled. 'Which ship were you on during the battle, PO?' he asked Mitch.

Mitch snapped to attention. 'The *Exeter,* sir,' he answered in a surprisingly sober tone.

'Ah yes,' replied Mountbatten. 'Captain Bell. Fine ship. Where are you serving, now?'

'*Decoy,* sir,' answered Mitch.

'Ah, one of your men, Peter,' replied Moutbatten, turning to our captain, who was hidden amongst the party.

Captain Hill-Norton stepped forward. 'Yes, sir' he said. 'Petty Officer Mitchell is our quarterdeck PO.'

Mountbatten looked at me, and raised his eyebrows. 'You were a bit young in 1939, weren't you, PO?'

Before I could answer, Mitch coughed, and said, 'beggin' your pardon, sir. The Doc is here to look after me, so he is.'

The Earl glanced at our captain, then asked, 'Why? What's wrong with you?'

'Be Jezus, it's me heart, sir,' replied Mitch, staring directly in front of him. 'The Doc is here in case I have another heart attack, sir.'

'When was your last attack?'

'On D Day, sir.'

Mountbatten's head went back and he roared with laughter. 'Great Scott,' he replied. 'You were not alone. Most of my staff had one that day also.'

After his Lordship moved away, our captain glared at us. 'Heart attack, my foot,' he growled, before moving on.

The film was excellent. From what I heard, it was a fairly accurate account of how the *Graff Spee* was cornered outside Montevideo on 13th December 1939.

At one point, the wheelhouse of the *Exeter* was destroyed. This meant the ship had to be steered from the tiller flat in the quarterdeck. Because all lines of communication were damaged, a human chain was formed, relaying verbal orders to and from the bridge.

After the film we were in the NAAFI. Mitch was at the bar ordering drinks. The chief cook took me to one side. 'You know, Doc, 'he said gravely, 'Mitch was in that chain. Volunteered to run the gauntlet from the quarterdeck to the bridge. Copped a piece of shrapnel, fell, and smashed all his teeth. Got the DSM, he did. But don't tell anyone. He likes to keep it quiet.'

I looked at the drunken figure of Mitch, slouched across the bar, trying to attract the attention of the barmen. Some hero, I thought. From now on, you can have as many sets of false teeth as you like.

On Thursday July 26 Nasser nationalised the Suez Canal.

There was also news of Egypt wanting to borrow money from America to build a dam at Aswan. If this wasn't forthcoming, Nasser might turn to Russia, thus stoking the fires of the Cold War.

'That bugger's been spoiling for a fight for some time,' said Harry Smyth, the wardroom PO Steward. Harry was a small, quiet man from Lambeth in London, who normally did not say much. 'Not content with kicking our lads out of the Canal Zone, now, he wants to grab everything for himself.'

'What will it mean?' I asked him, looking enquiringly around.

'The canal is our lifeline,' he replied. 'All our oil comes through there. The sod is holding the country to ransom.'

On the same day, our old Jimmy left the ship to take command of a frigate. I was sorry to see him go. He was a good officer, and I stood to attention on the brow as he left the ship.

He was replaced by Lieutenant Commander O. Lascelles. MBE, DSC. RN.

'I've served with him before on the *Caprice*,' said Jan Hawes. 'He's a hard bugger and stands no nonsense.'

Our new first lieutenant was tall, broad-shouldered, with fair hair and piercing blue eyes. During his first official rounds, he entered the sick bay without knocking.

After a quick, but thorough inspection, he said, 'I want the medical parties exercised regularly and all the first aid boxes checked.' He paused, and opened a cupboard. 'Where is the morphia kept?'

'I keep several monojects here, sir,' I replied. 'And the rest are in your cabin.'

'I want every senior officer to have some,' he replied. 'If we go into action, they may be needed.'

Go into action, I thought. The only action we had seen was chasing a few fishing boats all over the Mediterranean. What the hell was he talking about?

I was soon to find out.

Nobody was quite sure what was happening in Egypt. The newspapers told us the Queen had signed a proclamation recalling reservists to the colours, and ships were being taken out of mothballs.

'My missus told me in a letter the *Theseus* and *Ocean* sailed from Pompey full of troops and aircraft,' said the Chief ERA, as we grouped around the main notice board reading the latest report.

'Says here,' added the Chief Chippy, 'a troopship called the *Dilwara* has left England with a couple of infantry divisions, bound for Malta'

'Holy Mother,' cried Mitch. 'So that's why the *Birmingham* and *Jamaica* are here. Dear old Malta's going to look like it did during the war.'

When Joe told me in a letter that 3rd Paras were undergoing intensive training before leaving for Cyprus, I realised something big was brewing.

'There is even talk of us practising night jumps,' Joe went on. 'They won't tell us anything, but the word going around is some sort of invasion is being planned.'

Invasion! I cried inwardly. Now I'll really have something to tell the lads back home.

Throughout August we were at sea undergoing extensive exercises. Our new Jimmy really put the crew through their paces. Action stations were sounded without warning. My first aid parties practised everything in the manual, from treating burns to bullet wounds.

During the first week of September, in company with the

carriers *Theseus* and *Ocean,* we put to sea. In true naval tradition, Admiral Guy Grantham, the Commander-in-Chief, Mediterranean, standing on the balcony in St Angelo, saluted the fleet as it sailed out of Grand Harbour. During the week that followed, we practised landing craft exercises with the Royal Marines Commandos, while jet fighters screamed overhead, making low-level sorties.

'Just like D Day again,' quipped Mitch.

'Don't tell me you were there as well?'

'Certainly was,' answered Mitch. 'On the *Belfast.* Only it beats me why we're getting involved in Egypt when we're already fighting EOKA terrorists in Cyprus not to mention the Mau Mau in Kenya.'

'Sod off, Mitch,' replied Paddy Alexander. 'That bugger Nasser thinks he's another Hitler. If he's not stopped now, there's no telling what will happen next.'

But nothing happened.

The captain addressed the crew over the tannoy. He told us a special Association had been formed by those countries using the canal, hoping to pacify Nasser. Meanwhile, we were to continue exercising in case hostilities should break out between ourselves and Egypt

He ended by telling us in two weeks we would be going to visit Iskanderun. This, we were told, was a port on the coast of northern Turkey, where there was also a large American oil refinery. The news naturally brought forth loud cheering throughout the ship.

The news bulletins informed us that Nasser had rejected the British and French offers to negotiate terms for the Suez Canal.

However, nobody knew for certain what was happening. Rumours spread around the ship like wildfire. At one time, someone told me we were joining the Americans for an all-out assault on Alexandria.

One evening in the mess, a few of the PO's were playing uckers. Others were writing letters or lay in their hammocks reading.

'It says here, in the *Express,*' came the voice of Daisy May from inside his hammock, 'that a few squadrons of Canberra bombers are due to arrive in Cyprus. '

'Fine bloody war this will turn out to be,' growled Paddy O'Connor. 'The Gyppos will know everything we are up to. Those politicians want their heads testing, so they do.'

'I must say, it does sound a bit stupid,' I replied, lighting a cigarette. 'Maybe they are trying to scare them off.'

'No chance,' added Jan Hawes, 'Nasser has the help of the Ruskies. They even sent him 'planes, and equipment. It's us who should be bloody scared.'

'Anyway, boyo,' replied Sharky Ward, 'things seem quiet enough at the moment. Maybe it's the lull before the storm.'

Jan threw a six and beamed across at him. 'There,' he beamed. 'Home at last.'

'I wish to fuck we were,' muttered Daisy. 'Then we'd all get some peace.'

Before we sailed for Turkey, we re-ammunitioned ship, then took on fuel from the RFA (Royal Fleet Auxillary) tanker *Tiderace.*

Our journey to Turkey proved to be the roughest to date.

The ship shook and shivered its way though the rough seas, sending mountains of green water cascading over our bows. Lifelines were rigged along the upper deck for those on duty.

Once again, at night I bounced from side to side in my bunk. By the time we arrived in Iskanderun I was black and blue

However, before we reached Turkey, I was faced with a tricky problem.

Commander Bishop, the engineering officer, came into the sick bay. He was normally a pleasant, jovial man, who had never reported sick.

'Do you have a lozenge or something, PO,' he said hoarsley. 'I've got a bit of a sore throat.'

His left tonsil was enlarged, as were the glands in his neck and he had a fever.

'I'm afraid you've got a raging tonsillitis, sir,' I said to him. 'Are you allergic to penicillin?'

'No I'm not,' he replied. 'Don't tell me you're going to give me a bloody injection?'

I nodded my head. 'Yes, sir, I am,' I replied. 'And I'm afraid I'll have to ask you to turn in.'

'Rubbish,' he exploded. 'I can't do that. I'm too busy. Just give me a gargle or something, I'll be fine.'

'Sorry, sir,' I replied adamantly. 'This could lead to complications if you don't do as I ask.'

'Complications. What complications?'

'Chest infections, pneumonia, pleurisy, to name a few,' I said.

'Balderdash,' he snorted. 'Just give me the damn penicillin. and I'll be off. We're doing speed trials this afternoon.'

The commander had an acute infection. If he would not do as I asked, there was only one course open to me.

I took a deep breath. 'Sir,' I said.' You are not well. If you don't get turned in, you'll leave me no alternative but to report your condition to the first lieutenant. '

With a look of astonishment, he said, 'Will you, by Jove! We'll soon see about that,' and stormed out.

The Jimmy was on the bridge standing next to the captain. Nearby stood the chief yeoman. Both lookouts were closed up and everything was quiet.

The captain overheard me explaining the problem to the first lieutenant.

'Leave this to me, Number One,' said the captain, grinning. 'I'll have a word with Jeremy.' He then looked at me, and added, 'Are you sure about this, PO?'

'Yes, sir,' I replied confidently. 'I am.'

'Hmm…'he said with a wry smile. 'Very well. Carry on.'

At first the commander was angry, but the captain's words seemed to calm him down. During the next 48 hours, I was kept busy visiting him in his cabin with gargles, penicillin injections and plenty of fluids. By the time we arrived in Iskanderun the commander was recovering well.

Our visit to Turkey was brief but pleasant. The ship's soccer team lost 2-0; Seldom got drunk and fell overboard and was charged with breaking ship. Scouse Kilbane and others visited the town's only brothel. I would be seeing all of them in due course.

Normal routine was quickly resumed – that is, until we were torpedoed!

On a dull, overcast, Friday morning the ship left Turkey.and joined company with HMS *Jamaica,* off the coast of Crete. Above, the dark, cumulonimbus clouds stretching away to the horizon, gave warning of strong winds and heavy rain.

Daily Orders informed us a torpedo shoot would take place at two o'clock. All hands were to keep clear of the area aft of midships. This meant I would be confined to the sick bay while firing was in progress. However, I managed to watch from X gun deck as the five, elongated metal tubes containing the deadly weapons were trained outward. The guardrails were removed and everything was ready.

One by one, the gleaming, cigar-shaped weapons were propelled into the sea, leaving a long stream of white turbulence in their wake.

Once again my Walter Mitty mind went into overdrive. Watching the foamy lines streaking towards an imaginary enemy, I waited for the sea to explode, and a pall of smoke rise into the air.

The mellow voice of Jan Hawse interrupted my day-dreaming.

'Those are Mark V fish, my handsome,' he said, standing next to me. 'If they were primed, they'd carry enough explosives to blow us all to kingdom come.'

'Thank God they're going in wrong direction, then,' I said, warily.

The torpedoes were recovered by whaler crews, and by means of a derrick, hoisted onboard and replaced into the tubes. It was a lengthy process, which took most of the afternoon.

The next day was Sunday. The weather had suddenly brightened and the off-duty watches had a make-and-mend. After tot-time, the crew either got their heads down, caught up with their dhobying or wrote letters.

An air of tranquillity prevailed throughout the ship. We had completed our last Cyprus patrol, and were heading back to Malta.

Around one o'clock, I flopped on my bunk and opened an old copy of "Tit Bits". Just as my eyes were becoming heavy, an ear-shattering explosion sent me flying onto the deck. My head hit the side of a metal cupboard, sending stars flashing before my eyes.

Drawers flew open and the sick bay door came crashing down. The small mirror on the bulkhead cracked. Pieces of fibreglass casings from the neon lights hit the deck and a flurry of dust filled the air. The acrid smell of cordite stung my eyes. Holy Mother of God, I thought, we've hit a mine!

Rubbing my eyes, I staggered to my feet and gingerly made my way through the gap once occupied by the door and into the passageway.

I could hardly believe my eyes. To my amazement, the round head of a shiny blue torpedo protruded through the bulkhead of the after deckhouse. Around the gleaming warhead shrouds of metal curved outward like twisted fingers.

Just then, the chief cook appeared from the galley. His chubby face was pale with shock. 'Fuckin' hell,' he gasped. 'We've been torpedoed. The bloody thing could go off any second,' and rapidly disappeared.

The chief stoker and two ratings came up a hatchway.

'What the hell was that?' asked the chief, looking around. When he saw the torpedo poking through the bulkhead, his eyes almost left their sockets. 'Christ Almighty,' he cried. 'Get everyone out. And be quick about it.'

The first lieutenant and two other officers arrived. 'Clear the area,' he ordered. He shot a glance at me. 'Is any one hurt?'

'I don't know, sir' I replied. 'I'll check.'

The after officers' flat and messes were not damaged. But I was amazed to find another piece of the torpedo in the engine-room air intake. By some miracle, nobody was hurt. I reported this to the Chief GI.

A crowd of sailors appeared in various states of undress.

'Everyone for'd,' echoed the Chief GI, who had joined the officers. 'And be quick about it.'

'What the hell happened, chief?' asked Vince, a bearded AB. 'Are we gunna abandon ship?'

'Cut the cackle,' roarded the Chief GI, 'and move yourself.'

Outside, the after middle torpedo tube was empty. Bits of the cat-walk – a narrow, overhead bridgeway connecting the various parts of the ship - were strewn over the deck.

The solitary figure of Yorky suddenly appeared on the funnel deck. He was dressed in a pair of underpants and flip-flops. His red beard contrasted sharply with near-nakedness.

'What the fuck's going on?' he yelled at nobody in particular. 'I was just about to do me dhobying when I was blown on me back. Me bucket flew over the side, and I've lost all me gear.'

His sudden appearance lifted the tension. Even the captain raised a smile as we moved for'd into the canteen flat.

Shortly afterwards, the voice of the Jimmy came over the tannoy. He explained that the explosion was caused by faulty mechanism in a compressed air bottle. The force of the blast had broken the torpedo in two, one section entering the after screen door, and the other into the engine room air intake.

The duty watch cleared away the debris, and the Chief Chippy fixed the sick bay door and replaced the lighting fixtures.

'We was bloody lucky,' he said, screwing on a neon light

covering. 'If we hadn't had a make-and-mend, we'd have had a few injured men.'

Just then, Mitch appeared. His weather-beaten face broke into a radiant grin. 'Don't worry, Doc,' he said. 'The teeth are OK. But in all my years at sea, this is the first time I've been torpedoed by my own ship.'

Early next day we sailed into Valetta and tied up alongside the repair vessel, MV *Childers.*. The ship was immediately invaded by dockyard maties as they set about replacing the damaged torpedo tube.

Once again, the harbour was filled with warships. These were joined by the aircraft carrier HMS *Albion* and HMS *Tyne*, a large supply vessel. The presence of many landing craft and a squadron of Canberra bombers meant the place was rife with speculation.

The newspapers were full of belligerent exchanges between Israel and Egypt.

Jan Hawse sat in the mess reading a copy of the *Daily Express*. 'It says here,' reading from his newspaper, 'that if Israel and Egypt go to war, our lot will have to intervene'

'Doesn't make sense to me,' Mumbled Harry Smyth, the Wardroom PO Steward. 'Why the hell should we get involved?'

'Oil, me old cocka, oil,' replied Sharky Ward. 'If Nasser blocks that, we're all up the creek.'

During the next few weeks I was able to catch up with giving some of the crew routine injections and arranging annual chest X rays and medical examinations. I also had to go to Bighi to collect extra medical stores.

This was the moment I had been dreading. Despite efforts to forget Anita, her memory was still sharp in my mind.

A lump came to my throat as I went up in the lift and entered the receiving room. Suddenly, my anxieties were momentarily forgotten. Talking to the duty PO was none other than Sam Small. Dressed in white shorts and shirt, there was no mistaking his flaxen hair and finely chiselled features.

When he saw me, his eyes lit up.

'Lightburn, you bugger,' he exploded, shaking my hand. 'How the hell are you? When did you pick up your PO's rate?'

'I'm just acting local, Sam,' I replied. 'How long have you been here?'

'I'm on the *Albion*. What about you?'

'The *Decoy* – one of the *Darings*'

'Small ships, eh,' replied Sam with a tinge of envy. 'Lucky you.'

He had brought a party from his ship for X rays, and was waiting for them.

For a while we caught up with events at home.

'What happened to the lads of the football team?'

He went on to tell me Harry Johnson and George Storey were at HMS *Rooke,* a shore base in Gibraltar. Taff Baxendale and Lofty Day had been drafted to the aircraft carrier *Bulwark*

'Joe England and Pete Smart are still in the bone-yard,' he said. 'Oh, and by the way, there's a bloke onboard who wants to meet you.'

'Oh yes,' I replied, raising my eyebrows. 'Who's that, then?'

'His name is Malcolm, something or other. He's a PO Tel. Says he is the fiancé of a nurse you knew at Culdrose called Iris.'

I gave a start. 'What does he want me for?' I quickly asked.

Sam shot me a queer look and shrugged his shoulders. 'He didn't say. But Iris told him you were a lecherous bugger. Don't tell me you've been giving his girl one?'

'No, no, not me, Sam,' I said innocently, then added, 'When is *Albion* sailing for UK?'

'We're here,' he said, 'until this business with Nasser is over.'

'Ha, yes, of course,' I replied weakly. 'Well, if you see this PO, tell him we're sailing shortly. So I'm afraid he'll miss me.'

'You can tell him yourself,' said Sam, offering me a cigarette and lighting it. 'Here he comes now with the others.'

A dozen sailors appeared. One of them, a tall, thick-set petty officer with a ginger beard, approached Sam.

'All present and correct, Doc,' he said in a thick, Devon accent. 'What time is the launch coming?'

'In ten minutes,' replied Sam with a twinkle in his eye. 'By the way, Ging,' he went on, turning to me, 'this is Tom Lightburn. He knew your Iris at Culdrose, didn't you, Tom?'

My heart stood still. His dark brown eyes stared at me. For a second I thought he was going to hit me.

'So,' he boomed, 'you're the one. She told me about those dirty weekends.'

I gulped.

'She did,' I replied, stepping away from him.

314

'Yes, you dirty lucky bugger,' he said. 'She wrote and told me all about you and Julie, the dental nurse having it away in Penzance. Iris says if I met you, to ask you to write to Julie. OK?'

'Oh, right.' I replied, breathing a sigh of relief. 'I would have done, but we've been at sea a lot. You know how it is…?'

Ginger said goodbye then, with the rest of his party, made his way to the lift.

Sam and I shook hands again. 'Take care of yourself, Tom, lad,' he said. 'Oh, and by the way. You remember Charlotte, the nurse I caught you talking to that night on C2 ward?'

'Charlotte, the…'

'Yes, well,' he said, interrupting me. 'We are getting married when I get back.'

'That's great, Sam,' I said, biting my tongue. 'Congratulations. I hope you are both very happy.'

After Sam and his party had left, I was quickly brought back to earth. I decided to go and see Desperate and any other of the lads from Plymouth.

'Desperate's still on the medical ward,' said the duty PO, checking his list. 'You'll just catch him before he goes off duty.'

Making my way across the small square and up the stairs I felt slightly sick and my mouth went dry. This was the ward where I met Anita. I entered, half expecting to see her.

Desperate still had his perpetual five o'clock shadow, grinned when he saw me. After introducing me to the sister, we adjourned to the galley.

'Jock McBride and Lofty Small are on the surgical ward,' he said, handing me a mug of tea.

'What happened to Simbo?' I asked, taking a welcome gulp of tea'

'He's still in HMS *Tamar,*' he replied. 'Along with Taff Elias and Johnny Halligan.'

There was an awkward silence, before Desperate spoke again.

'I'm sorry about Sister Johannsen,' he said quietly. 'I thought you might have heard. Didn't mean to spring it on you like that.'

'That's all right, Des,' I said, placing a hand on his shoulder. 'Forget it.'

Desperate finished duty, and together we went and collected my medical stores.

We then went to see Lofty and Jock on the surgical ward.

They were busy making beds. Upon seeing me, they stopped what they were doing. They both came towards me, grinning their heads off.

'My God!' cried Lofty. 'You look like a Dutch Admiral with that brass hat.'

I laughed, and told them my rank was only temporary.

'Bloody hell, fellers,' I said, shaking each by the hand. 'It seems ages since Des and I we were kicked out of the "Paramount", doesn't it?'

'You're right there, man,' replied Desperate. 'And believe me, a lot of beer's been drunk since then, Tom.'

'Aye,' said Lofty, giving Jock a playful dig in the ribs. 'But you've not paid for it. You tight-arsed bugger.'

'Which reminds me,' said Jock. 'If we hurry we'll be able to have a few wets in the canteen before they close.'

Information about Egypt and Nasser was scarce. A news bulletin told the crew that expatriate staff in the Suez Canal company had left Egypt. So clearly, something was stirring in Whitehall. There seemed to be a lull on the political front, but in Grand Harbour and Sliema, the build-up of ships continued.

A week later we put to sea.

Training exercises were intensified.

Using a stopwatch, the first-lieutenant timed how long it took Big Geordie and his first aid party to convert the wardroom into an emergency operating station.

'Fifteen minutes is far too long, PO,' he snapped, at me. 'Dismantle everything, and do it again.'

'Bloody Captain Bligh,' growled Tiny Small, as he removed the deck-head lighting. 'Thinks he's back on the soddin' *Bounty*.'

After two more attempts, we finally did it in ten minutes.

I even managed to arrange with Sharky Ward, the corpulent PO Cook, to use large pans of water in the wardroom galley to sterilise instruments should this become necessary.

When we returned to Grand Harbour, I received a signal from the squadron medical officer, ordering me to collect an emergency surgical dressing chest from Bighi – a sure sign something was up.

Packed in straw, the chest contained a host of stainless steel, surgical instruments. Among them was a small saw. My God, I

316

thought, gingerly running my fingers along its serrated edge, I hope I don't have to use this.

There were sets of retractors, scalpels and a range of forceps I had never seen before. There were also masks made of metal mesh. A pad was placed into these, held over the patient's mouth, and chloroform added as an anaesthetic. Everything, in fact, a surgeon would need to carry out an emergency operation.

I had the chest removed to the wardroom where it was covered, appropriately, with a red tablecloth.

During the next two weeks the October weather at sea was extremely rough. We were in and out of Malta, doing gunnery shoots, and acting as guard ship for HMS *Albion*,

On our way back to Malta, the ship was tossed about like a cork. Many were seasick and the toilets became blocked with vomit.

The sick bay was invaded by sailors looking like death warmed up. Among them was the gaunt figure of Junior Seaman Nobby Clark.

'It's me guts,' he Mumbled, holding his arm across his abdomen. 'I can't keep anything down.'

I reached for the hyocine hydrobromide tablets. 'Take a couple of these,' I said. 'Try and get some fresh air, and eat some dry bread. At least you'll have something to bring up.'

A few hours later, Seldom bust into the sick bay. His sou'wester was dripping and his black oilskin glistened with rain.

'You'd best get for'd to 30 mess, Doc,' he blurted, wiping his face. 'Young Nobby Clark's in agony.'

I grabbed my foul weather jacket and followed him. The stuffy atmosphere of the mess was heavy with tobacco smoke. Numerous hammocks swung in unison with the motion of the ship.

Several sailors were gathered around Nobby's hammock. One held a bucket, and said, 'He's been sick quite a lot, Doc,'

'Is it your stomach again, matey?' I asked.

His pale face was contorted in agony. Through clenched teeth, he Mumbled, 'Yes. It's killing me, Doc.' He had both knees drawn up and both arms were across his stomach. Clearly, this was something more serious than sea-sickness.

As quick as I could, I gave him an examination. The right side of his abdomen was tender and the muscles were tense. This was a

317

symptom called 'guarding,' Dr Young at Culdrose had shown me. His pulse was full and bounding, and his temperature was a shade above normal.

Christ Almighty, I thought, he's got acute appendicitis.

'You'll be all right, Nobby,' I said, trying to re-assure him. 'Just lie still.'

I looked at Pincer Martin, who was the killick of the mess. 'Keep an eye on him, Pincher,' I said, 'and don't give him anything to eat. I'll be back shortly.'

On the bridge, the captain and other personnel were closed up.

The first lieutenant was standing by the chart table. 'Excuse me, sir,' I said nervously.

He gave me a sharp glance. 'What do you want, PO?'

'I think a rating has acute appendicitis, sir,' I replied, licking salt away from my lips. 'Junior Seaman Clark.'

'What?' he quietly gasped. 'Appendicitis? Are you sure, man?'

Oh hell, I thought. Here I go again. If I'm wrong, this will definitely be the end of me.

'Yes, sir,' I replied. 'As sure as I can be.'

The shadowy figure of the captain appeared. Like the others he was wearing a black oilskin. His bronzed face was wet and water dripped from the peak of his cap. 'Do we have a problem, Number One?'

'One of the crew is sick, sir,' replied the Jimmy. 'If you'll excuse me, I'll go down below and see how bad it is.'

The captain gave a curt nod. 'Very well,' he said. 'Keep me informed.'

We clambered down a few ladders into the mess.

'How are you feeling, Clark?' asked the Jimmy. 'Are you, err...in much pain, my boy?'

'Y...yes, sir,' stuttered Nobby, still clutching his stomach. 'It's bloody agony.'

'I see,' replied the officer calmly, and moved away.

I followed him outside.

'Right, I'll inform the captain,' he said, quietly. 'We are too far away from *Albion*, to ask for a doctor. If we make a dash for Malta, we could arrive there by dawn. Make out a signal and I'll have it sent off immediately. Meanwhile what are you going to do with Clark?'

'I'll keep him where he is, and give him a large dose of

penicillin, sir,' I replied.

An emergency signal was sent off, requesting a medical officer to meet us in Grand Harbour.

'We're going to get you to Malta, Nobby.' I told him. 'Don't you start worrying, now, you're going to be all right.'

The ship thundered through the sea like a thoroughbred. A pipe was made informing the crew special sea duty-men would be required at three-thirty in the morning.

The next eight hours were the longest of my life.

After giving Nobby two large injections of penicillin, I remained by his side. Christ, I thought, checking his pulse every fifteen minutes, never a dull moment in this ship. A chilling thought ran through me. If his appendix was to burst, he would certainly die from peritonitis.

Nobody in the mess slept that night. Even those with the middle watch asked how Nobby was. Others hovered around, making sure I had a regular supply of kye.

By the time the launch came alongside I had no nails left. The welcome figure of a surgeon lieutenant accompanied by a sick berth PO came into the mess.

I ordered everyone to leave and explained the problem.

'I think you are right,' said the doctor after a brief examination. 'Let's get him ashore.'

With the help of the first aid party, we tucked Nobby into a Neil Robertson stretcher and lowered him into the launch.

'We'll take it from here,' said the PO. 'You look all in. Go and get your head down. We'll send a signal informing you of what happens.'

The following day a signal arrived telling us Nobby had been operated on and was recovering well.

Two weeks later Israel attacked Egypt.

20

We heard the news of the attack while on our final Cyprus patrol. A buzz of excitement spread throughout the ship like a cyclone.

Big Geordie popped his head into the sick bay. 'Now we'll see some action,' he cried. 'Get those scalpels sharpened, Doc. Looks like you're gonna need them.'

'Blood thirsty bugger,' I replied. 'Close the door and sod off.'

The next day the captain told us over the tannoy that Britain and France had appealed to both Israel and Egypt for a cease-fire. 'The likelihood of this happening is remote,' he said. 'Therefore, an invasion of the Canal Zone will probably be imminent. I will keep you informed of further developments.'

'If we go in, Mitch,' said Wiggy Bennett, 'do you think the Gyppos will fight?'

We were in the mess one evening.

'Of course they will,' replied Mitch. 'They're not going to stand and watch while us and the frogs take over their land, are they?'

Daisy May looked up from his letter writing. 'My missus tells me in her letter, the Ruskies have sent them some Ilyshin jets as well as MIGs.'

'How come your missus knows more than us?' asked Wiggy.

'My missus knows more than Anthony Eden,' replied Daisy, with a grin. 'She gets her gen from the women at the bingo.'

We gave a half-hearted laugh.

'Aye, maybe she does,' replied Jan Hawes, hanging up a well-ironed shirt. 'But they've got a few submarines *and* motor torpedo boats.'

'Not to mention some tanks,' said Mitch, taking out his teeth carefully wrapping them up in a handkerchief. 'We sold them a few, and so did the reds.'

'Maybe so,' said Daisy, 'but they haven't much of an army, have they?'

'I wouldn't be too sure of that, my lad,' chimed in Sharky Ward, the portly officers, cook. 'They'll be on their home ground. And besides, if they all dress in that long, white gear, our lads won't be able to tell the difference between soldiers and civilians.'

'You'll be all right, then, chef,' quipped Jan Hawes, looking at the chef's working rig. 'If you go ashore dressed like that you'll be as safe as houses.'

Harry Morrison, who was playing cards with two others, cried, 'gin,' then went on, 'Hey, Doc, you might even get a chance to use those saws and things you brought on board.'

All the talk of Egyptian fighters, tanks and MTB boats left me feeling uneasy. That evening I double-checked the morphia, and the first aid boxes. My worries were compounded next day when we heard the Israelis had invaded the western banks of the Gulf of Aqaba

At first nobody understood why this had taken place. One morning, Sub Lieutenant Forbes came into the sick bay for an aspirin. I asked him what was going on.

'As you know, PO, Israel and Egypt are sworn enemies,' he explained. 'For some time now, the Egyptians have prevented Israeli shipping from using the canal. They have also blockaded the Gulf of Aqaba. If the Israelis occupy the west side of Aqaba, this will allow their shipping safe passage into the Red Sea. That Egyptian warship we saw in the Red Sea was on blockade duty.'

At four in the morning on the 31st October we arrived off Port Said.

Sleep seemed to elude me. I sat up and looked out of the porthole.

Shafts of pale moonlight beamed down onto the rolling sea like inverted searchlights. The sickening thought that an Egyptian submarine might be lurking beneath the waves flashed through my mind.

Suddenly, Action Stations sounded.

In a matter of seconds I donned my ant-flash gear, boots and lifejacket. My heart beat fast and I started to sweat. In my breast pocket was a photograph of Mum and Dad, along with a roll of pound notes curled up in a condom. If I drowned, at least I wouldn't die a pauper.

The first aid parties arrived, collected their medical bags and hurried away.

After checking they were at their posts, I reported this to the bridge.

The voice of the first lieutenant warned of an attack by Egyptian motor torpedo boats. My God, I thought. Now we're for it.

Danny Wilde bounded into the sick bay. He face was drawn, and he was sweating. 'Do you think they'll torpedo us?' he asked.

Behind him stood Big Geordie. 'Don't worry, Danny,' said the big man. 'If they do, and we have to abandon ship, the sharks will soon put paid to you.'

'Sharks!' exclaimed Danny looking at me. 'There's no sharks in the Med, is there, Doc?'

Big Geordie, standing behind him, quickly nodded at me.

'Of course there is, Danny,' I replied, feeling his arm. 'But, I doubt if they'll fancy you. You're too skinny.'

For the next two hours we anxiously waited for an attack which never came. At six in the morning we went to Defence Stations. Two hours later the alarm went again, but once more an expected attack proved false.

Similar scares occurred throughout the next few days.

News telling us of the shooting down of a Wyvern helicopter from HMS *Eagle* plus the loss of a Sea Hawk fighter from HMS *Bulwark* increased our anxieties.

Tension was etched on the faces of the crew.

Seldom came into the sick bay, complaining of a headache. His face was pale and he looked tired. There was really nothing wrong with him, except an acute attack of nerves.

'Those bloody Gyppos really mean business. Don't they Doc?'

'Sit down and relax, Seldom. You'll be fine,' I replied. 'Have a cup of tea, and remember - we mean business as well.'

On Saturday 3rd November, we were once again closed up at action stations. The time was one in the morning. My body craved sleep. I splashed cold water on my face, and crept out onto the torpedo deck to take a breath of fresh air.

The cool night air was a welcome relief from the warm, stuffiness of the sick bay. The ship was steaming steadily through the sea. The silhouettes of other warships were barely visible in the dark. Everything was quiet. The moon flitted between dense clouds, sending occasional shafts of light dancing across the waves. It was hard to believe we were in harm's way. After a few deep breaths I returned inboard.

Quite abruptly, the serenity of the scene was shattered.

Once again we went to action stations.

'The ship is under attack by Egyptian 'E' boats,' came the Jimmy's calm voice over the tannoy.

My heart leapt in my mouth. I waited for an explosion, and imagined myself struggling in the water, while watching the ship slowly sink.

Without any warning, the for'ds guns of A and B turrets opened up. The sick bay shuddered as the shock wave vibrated through the ship. After two more salvoes, the firing stopped.

Shortly afterwards, the first lieutenant informed us the attack had been repulsed.

After we had stood down, I met Pincher Martin on the upper deck. He had been closed up on the starboard Stag (Stabilised Tachometric Anti-Aircraft Gun,) mountings. From there, he witnessed everything.

'They suddenly appeared from nowhere,' he said excitedly. 'At first, they were like little white specks. Then they made a fuck up. The silly buggers switched on their searchlights. That told us where they were. When we fired a few salvoes of star shells over 'em.' He stopped talking and laughed. 'You should have seen them. They turned, and ran like rabbits.'

On Daily Orders next day, the crew were informed that all outgoing mail would be censored.

'That's a diabolical liberty, that is,' cried Pete. 'There goes my sexy letters to the missus,'

'What about my pen friend in Paris,' muttered Sharky Ward. 'The frogs are with us out here, ain't they?'

'Don't tell me you send her *French Letters,*' laughed Taff Leighton.

'Piss off,' replied Sharky, 'you sheep-shaggers can't even write. Let alone spell.'

However, it did serve to remind everyone of the serious situation we were in.

Early next morning, I went onto the bridge to fill in the number of sick in the log. Everyone had binoculars trained away to starboard. Nudging Sharky Ward, I asked, 'What are they all looking at, Bunts?'

'It's the Yanks,' he whispered.

'What are they doing there?'

Sharky put down his binoculars. With one hand he wiped his eyes. 'They're against us invading the Canal Zone. Something to do with the President's re-election coming up.'

Later that day the first lieutenant voice came over the tannoy.

'HMS *Newfoundland,* has engaged and sunk an Egyptian warship in the Gulf of Aqaba, and has sustained several casualties,' he paused. 'I will keep you informed. That is all.'

I immediately thought of Reg McKnight who was onboard *Newfoundland,* and prayed he was all right.

A feeling of disquiet spread around the ship.

'Bloody hell,' gasped one of the crew. 'For all we know, we could be next.'

On Sunday 4th November I was in for another shock. Glancing outside the pothole, I could hardly believe my eyes. As far as I could see, ships ranging from landing craft to cruisers stretched away in the distance.

Straight away, I dashed onto the upper deck and joined several others.

Set against a dull, grey sky, signals flashed between ships like miniature gunfire. Jet fighters from aircraftcarriers screamed overhead, forming a protective umbrella against intruders.

'My God, Slinger,' I cried. 'This reminds me of when my Dad described the invasion of Sicily. "Ships as far as the eyes could see," he told me. This is what it must have been like.'

The first lieutenant announced we were to escort the landing craft towards Port Said, and added, 'Lower deck will be cleared at 1400. All hands will muster on the fo'c'sle for an address by the captain.'

'Allo, allo, allo!' cried Paddy Alexander. 'What's the old man got up his sleeve this time.'

At precisely two o'clock we found out.

Captain Hill-Norton, immaculately clad in his tropical uniform, stood on a raised platform. Palcing both hands on his hips, he surveyed the ship's company. In a sharp, well-modulated voice, he began, 'I expect you all know why you are here.'

Wiggy Bennett was standing next to me. 'Look at him,' he uttered from the corner of his mouth. 'He thinks he's bloody John Wayne. Of course we fuckin' know why we are here.'

A low murmur swept through the crew. The Captain waited till this had died down before continuing. 'At 0200 tomorrow, 3rd Para will be dropped to take Gamil airfield, some distance down the canal. French paratroops will land and occupy bridges further afield.'

The mention of 3rd Para brought me up with a jolt. This was Joe's battalion. Remembering what was said about the Egyptians retaliating, my heart sank.

I gave the Chief GI a sly nudge.

'Will we be giving the Paras support, chief?' I whispered.

He gave me daggers. 'No we wont,' he replied bluntly. 'We'll be too far away. Now shut up and listen to the skipper.'

The captain set his jaw and went on. 'In company with *Jamaica*, *Duchess* and *Diamond* we will give covering fire to units of 40 and 42 Royal Marine Commando, who will be landing on the beach. Supporting them will be a squadron of Centurion tanks.' Once more he paused.

My palms began to sweat and I could feel the tension rising.

The captain coughed before carrying on. 'When the marines are ashore, *Decoy* will take a position parallel to the coast. We will be the closest ship inland and will engage the enemy. I am confident the ship's company will perform with efficiency. Good luck to you all. '

Everyone glanced nervously at one another.

'The closest ship to the coast,' re-iterated Mitch. 'Jesus Mary and Joseph, we'll be sitting ducks. I'm due for me pension when we get back, and I want to live to spend some of it.'

I grinned at him, and replied, 'Never mind, Mitch. Maybe you'll get another medal to go with the others you've got.'

'Fuck your medals,' he said, shaking his head. 'I've seen too many good men killed already.'

On several occasions I watched as aircraft from the carriers passed overhead towards Port Said. This was followed by the faint clumping sound of bombs exploding, as palls of black smoke appeared in the distance.

'I wonder what they are hitting?' mumbled Big Geordie.

He and the other members of the first aid parties were on the quarterdeck. I was giving them a final briefing before we went into action.

'Nasser,s palace, I hope,' replied Pete. 'Then maybe we can all go home.'

'Right, lads,' I said. 'This is it. This is what we've been training for. By now everyone should know exactly what to do. Any questions?'

Some shook their heads, others met my gaze with a blank

stare.

'If anyone needs help, send for me. Good luck.'

That night, the thought of Joe parachuting onto enemy-held territory kept me awake. Around four I heard the drone of aircraft. We were at Defence Stations and I was fully dressed. In a flash I leapt out of bed. The deadlights covered the scuttles, and the ship remained 'darkened,' as a precaution against enemy attack. Pulling aside the black canvas covering, I opened the hatchway that led onto the ship's waist. Dawn was breaking and streaks of sunlight cast an eerie glow against a grey sky. All around, I could see the dark shapes of several warships ploughing through the ocean.

Suddenly, my stomach churned over.

The drone of aircraft could be heard some miles away. In the distance dim lines of red tracer bullets arched into the sky. My God, I thought. Joe and his mates are jumping through that. The image of Joe, his parachute engulfed in flames, flashed through my mind. A lump came to my throat. Once more I recalled my cryptic comment to him. 'Anyone who wants to jump out of a perfectly good aircraft, must be bloody crazy.'

Now, watching the sky ablaze with enemy fire, my words seemed painfully accurate. Then I remembered it was 5th November. By Christ, I told myself, if Joe and I survive, this would be one Bonfire Night we would never forget

Quite abruptly, the red lines in the sky disappeared.

Everything went quiet except the steady throb of the ship's engines. The sudden silence was uncanny, and as the day unfolded an air of apprehension spread throughout the ship.

'Do you think the Paras made it?' I asked Paddy Alexander.

'You bet,' he replied. 'To be sure, it'll take more than a few jippos to stop those lads, I can tell you.'

Daily Orders informed everyone we would go to action stations at midnight.

The sky was overcast and there was a heavy swell. On the horizon, I could see a forest of masts as more vessels from Malta and Algiers joined the fleet. Helicopters buzzed from ship to ship while high in the air, Avengers and Sky Raiders hovered around like mother hens protecting their young.

What happened next took my breath away.

'There it goes,' cried Mitch, who had joined me on the port

waist. 'The dear old battle ensign!'

I watched with pride as the white ensign was slowly hoisted to the yardarm. For a few seconds it hung on the breeze before fluttering into full splendour.

'Never thought I'd live to see that again,' said Mitch quietly. 'Now the shit will really hit the fan.'

I did not reply. Instead I stood transfixed. This was a ritual carried out by every British warship from Trafalgar to D.Day, signifying action was imminent. It was a sight I would never forget.

'I expect you'll be busy tonight, Doc,' went on Mitch.

'Cheerful bugger, aren't you?' I replied. 'Where's your action station?'

'On the starboard Stag gun with Pincher Martin,' he replied.

'Well, try not to get your balls shot off,' I replied.

'It's not me balls I'm worried about losing,' he said, flashing his false teeth at me. 'It's these new choppers you got me in Malta.'

After supper the medical parties collected their first aid bags. One or two tried to make weak jokes.

'Glory be, I hope your knives are sharp, Doc,' said Paddy Murphy.

'Of course they are, mon,' added Big Geordie. 'The chief cook sharpened them himself.'

Each senior officer was issued with morphia, and field dressings were distributed to those in exposed positions.

Around ten o'clock in the evening, the burly figure of Jan Hawes came into the sick bay. He already wore his anti-flash gear loosely around his neck.

'Hey, Doc,' he cried excitedly. 'You'll never guess what happened. The bloody Yanks turned on their searchlights. The whole allied fleet was illuminated.'

'Bloody hell, Jan.' I replied, 'the jippos will have a field day. Why did they do that?'

'Buggered if I knows' he replied, rubbing his nose with the back of his hand. 'Those Yanks 'ave been following us for days. Anyway, apparently the C in C told 'em to fuck off and eat their ice-cream.'

'Did they switch off the lights?'

'You bet.'

At precisely midnight action stations sounded.

I quickly checked to see that each first aid party was closed up.

Quite unexpectedly someone knocked on the sick bay door.

The cherubic features of the chief cook appeared. 'Grub up, Doc,' he said cheerfully. 'Do you want your sarnies here, or down in the mess with your lads?'

'I'll have mine with the first aid party, thanks chief,' I replied. Another cook carried a fanny full of steaming hot soup. The chief held a tray packed with sandwiches. I followed them down a ladder into the after mess.

The dim, red emergency lighting cast shadows on the faces of the men. They were sitting around a long table, some with their heads resting on their hands, others talking quietly.

'Come and get it,' cried the chief, placing the tray on the table. His assistant did the same with the soup.

Bungy Williams reluctantly accepted a sandwich. 'Bloody hell,' he growled. 'When this lot is over, I'm never going to touch corn dog again.'

'Don't speak too soon,' muttered Shiner Wright, who surprised everyone by paraphrasing the bible. 'Before the cock crows we might be hit thrice by Gyppo shells. So eat, drink and be merry, my sons.'

With his chilling remarks churning around in my head, I returned to the sick bay. The atmosphere inside was warm and claustrophobic. My anti-flash gear made my scalp itch, and beads of sweat ran down my face.

A knock came at the door, and the burly figure of Big Geordie appeared. He too was sweating profusely.

'Any tea on the go, Doc? That soup tasted like tar,' he said. His voice sounded calm, as if what we were doing was an everyday event. His casualness helped to relieve the mounting tension inside my stomach.

'Can't you think of anything else but your stomach?' I replied, half heartily. 'Help yourself. You know where everything is. How are the rest of the lads bearing up?'

'They're all right,' he replied, taking off his anti-flash gloves. 'Paddy Murphy's pissed off with the whole thing. He says it's all the fault of the English. He reckons they have no right to be invading poor little Egypt.'

'Maybe he should have joined the American navy,' as he handed me a mug of tea.

For the next three hours the tension mounted, but nothing

happened.

In the after first aid party, most were sitting against the bulkhead cradling their medical bags in their laps. Others sat at a table, resting their heads in their arms. Big Geordie looked up as I entered the mess.

'Do you think the Gyppos will fight, Geordie?' I asked, sitting down next to him.

He looked at me with tired eyes. 'I overheard the Jimmy telling the navigator if the Ruskies help them, we could be in for a real battle.'

The expressions on their drawn faces told me they were more than a little scared. I wanted to say something cheerful. I was about to speak when a voice on the tannoy announced firing from A and B guns would commence in ten minutes time.

'This is it, lads,' called out Shiner Wright, standing up and stretching his arms.

'And about bloody time, too,' cried the dimunitive figure of Harry Bridges, the canteen manager. 'The sooner we get this soddin' thing over, the quicker I can get my inventory finished.'

Once again I wished them good luck, and returned to the sick bay.

Shortly afterwards, all hell broke loose. The whole ship shook as A and B guns opened up. The percussion sent shock waves running through the ship like an earthquake. The earplugs I wore did not prevent my senses from being dulled. I put both hands over my ears and held my breath. Each salvo made the ship shiver. Every bottle in the sick bay rattled. The large medicine cabinet rose and fell and I thought the bulkheads would cave in.

Quite abruptly, the firing stopped. Even so, the noise continued to reverberate around in my head. The ship rocked angrily from side to side. When I removed my earplugs the silence was deafening.

Leaving the sick bay, I undid the clips on the afterdeck house hatchway, and gingerly stepped outside. As I did so, the chief cook came from the galley and followed me. He gave me a crafty wink and smiled.

'We could both lose our rate for this,' he said.

'I know, chief,' I replied. 'So what? We could all be killed before the day is out'

All of a sudden, the swish of shells passing above our heads instinctively made us duck. We learnt later these were from the

French battleship, *Jean Bart*. After a few salvos, the firing stopped, apparently, they were causing too much damage!

The sudden daylight hurt my eyes and made me blink. Silhouetted against an orange–coloured sky, the dark outline of Port Said's minorets resembled a scene from the Arabian Nights.

Without warning, A and B turrets re-commenced firing. The chief and I crouched down by the side of the torpedo tubes, watching yellow flashes as they exploded along the coast. Not far away from the ship several landing craft, crammed with green-bereted Royal Marines, headed for the shore. Walls of watery spray cascaded over the bows of each craft as they ploughed forward, shrouded in smoke. The LCIs were roughly 100 yards from the beach, when, out of the sky roared several jet fighters. With arrogant pride, one waggled its wings before soaring away.

The deck shook under our bodies and the noise was deafening. We were momentarily distracted by the sight of the captain. He was leaning over the starboard wing, frantically waving his cap at the marines.

The chief nudged me in the ribs. 'He's crazier than us,' he yelled, shaking his head in disbelief. 'He didn't say we'd be *this* close to the shore.'

As each LCI hit the beach the marines stormed ashore. Opposition was almost non-existent. Hunched and alert, they cautiously moved inland. Ahead of them, cloaked in early morning mist, was a small pier and a large building, which I later learned was a gambling casino.

From inland, a thick pall of black smoke curled into the dull, morning sky, evidence of earlier bombing raids. The acrid smell of cordite stung my nostrils as a grey fog of gun-smoke drifted lazily across the ship.

Without warning, our gunfire ceased. However, a series flashes from the shore was quickly followed by plumes of water erupting close by the ship.

'Christ Almighty!' I gasped. 'They're firing at *us'*

The jets of water came closer and we heard the sharp pinging noise nearby.

'Holy shit,' cried the chief. 'That's shrapnel!'

A crimson glow appeared in the sky over Port Said.

Quite suddenly a lone jet swooped down, firing daggers of yellow rockets. The enemy gunfire abruptly ceased.

'Well, you know what they say, chief,' I replied, looking upwards. 'Red sky in the morning, shepherds warning – let's get the hell out of here.'

Back in the sick bay, I removed my earplugs.

The first lieutenant informed us the ship would be turning to port. His voice was remarkably calm. 'We will move close to the shore, and bring all guns to bear on the enemy.'

Grabbing hold of the bunk stanchion, I steadied as the ship heeled to port.

'Bollocks,' I cried, hurriedly re-placing my earplugs. 'Here we go again.'

The groaning noise of shells being loaded in the hoist of X gun echoed through the bulkhead. Practice shoots in the past only consisted of a few salvoes. But that was nothing compared to what happened next. I sat down at the desk, placed a pillow over my head, and waited.

The sudden impact of the firing sounded like someone hitting the side of the ship with a large hammer. The recoil made the ship rocked like a child's cradle. Every bone in my body seemed to vibrate and once again my ears felt as it they would burst. Salvo after salvo thundered away. I pushed the pillow tightly against both ears. I tried to pray but the noise paralysed my brain.

The chair I was sitting on rose in the air. Still clutching the pillow over my head, I was thrown backwards onto the deck. Suddenly, I felt warm fluid run down the front of my face. My God, I thought, I'm injured. I glanced around, half expecting to see a gaping hole in the bulkhead. Instead I saw water dribbling over the edge of the sink. For a while I sat watching the water cascade onto the deck. It ran into a corner forming a clear pool that swished from side to side.

Quite unexpectedly, the door slid open and in came Harry Morrison. He was in charge of the for'd medical team. Although I could not hear him, I saw he was laughing. I quickly removed my earplugs.

The sudden sound of the engines was deafening.

Harry continued grinning as I staggered to my feet. 'Are you all right, Doc? You look as white as a sheet.' He glanced about. 'Bloody hell, it looks as if it's been snowing in here.'

For the first time I noticed everything was covered in fine white dust. The neon lights hung limply from the deck-head, and several electrical fittings had come loose.

A glance in the mirror showed a white-faced person who resembled the abominable snowman!

'We... we weren't hit, or anything, were we?'

'No,' laughed Harry, handing me a cigarette and lighting it. 'The firing stopped a good ten minutes ago.' He looked around again. 'All the messes are like this. The ship's in a hell of a state. The firing brought down lights, cables and everything else.'

'Anyone hurt?'

'No,' replied Harry, shaking his head. 'No, just several cases of acute diahorrea. Nothing serious.'

The time was just after nine-thirty. We had been closed up for almost ten hours.

We remained at defence stations for the remainder of the day. Sitting at my desk, I fell asleep with my arms across my forehead. I was awakened by John Smith, the coxswain.

'Wake up, jack, it's past tot time,' he said jokingly. He still wore his anti-flash gear. 'Didn't you hear the pipe?'

My mouth felt like a vulture's crutch and my bladder was bursting.

'What's happened?' I said, blinking my eyes.

'The Gyppos have signed some sort of treaty,' he said. 'It's been the shortest war on record.'

'Thank fuck for that,' I muttered, standing up and yawning. 'Now. What was that you said about tot time?'

Three days later, in company with *Duchess* and *Diamond,* we entered Port Said.

The harbour resembled a nautical graveyard. Funnels, masts and hulks of ships sunk by the Egyptians poked out of the grimy, green waters. Tugs with divers were busy clearing away wreckage as ships came alongside a crowded wharf. The once beautiful Custom House with its three green domes lay in ruins.

On the way to the sick bay, I met the canteen manager.

'It's all his bloody fault,' said Harry, nodding towards an imperious-looking statue guarding the entrance to the harbour.

'What is?' I asked, glancing at him.

'All this', he replied, gesticulating with a hand. 'That's the statue of Ferdinand De Lesseps. He built the soddin' canal just over a hundred years ago. And he was frog!'

The welcome sight of mail arriving on board cheered everyone up. I was especially relieved when I learnt Reg was all right. Apparently, Mum met Reg's mother, who said he was unhurt and due home.

Two days later, with a cloud of black smoke still lingering over Port Said, we sailed for Malta – at last I could get a decent night's sleep.

21

We arrived in Grand Harbour on Sunday 11th November and tied up alongside HMS *Corruna* at Hamilton Wharf.

The next day I took a party of ratings to Bighi for routine chest x-rays. The sight of the hospital's high walls still evoked painful memories. I closed my eyes, telling myself she was gone and I would be soon be on my way home.

The x-ray department was situated next to the surgical ward on the far side of the hospital.

Sitting at a desk was Brum Appleby, a fellow footballer I knew from Stonehouse.

'Hello, Tom,' he said, shaking my hand. 'You look uglier than ever. How's the soccer?'

'Haven't had much time to play any lately,' I answered. 'Been rather busy at sea.'

'Of course,' he replied. 'The Suez business. We've got quite a few casualties in here.'

I was in no mood for talking and gave a quick shrug of my shoulders.

While the group were x-rayed, I wandered into the surgical ward. The first person I saw was Jock McBride.

'Tom, lad, great to see you, mate,' he said, shaking my hand.

'And you, Jock,' I replied. 'How are the others?'

'Des comes off nights next week and Lofty is on the medical ward.'

'Look, Jock,' I said. 'It's my birthday on the eighteenth of this month. Do you think we could all meet up for a few wets somewhere?'

'Let's see,' he replied. 'That's next Sunday. We should all be off duty. What about meeting up at the Vernon Club in Valetta? Say about eight?'

'A great idea, Jock,' I answered, giving his arm a friendly dig. 'Sunday it is.'

After introducing me to the sister, we walked slowly around the ward. Lying in bed were young men, their faces swathed in bandages. Others had arms in slings, while several sat around in dressing gowns, reading or playing cards.

'Are they all from Suez?' I asked.

Before Jock had time to answer, a voice cried out. 'Of course we are, you daft bugger.'

I could hardly believe my eyes. Standing in front of me was Joe. He wore a white dressing gown and his mop of fair hair was cropped short. The only thing that hadn't changed was his grin.

'Joe!' I exclaimed as we warmly shook hands. 'I don't believe it. How are you?'

'I'm all right.' He tapped his left thigh. 'A slight nick on my leg. They're flying me back to Aldershot tomorrow. What about you?'

'I'm OK,' I replied. 'We got back the other day.'

I told him I had watched the parachute drop. 'For a while there, I thought you'd had it.'

He glanced at the deck. 'The bastards killed a few of us. I was lucky. This is only a scratch.'

I told him about Phil and Reg. 'We sail for UK in late December,' I said. 'At least you'll be home for Christmas.'

With a forlorn look in his eyes, he replied, 'Don't worry, Bud, I'll take your Mum and Dad to the "Brighton" and have a few wets for you.'

Our conversation was interrupted when the medical officer entered the ward. Jock called the ward to attention. Joe and I looked at one another.

A lump came in my throat. 'Look after that leg of yours,' I said, shaking his hand.

'It's a good job it isn't my drinking arm,' he said, grinning. 'Then I really would be in trouble.'

At the door I turned, gave Joe a quick thumbs up, and left.

The Vernon Club was popular with all the services. The beer was cheap and there was an occasional open-air dance.

The bar was crowded with men and women in uniform. Jock, Lofty and Des were waiting and we settled down to some serious drinking.

A lot had happened to me since we first met in Portsmouth. During that time, each of us had, in one way or another, faced death. Myself, on a personal note; they on the hospital wards. Their tanned faces looked older, but their laughter brought back a host of happy memories.

'That badge of yours looks smart, Tom,' said Lofty, touching my good conduct badge. 'No more comments about you being a 'mickey-mouse' PO, eh?'

'You're right, there, Lofts,' I replied, with a grin. 'You can call me 'Stripey.'

'I wonder how old Obadiah is?' Des said, before taking a large gulp of his beer.

'Probably still getting nagged to death by that battleaxe of a chief wren,' replied Lofty, passing his cigarettes around.

'Still pulling his wire, more's the like,' cracked Jock.

We instantly broke out into a chorus of, 'My name is Obadiah – and I always pull my wire!'

'A toast to Obadiah, and to all the Obadiahs of the world,' cried Des, raising his pint glass.

After a few more drinks, we re-acquatinted ourselves with the "Egyptian Queen" and a several other well-known watering holes.

Much later, with our arms around one another, we staggered through the main archway leading to the bus station. Our garbled rendering of *Maggie May* was interrupted when Des did a five-finger spread against the archway wall.

'Come on, Tom,' said Jock, 'we'll give you a destroyer escort to Customs House steps. Then we can catch a taxi around to the bone-yard.'

The wharf was quiet.

'I wonder when we'll meet again,' slurred Lofty, leaning against me.

'Och, away with you,' replied Jock. 'We'll all eventually stagger through the gates of Stonehouse.'

'Take care of yourselves, lads,' I said, shaking each warmly by the hand. 'See you back in Guzz.'

As I stumbled into a dico, Jock just managed to prevent Des falling into the harbour.

Leaning precariously forward, Desperate took out a small paper bag. Waving it in the air, he yelled. 'You forgot the toffees I bought you, Tommy Bach.'

'Keep 'em, Des', I shouted. 'Give them to the next girl you meet at the pictures.'

As the oarsman slowly paddled the boat away, the sound of them singing Devonport's national anthem echoed across the harbour.

Half a pound of flour and lard,
Makes lovely clacker,
Just enough for you and me,
Cor, bugger Janor!
Oh! How happy us will be,
When us gets to the West Country,
Where the oggies grow on trees,
Cor bugger Janor!

During the next three weeks, the crew prepared for the forthcoming Admiral's Inspection. Every piece of brass was polished and re-polished. Each mess deck was scrupulously cleaned. The ship was re-painted from stem to stern – even the bilges were scrubbed till they gleamed like silver.

While walking across the upper deck, I overheard the chief GI talking to a group of ratings.

'I want to be able to see my face in your shoes,' he growled.

'What about the soles of our shoes?' quipped Seldom.

'Polish them too,' replied the chief.

'The inspection will take place on Monday, 17th December,' said the first lieutenant. We were in his cabin. 'It will be a more detailed examination of your records than Portland. If anything's not up to scratch, I'll have your rate off you. Do I make myself clear?'

I tried to swallow. 'Yes, sir,' I replied. 'Who will be doing the examining?'

'I expect it will be a surgeon commander and his staff from St Angelo.'

The big day finally arrived. Everyone on board was nervous. The voices of chief and petty officers rang around the ship barking orders. The sound of footsteps scurrying about echoed along the passageways.

I laid all the documentation out on the desk then unlocked all the cupboard doors and drawers, ready for scrutiny. All dangerous drugs were checked and accounted for. Hopefully, I had left nothing to chance.

The sick bay looked immaculate. The deck, desk and scuppers gleamed like glass. Medicine chests and cabinets shone, and the

337

stringent smell of antiseptic hung in the air. I had even polished the soles of my shoes.

Pacing up and down, my stomach churned over. Shortly before ten o'clock the door opened.

Straight away, I recognised the stocky figure of Boyd-Martin, my old boss from Culdrose. The four gold rings on each sleeve told me he was now a surgeon captain.

Behind him came the squadron doctor, Surgeon Lieutenant Jones. He was followed by a portly, sick-berth chief petty officer.

The surgeon captain sniffed the air, glanced around and removed his gold-braided cap. His hair was thinner and greyer than before, but he still wore that familiar jaundiced expression. 'Ah, Lightburn,' he said, raising his bushy eyebrows. 'We meet again, I see.'

Standing stiffly to attention, I replied, 'Yes, sir.'

Turning to Surgeon Lieutenant Jones and the chief, he said, 'Lightburn, here, was my leading hand at Culdrose.' He then looked back at me. 'I see you've been promoted again.'

'Yes, sir,' I replied again.

'Well stand easy, my boy,' he said with a weak smile. 'We're not going to eat you.'

He walked around, briefly glancing here and there. I waited nervously as he checked the dangerous drug records and store account. 'Good,' he said. 'They're in order.'

I breathed a sigh of relief. At least we had started off on the right foot. Any discrepancy would have had serious repercussions.

Looking at the chief, Boyd-Martin said, 'Surgeon Lieutenant Jones and myself will be either with the first lieutenant or in the wardroom if you want us, chief. We'll leave you to carry on here.'

After they left, the chief unbuttoned his jacket and sat down. 'Thank goodness for that,' he said in a rich West Country accent. Now we can have a bloody smoke. My name's Trevelyan Roberts.'

We shook hands, and I introduced myself.

'Got any tea going, Tom?' he asked, giving me a cigarette and lighting one for himself.

'Would you like a drop of neaters in it?' I asked, taking a green medicine bottle from under the mattress of my bunk.

His eyes lit up. 'Handsome!' came his enthusiastic reply. 'I expect those two will be knocking a few back in the wardroom. So why shouldn't we?'

Over a mug of tea, well laced with rum, he examined the rest of my documentation. 'They're all in order, my handsome,' he said, glancing at his empty mug. 'Now, how about another cuppa?'

'Do you want to go down to the engine and boiler rooms, chief?' I asked. 'I've opened all the first aid and stretcher cabinets.'

'I don't think so,' he replied. 'My arthritis is playing me up. I go outside in a few weeks time. Besides,' he went on, 'everything is top line here, so let's wait for the brass to return, eh?'

Shortly before eleven-thirty, both officers returned.

The chief stood up and quickly buttoned his jacket.

The rubicund glow on the faces of both officers told its own story.

'Your first-lieutenant and Doctor Jones have given you a good report,' he said, smiling at me. Then, turning to the chief added, 'How is everything here, chief? Top line, I hope?'

'Yes, sir,' replied the chief. 'As you say, sir. Top line.'

'Good!' exclaimed the captain. With a quick glance at Doctor Jones, he said. 'We might as well adjourn to the wardroom.'

'Splendid idea, sir,' replied Doctor Jones. 'Well, Lightburn,' he said shaking my hand, 'I don't suppose we'll meet again before you sail for home, so thank you for all you've done.'

'Thank you, sir,' I said, shaking his hand. 'And give my best to PO Burgess.'

As I slid open the door for them, Surgeon Captain Boyd-Martin gave me a wry smile. 'Petty Officer Manley obviously taught you well at Culdrose.'

I gave him a re-assuring grin, and nodded. 'Yes, sir,' I replied. 'He certainly did that.'

'Special sea-duty-men to your stations. Close all screen doors and scuttles. Assume ABC 3, condition x-ray. Hands fall in for leaving harbour.'

This was the pipe I had been waiting for since I woke up at six o'clock. My heart pounded in my chest - at long last we were on our way home.

The ship slipped her moorings and slowly moved away from the wharf. As usual the sky was pale blue, and the waters of Grand Harbour sparkled in the strong morning sun. From the battlements of St Angelo came the strains of a trumpet.

'Face the starboard.'

Everyone snapped to attention. From a high balcony overlooking the harbour, the authoritative figure of Guy Grantham, the Commander-in-Chief, Mediterranean, gave the ship a farewell salute.

Away to our left, a small crowd gathered at the Barraca Gardens. They waved as the ship slowly nosed its way towards the breakwater.

Jerry Johnson, who was fallen in next to me, groaned, 'This sun is playing tricks. I'm sure I saw big Betty from the "Gyppo Queen" wave to me.'

'You're hallucinating, Jerry,' said Harry Morrison, from the corner of his mouth. 'She was waving to me.'

Across on the cliffs of Kalkara, the yellow columns of Bighi shone like gold.

Suddenly, I gave a start. For a fleeting second I thought I saw a white-coated nurse with blonde hair on the balcony – perhaps I too was hallucinating.

Epilogue

In January 1974, I was serving in HMS *Endurance,* the Royal Navy's survey ship. Following a visit to the Antarctic and South Georgia, we had the task of acting as guard ship for the Whitbread round-the-world yacht race. This entailed remaining at Cape Horn for long periods, through the world's most perilous seas. Our work completed, we set sail for Valparaiso, in Chile, and a well-earned run ashore.

Valparaiso was a busy, bustling port, full of merchant ships and tankers. We arrived on a fine day with a clear blue sky and a hot sun beating down on our heads. I was fallen in for entering harbour with the other senior rates.

Looking across the harbour, my curiosity was suddenly aroused. Tied up alongside the wharf were the unmistakable clear-cut lines of an old Daring-class destroyer.

As soon as we were berthed I decided to take a closer look. My footsteps faltered. As I drew nearer I immediately recognised her. It was none other than HMS *Decoy,* the first ship I had sailed in almost twenty years ago.

But why was she here? I wondered. Perhaps I could find out by going aboard.

The hairs on the back of my neck stood on end as I gazed nostagically over her familiar sleek lines. Her once stovepipe funnel had been altered and the bridge was now enclosed. However, her guns still defiant, brought back vivid memories of painful eardrums and shattering glass.

A few swarthy dockyard workers greeted me with a smile. Dressed in my tropical whites, they probably thought I was one of the ship's officers.

On several areas the ship was mottled with patches of red lead. The grey paint on parts of her superstructure was peeling and the metal deck, once the colour of lawn green, was now covered in dust and grime. Clearly, she was in a state of chronic disrepair.

The sight of the empty space once occupied by the torpedo tubes made me grin. Maybe someone had heard they sometimes exploded.

With mounting excitement I went into the after deckhouse.

The dank smell of stale dust and grimy cobwebs hanging from the overhead pipes was further evidence of long-term neglect.

The sign on the sick bay door was gone, and as I slid open the door, I felt as if I was stepping back in time.

Once inside, I was momentarily blinded by the sudden dimness. Gradually my eyes adjusted to the light.

Everywhere I looked brought back a memory.

The sink where I cowered during the Suez bombardment was now coated with thick verdigris. The faded sheen on the brass scuttles would have given my old first lieutenant a heart attack. The medicine cabinet was badly in need of a polish and inside, its racks lay empty and forlorn. I gently pushed the frames of the cots. They didn't move. Opposite, stripped of bedding, was my old bunk, reminding me of so many sleepless nights.

Faces and names came flooding back into my head. What had happened to Seldom, Pete and Big Geordie and the others, I wondered? Scattered, no doubt, to the four corners of the earth. I smiled, thinking of Mitch, hoping he hadn't lost too many sets of false teeth. For the first time in years I remembered Anita but thankfully, the sudden, grating sound of a drill brought me back to reality.

After a final look, I closed the door and left.

Walking down the gangway, I asked myself, what on earth was the ship doing here?

Years would pass before I found the answer.

HMS *Decoy* was one of nine Daring-class destroyers built after the Second World War. Laid down in Yarrow in 1946, she was launched in 29 March 1949 and commissioned on 28 April 1953. After Suez, she served in every theatre in home waters and the Mediterranean. Following her last commission in 1967-70, she was taken out of service.

With the exception of *Decoy,* all the Daring-class destroyers were scrapped in 1973. My old ship was eventually sold to the Peruvian navy and re-named *Ferre.*

As someone once remarked, 'Your first ship is like your first love. You never forget her.' How right they were.